Mobile Phones and Tablets Repairs:

A

Complete Guide for Beginners and Professionals

Chukky Oparandu

Illustrated in pictures and Diagrams

Mobile Phones and Tablets Repairs:
A Complete Guide for Beginners and Professionals
Copyright © 2016 by Chukky Oparandu

ISBN-10: 9789534116
ISBN-13: 978-978-953-411-1

Mondraim Books
A Division of Mondraim Ltd.
Nigeria.

Printed in the USA by CreateSpace, Charleston SC

Available from Amazon.com, CreateSpace.com and other retail outlets
Also available on Kindle and other devices
For information regarding special discounts for bulk purchases,
Please contact info@mondraim.com or call +234-8035887084

Warning and Disclaimer

Dedication

To my darling Wife, Linda;

Chukwuma Junior, Onyinyechi, Iheoma;

And my beloved mother, Joyce;

The treasures God blessed me with, I dedicate this work.

Contents

**PART 3   MOBILE PHONE SOFTWARE AND
SOFTWARE REPAIR TECHNIQUES**

Acknowledgments

I want to acknowledge the God of the universe who through the Holy Spirit inspired the writing and compilation of this work. The motivation to keep going could not have come from anywhere else other than the divine.

Among mortals came moral, intellectual and other forms of material support. I thank my sisters, Nkeiru, Amarachi, Chidinma and Akunna for their moral support. I thank particularly Dr. Rabe Nasir Mani, who has been a mentor to me for his input. Your encouragement has been and will continue to be helpful in my career goals sir. The same appreciation goes to Alhaji Garba Sanda Mani. I value your support sir.

I cannot forget the motivation and support I got from the staff of the Katsina Youth Craft Centre and the Department of Science and Technology, Katsina where I have been privileged to tutor and mentor an enormous number of youths in Computers, mobile phones and tablets repairs. The result is in the testimonials of successful enterprises set up by the youths in the state and across the nation.

I want to thank particularly my members of staff especially Mr. Abiodun Soniyi who has been with me for close to a decade. I appreciate your loyalty and dedication to duty even as this work was being compiled. Also worthy of mention are Jephta Idhu, Nasiru Kabir, the MCOMS Training Consult team, my brother Nnanna and a host of others too numerous to list here.

Thank you all.

Preface

It was Napoleon Hill who said that, *"Knowledge is only potential power. It becomes only power when, and if, it is organized into definite plans of action, and directed to a definite end."* [1]

In every economy in this 21st century, Tech Business would thrive and serve as the catalyst for growth in all sectors of national economies. Truer is this fact in economies that are experiencing a recession- especially a mono-product economy like ours in Nigeria and most third world countries. It is an economy for knowledge or skilled workers. For instance, people would rather patronize the services' sector to repair their faulty devices than to change to new ones, especially when the national economy is experiencing a downturn.

Man's basic needs have changed from what it was in other era of existence;

- Shelter
- Clothing
- Food/water
- Information & Communication   (the new entrant)

Man today - even one who is unemployed - can hardly function without information/communication. If you are stranded to the lowest low, once you have life as a result of food/water, clothed - even if with just one garment under a shelter of any form, shape and size - getting out of your condition faster will require that you gain relevant information and the ability to communicate for help. And today, with the internet and the mobile phone, man is gradually evolving to that state where he can hardly do without his mobile handset!

Why am I saying this?

The best business is that one that meets one of man's most basic needs - it will always have a 'demand' market.

Mobile Phones and Tablets Repair Services and Solution ICT subsector is a multibillion dollar sector open to all that are interested. It is a veritable self reliance investment vehicle for arriving to any future career destination even if not a permanent career venture. This book is a response to the growing demand for comprehensive professional information that could assist young people all over the world who desire entry to the technical service industry in the mobile device category. The future is in the mobile phones, tablets and notebook devices computing segment, a departure from the dominance of desktop computers in the last two decades.

The book is organized in a way and format that teaches the reader who follows through, chapter by chapter as if he/she was attending a live training lab. At the end, the author's hope is that the reader will learn many key start-up and detailed Mobile Phone repair procedure information that can help to kick-start a small or large scale service center in any locality of choice.

The author of this book has consistently trained and empowered thousands of youths through partnership with Katsina State government, Nigeria at the Katsina Youth Craft Centre, Katsina - a multi-million dollar youth skill acquisition centre and some NGOs. The result has been phenomenal. If there is any such time when the youths should be encouraged to look beyond the usual "Go to school, get a certificate, find a paid job" cycle, it is now. Facebook's Mark Zuckerberg, Apple inc. founder Steve Jobs and many others who thought out innovative solutions to societal needs through information technology should serve as worthy examples to emulate.

Let me also end with the words of Napoleon Hill to that student, that graduate, that unemployed youth or adult who is interested in becoming a master of his destiny, and who has chosen to learn by opening the pages of this book;

"Knowledge has no value except that which can be gained from its application towards some worthy end. This is one reason college degrees are not valued more highly. They represent nothing but miscellaneous knowledge". [2]

~ Dr. Rabe Nasir Mani
Special Adviser to the Governor,
Department of Science and Technology, Katsina.

Author's Note

Why this book?

The writing of this book is informed by popular demand. Online and in some poorly prepared pamphlets, there have been some snippets of half baked repair guides. But there has not been a complete story in one resource for those who are yearning for access to this technical knowledge and industry.

In book stores the world over, there are no such complete repair guides for mobile telephones and tablets repairs even though you will find many for PCs. So I undertook this task for the millions of youths out there who are budding, seeking for means of learning and self reliance. I have seen lives changed through this technical service. In this century, the age of mobile communication and computing, it is one of the hottest tech repair service segment.

Not everyone owns a PC (desktop or laptop) and definitely not everyone owns a mobile phone at the moment. But you will agree that more number of people already own and will own a mobile device in the future than a PC. Therefore a good mobile phone technician has a brighter and faster earning potential than a PC technician. Secondly, a good mobile phone technician can also be a PC technician and vice versa but for a PC technician, he may yet need some further training especially in Microelectronic device handling and BGA soldering.

Consider that by virtue of what is essential for living in the 21st century and beyond, every individual on earth (billions of population of humans) will eventually own a mobile device. That is a huge market! To be successful or wealthy, you have to exchange something for something. Exchanging personal services for money is a great tool and goal for entrepreneurship. With my education and having spent over twelve years running Service Centers that fix myriads of Computers, Microelectronic mobile devices, IT consulting and Training, I believe I qualify as an authority in this area of expertise. This is my gift to the upcoming generation. You can be successful if you believe and work hard. You too can learn if you are determined to and focus.

I have trained through government support thousands of technicians spread all over Nigeria and Niger Republic – with or without higher education. Education is important, in fact very important if you pursue it with a sense of purpose in an area. But education or the lack of it is not usually the main limitation. Rather, it is a lack of a sense of purpose. That sense of purpose should be to the intent to acquire and apply knowledge towards a specific end; otherwise you succeed in only becoming a certificated illiterate. The time to take that bold step is now. Stir up your brain, dream dreams and the sky will be your stepping stone.

Highlights of What to Expect in this Course

To master the craft of mobile phones and tablets repairs commands a tremendous power for you to make money. Fixing mobile phones is a specialized technical knowledge area. Being a master, an expert at your job and be among the distinguished top earning "tech-entrepreneur" through managing a successful support service centre demands that you are well grounded in the relevant knowledge, technical details and smart-skills (the total package) involved. This book is the answer to that need. Chapter by chapter, you will go from a complete novice in technical skills and knowledge to one that can begin to earn a decent wage the moment you finish walking yourself through the pages of this book.

Part 1 of the book begins with chapter 1 "Introduction to Mobile Communication Technology" which summarizes and introduces you to the concepts of a communication system along the context of mobile communication, the various implemented technologies and standards as well as the physical attributes and features of a mobile phone.

Chapter 1 is followed by chapter 2 which walks you through a visual understanding of the internal structure and components of mobile phones and devices.

Chapter 3 shows you briefly the various tools and equipment you will require on the job and ends the first part of the book. The second part of the book begins with chapter 4 where you are taught the specific practical skills you will be applying daily on the job using the tools and equipment you have been shown in chapter 3.

Chapter 5 introduces you to hardware repairs. Everything that relates to mobile phone motherboards, its components, their interconnections and structure is discussed in details. You need to absorb the information in this chapter for all it is worth.

Chapter 6 is one of the longest chapters in the book as it is a foundational course on electronics. The chapter fills you in on the relevant perspectives needed for purposeful work in the field. Attempt is made to bring new entrants to technical service to speed as well as direct the attention of students and professionals to ways the knowledge acquired or being refreshed in this book could be turned into practical economic value in offering technical services.

Chapter 7, "Hardware Faults, Faults Detection and Repair Procedures" launches the reader into a step-by-step guide to repairs, applying in tow, skills and knowledge gained in the previous chapters.

Part 3 of the book which focuses on software repairs opens with chapter 8. In this chapter, you are introduced to concepts on software, software repairs and software repair tools guide. The information in this chapter will prepare you for the task ahead in an organized fashion, eliminating the confusion that faces new entrants to software flash programming given the overwhelming volume of resources that abound.

Chapter 9 continues with software but delves into software repair procedures proper, empowering you with knowledge which you can apply instantly with certain useful free software even if you have no money to buy proprietary ones. Chapter 10 teaches you a number of settings and codes related information which is very helpful to start earning money quickly.

Finally, chapter 11 completes the course for you by teaching you practical entrepreneurial guides that would see you launching into the business, avoid the pitfalls of others before you and make it to the top faster.

Everything taught in this book has been practiced in a teaching environment and the impact has been tremendous.

PART 1
FOUNDATION KNOWLEDGE

Chapter 1

Introduction to Mobile Communication Technology

What is Communication?

Communication is the process of exchanging data between two or more entities. Communication can be defined as *"the purposeful activity of information exchange between two or more participants in order to convey or receive the intended meanings through a shared system of signs and semiotic rules.*

In the telecommunication industry, a communication system refers to a collection of disparate communication networks, transmission systems, relay stations, tributary stations and data terminal equipment (DTE) usually capable of interconnection and interoperation to form an integrated whole. The components of a communication system serve a common purpose, are technically compatible, use common procedures, respond to controls, and operate in union" [3].

Communication systems are designed along with the implementation of specific data transmission and reception technologies. This means that the end device in the system (mobile phones) must have the kind of radio access technologies that are compatible with the implemented technology within the communication system. The technology specification implemented by carrier companies determines the kind of radio access a mobile phone has to the network.

The RF components in any given phone vary in both sophistication and complexity depending on the access technology standard they can connect to. In recent times, multiple mode access phones are commonplace. Curiously, there exists no backward compatibility to older systems with the invention of newer technologies.

The word 'mobile' is derived from the Latin word mobilis – which means "to move", "able to move freely or easily", "able or willing to move freely or easily between occupations, places of residence and social classes" [4].

A Mobile device is a mobile, wireless or cellular phone - a portable, hand-held communication device connected to a wireless network that allows users to make voice calls, send text messages and run applications at any location, while stationary or in motion.

Below are sample pictures of different mobile phone designs as we explore the development of the mobile communication system briefly.

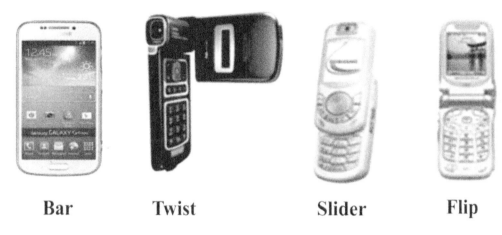

| Bar | Twist | Slider | Flip |

Figure 1.1: Various Phone Designs

Development of the GSM Cellular Technology and Phone

*"**GSM** stands for **Global System for Mobile Communications**, originally known as (**Groupe Spécial Mobile**), and is a mobile communication system or standard developed by the European Telecommunications Standards Institute (ETSI) to describe the protocols for second-generation (2G) digital cellular networks used by mobile phones, first deployed in Finland in July 1991. According to Wikipedia, as at 2014 it had become the default global standard for mobile communications - with over 90% market share, operating in over 219 countries and territories"* [5].

Mobile phones were developed for communication over distinct generations (depending on the span of years the technology infrastructure were developed and deployed) based on the GSM standard. Earlier mobile phones were bulky, expensive and were mostly installed in mobile trucks, cars or carried in briefcases. They only had capabilities for voice call or communications. Let us follow the sequence below;

1G

By the year 1980, the first generation 1G mobile phones were developed alongside first generation cellular networks. These networks only processed and operated on analog radio signals. They only had capability for voice and limited data running on AMPS/DataTac technologies (Advanced Mobile Phone System). The first Blackberry phone was made during this period, the Blackberry 850 [6].

AMPS   1G PHONE

Figure 1.2: Sample 1G Phones

AMPS: By 1983, the analog cell-phone standard called AMPS (Advanced Mobile Phone System) was approved by the American FCC and first used in Chicago. AMPS used a range of frequencies between 824 megahertz (MHz) and 894 MHz for analog mobile cell phones.

Another version was created which multiplied the access medium to three times its capacity for voice transmission using limited digital technology. It is known as NAMPS (Narrowband Advanced Mobile System) which only operated in the 800MHz band. This technology was the predominant implementation in the cellular systems accessed by the earlier "Basic" phones. Such phones could not support features such as email services or internet access because the NAMPS standard itself did not offer such features in the communication system.

During this period, the telecommunication companies were limited to their assigned transmission frequencies for voice and data, out of which

4

a channel is created using two disparate transmission frequencies – one for transmission and the other for reception. This analog communication system could only produce voice qualities almost at par with the traditional wired telephone system.

2G

The 2G standard marked the introduction of a full digital technology mobile system. It is the actual GSM standard and utilized circuit-switched network transmission method optimized for full duplex voice telephony. It was expanded over time to include data communications, first by circuit-switched transport, then by packet data transport through GPRS (General Packet Radio Service) and EDGE (Enhanced Data rates for GSM Evolution or EGPRS). Other technologies included in the standard are iDEN (Integrated Digital Enhanced Network), CDMA (Code Division Multiple Access) and TDMA (Time Division Multiple Access) [5]. During this period 2.5G networks were developed with the addition of HSCSD (High-Speed Circuit-Switched Data), WiDEN, and CDMA 2000 1x-RTT.

GPRS stands for General Packet Radio Service, a mobile data service for use on GSM networks. It is part of the 2.5G standards family.
iDEN stands for Integrated Digital Enhanced Network which was solely developed by Motorola for 2G mobile telecommunication standard family.
WiDEN is the Wideband Integrated Digital Enhanced Network which is developed for the 2.5G standard family.

Motorola Razor

Nokia 6233

Earlier 2G phones

Figure 1.3: Sample 2G Phones

5

3G

Around 2004, 3G or third generation mobile cellular networks were developed to provide actual multimedia features. With the introduction of this communication standard was added features and functionalities such as broadband data, voice and streaming video implemented with W-CDMA technology.

UMTS is short for Universal Mobile Telecommunications System, a 3G networking standard used almost all over the world as an upgrade to existing GSM mobile networks. UMTS makes use of WCDMA, a technology that shares many features with CDMA networks used throughout the world, though it is not compatible with them.

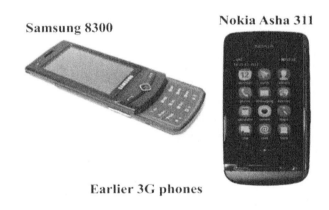

Figure 1.4: sample 3G phones

WCDMA stands for Wideband Code Division Multiple Access which is used in the radio leg of both UMTS and HSPA (High-Speed Packet Access) networks. In addition to supporting conventional voice, text and MMS services, WCDMA can carry data at high speeds, enabling mobile operators to deliver richer mobile multimedia services such as music-on-demand, TV, video streaming and broadband Internet access.
"The **3GPP** (Third Generation Partnership Project) developed third-generation (3G) UMTS standards" [7]

4G LTE

LTE (Long Term Evolution) is an advanced mobile cellular network standard in use today. It is not part of the ETSI (European Telecommunications Standard Institute) GSM standard. It is based on the GSM/EDGE and UMTS/HSPA network technologies, increasing the network capacity and speed using a different radio interface as well as core network improvements. It is a high-speed broadband standard for data and visual-centric information. Devices have data transmit speeds of 100mbps while in motion and 1Gbs when stationary.

Two main reasons 4G is faster than 3G are the implementation of Orthogonal Frequency-Division Multiplexing (OFDM) and Multiple-Input-Multiple-Output, or MIMO technique. OFDM is a technique for squeezing more data onto the same radio frequency spectrum thereby reducing latency (delay) and interference. Data is split up and sent through small blocks of frequency in parallel, therefore increasing the capacity of the network. MIMO is simply the use of multiple antenna arrays at both the transmitter and the receiver to improve communication performance.

Digital Mobile Cell Phones

Digital mobile phones use the same radio technology as analog phones, but they use it differently. Analog systems hardly utilize fully the signal frequency spectrum between the phone (Mobile Station) and the cellular network due to the fact that analog signals do not undergo compression and signal manipulations as easily as pure digital signals.

Digital systems are much more efficient for signal transmission and reception. With digital systems more channels can be packed into a carrier company's allocated bandwidth which is an obvious advantage unlike with analog systems.

Digital phones convert the human voice (which is an analog signal) into binary information (1s and 0s) and then compress it before transmission. This compression allows between three to ten digital cell phone calls to utilize the same frequency spectrum commensurate with a single analog call.

Most digital cellular systems use frequency-shift keying (FSK) method for data transmission over legacy networks. FSK uses two frequencies, one for 1s and the other for 0s, alternating rapidly between the two to send digital information between the cell tower and the phone. Through the process of modulation and encoding, the analog information signal is converted to digital data, compressed and converted back to analog signal, retaining a high level of voice quality throughout the process. This is possible due to the strong processing power packed into digital cell phones.

Cellular Access Technologies

Access technologies refer to the method through which the user's message signals (voice, text, and data) gain access to the communication medium. Since in every cell there are multiple network users, "Multiple Access" denotes that in each access technology specification, more than one user is able to utilize the cell.

Three common technologies used by mobile cell phone networks for transmitting information are:

- Frequency Division Multiple Access (FDMA) which assigns a separate frequency for each call. FDMA separates the spectrum into distinct voice channels by splitting it into uniform blocks of bandwidth. This system is used mainly for analog transmissions. While it is capable of carrying digital information, FDMA is not that efficient for digital transmission.

- Time Division Multiple Access (TDMA) which assigns each call a fixed portion of time on a designated frequency. TDMA on the other hand has three times the capacity of an analog system using the same number of channels and operate in the 800-MHz (IS-54) or 1900-MHz (IS-136) frequency bands.

- Code Division Multiple Access (CDMA) which gives a unique code to each call and spreads it over the available frequencies.

Mobile Phone Structure and Form Factors

There are various physical designs of a mobile phone. The form factor of a mobile phone refers to its size, shape and style, as well as the layout and position of its major components. Understanding these aspects of the mobile device design is important for a technician whose major job function includes primarily the task of disassembling and reassembling the phone to carry out corrective repairs.

There are three major form factors of mobile phones that have existed so far– bar phones, flip phones, and slider phones – as well as sub-categories of these forms. The "twist" design for instance was a subset of the flip type of mobile phones.

Bar Phones

A bar phone takes the shape of a rectangle, usually with rounded or curved corners or edges. This is the mobile phone form factor that is dominant in the market today among many manufacturers and brands. A common feature in the Bar-type mobile phones is the presence of the screen and keypad on the front face or fascia. Since the dominance of smartphones began, almost all the mobile phones manufactured till date are coming out in bar form factor.

Figure 1.5a: Sample bar phone

Touchscreen phones, Tablet phones or the coinage "Phablet" (which means that they combine the functions of a smartphone and a tablet) phones are all subsets of the bar form. The very wide screen sizes Phablets and Tablets differentiate one from the other. They are usually larger than that of most touchscreen smartphones with most screen sizes measuring between 5.5 to 7.9 inches. You can hardly fit a Phablet phone comfortably into your pocket.

Figure 1.5b: Sample bar Tablet phone

Flip Phones

A *flip* phone is designed with two sections that are connected by hinges, thereby allowing the phone to flip open and as well fold "closed" reducing the size of the phone. When it is flipped open, the speaker and microphone of the phone are placed closer to a user's ear and mouth respectively, thereby improving the phone's usability. When the phone is flipped shut, it becomes much smaller and compact.

Flip phones are phones which fold open vertically with two separate sections (top and bottom) divided by a hinge at the centre. The top section houses the screen and the speaker of the phone while the bottom houses the keyboard, the internal main PCB with associated peripherals and the microphone (mouthpiece). This design is best used for the 12-digit-keypad-type basic and feature class mobile phones rather than the full QWERTY keyboards which has become more common with the introduction of smartphones. Historically, flip designs were succeeded by slider designs.

Flip Phone
Figure 1.6: Sample flip phone

Slider Phones

Slider or slide phones are designed with two or more sections just like the flip phones, which slide past each other on rails. Similar to the flip, one section of the slider phones houses the display unit as well as the speaker for hearing during calls, while the other section houses the keypad assembly and slides out for user input. In some models sliding up or down provides distinct functions to the user and some sleek mechanisms are built-in to smart-pop the keypads out as soon as a user initiates the action of sliding.

Some keyboards slide out downwards while others are designed to slide out horizontally, placing the phone into a laptop kind of orientation that allows access to a computer QWERTY kind of keypad.

As is often said that history usually repeats itself, the slider phone form factor has declined, giving way to the return and dominance of the bar-type and its touchscreen/tablet/phablet subsets.

One of the drawbacks of the slider design as well as the flip designs was the use of flexible connectors to link the upper and lower (top and bottom) sections together which conveys current to power the screen, speakers, vibrators and any other device peripherals housed in the upper section from the battery in the lower (bottom) section. These "flex connectors" are delicate and wear out (break) after several cycles of "fold/open" or "slide-up/slide-down" motions necessitating technical service support to users.

Figure 1.7: Sample slider phone

Mobile Phone Classifications

Mobile devices are grouped into various categories of which one is the *Cellular Phone*. These mobile device categories are;

- Cellular or Cell Phones
- PDAs (Personal Digital Assistants)
- Smartphones

Mobile phones are further classified into three main classes;

- Basic (or dumb) phones
- Feature phones and
- Smartphones.

Now let us take a brief look at the differences between these terms.

What is a Cellular (Mobile) Phone?

A mobile phone is frequently called a cellular phone or cell-phone. These communication devices connect to a wireless communications network through radio waves or satellite transmissions. Most mobile phones provide voice communications, Short Message Service (SMS), Multimedia Message Service (MMS), and newer models also provide internet services such as Web browsing, instant messaging capabilities and e-mail.

What is a PDA?

PDA is the name given to small handheld devices that combine computing, telephone/fax, internet and networking features. It is an acronym for Personal Digital Assistant. A typical PDA can function simultaneously as a cellular phone, fax sender, Web browser and personal organizer. These devices are usually pen-based, requiring mostly the use of a stylus rather than a keyboard for input. PDAs today are available in either a stylus or keyboard version. Traditionally, PDAs do not incorporate phone or fax services.

What is a Smartphone?

A smartphone combines the features of the traditional PDA and cellular phone, with a higher leaning towards the cellular phone functionality.
These handheld devices integrate mobile phone capabilities with the more common features of a handheld computer or PDA. Smartphones allow users to store information, e-mail and install programs, alongside functioning as a mobile phone in one device. The features of a smartphone are usually more oriented towards mobile phone features than the PDA-like features. There is no industry standard for what defines a smartphone, so any mobile device that has more than basic mobile phone capabilities can actually be rated under the smartphone category of devices. Tablets fall under this category.

Smartphone historical milestones till date can be summarized thus:

- ☐ 1997– The term smartphone debuted
- ☐ 1999 - RIM began to make Blackberry phones
- ☐ 2007 - iPhone 1 was released
- ☐ 2008 - Android v1.0 was released
- ☐ 2015– iPhone 6 and Android 6.0 "Marshmallow" were released

What is a PDA Phone?

With the constant changes in technology, device functionalities and capabilities also change. In the recent past, it was easier to differentiate a PDA from a smartphone simply by looking for touch-screen capabilities. If it had a touch screen it was a PDA, if it didn't, it was a smartphone. For example, Sony Ericsson made their first Smartphone, which combined a touchscreen and a full QWERTY keyboard. The generic term for a PDA oriented device such as the Sony Ericsson phone described, having cellular phone capabilities is called a PDA phone.

Mobile Phones' Features

The following are some features and capabilities summarize the functionalities built into Mobile Cell Phones depending on the model:

- Voice call
- Storage of contact information
- Make task or to-do lists
- Keep track of appointments and set reminders
- Use the built-in calculator for simple math
- Send or receive e-mail
- Get information (news, entertainment, stock quotes) from the internet
- Play games
- Watch TV
- Send SMS messages
- Integrate other devices such as PDAs, MP3 players
- Virtual Private Network (VPN)
- Near Field Communication
- Wi-Fi Connectivity
- Bluetooth
- GPS
- Camera/ Video capabilities
- Internet Communication sharing (Hotspot)

- Third-party application support

Chapter 2

Mobile Phone Component Identification and Features

Mobile phones are just like PCs in their hardware component make up. Like a PC they have a processor, inputs and outputs, power management, radio (cellular) etc. The modern mobile phone is basically a micro computer. Unlike a PC that has PCI slots, SATA controllers and ports, memory slots, the mobile phone have these equivalents mainly soldered directly to the board. When you disassemble a mobile phone, every component part attached to the phone's motherboard is a peripheral component that aids the functionality of the main board or motherboard. But it cannot function effectively without these peripherals attached at various interfaces.

While one may buy these peripheral input/output components from any mobile phone parts store, the same does not hold true for the main board else you may buy it at almost the cost of a new phone. The actual cell phone, in my opinion is the motherboard with its internal electronics. Those internal electronic components are listed in this section and are the basic electronic components found in virtually all electronic devices in existence. What varies among varieties of electronic products are their form factors and circuit design. It is therefore important that every item found on the motherboard of the phone is properly identified by a technician. The function of a component must be known, its positional location identified and its functional or failure status determined by a technician.

The design of the motherboard is such that board space and cost is minimized. A smartphone motherboard is often made to be specific to a certain form factor or design dictated by the manufacturing company. The size constraints and costs make the phone design less generic. Today's smartphones utilize what is referred to as System on Chip or SOC technology whereby the processor and other key ICs (Integrated Circuit) integrate several functions into a single chip. Unlike the PC, today's smartphones are incredibly complex digital electronic devices. They are designed by a team of dozens of computer engineers and electrical engineers to produce durable, energy efficient, high-speed, slim, attractive, unique and affordable systems.

Therefore in concept and reality, a mobile phone especially a smartphone is basically a computer, though much more complex in design and production than a PC.

Finally, the spare parts found in the mobile phone as well as in all tablets made by the various manufacturers such as Apple, HTC, SonyEricsson, Nokia (Microsoft), Samsung, LG, Chinese phones etc. may differ only in their allocated fixed location within the phone and their shapes, sizes or other form factor. Besides that, the function of the component in the phone remains the same across models.

Peripheral Input/ Output Components

This refers to components that are attached as auxiliaries to the motherboard of the mobile phone besides the external casing of the phone. They include the following;

The Battery

The battery is the primary source of power to the mobile phone. It supplies optimum D.C (Direct Current) voltage of between 3.6v to 3.8v and is shut down by the phone at below 3.1v D.C. Most mobile phone designs provide for a user-removable back cover to gain access to the battery. In some designs, the batteries are sealed within the casing of the phone and can only be accessed by a technician disassembling the phone altogether.

Figure 2.1: Mobile Phone Batteries

Battery Connector

The battery connector provides interface between the phone's motherboard and the battery. Some connectors consist of 2 pins; some are 3 pins while others are 4 pins. The first and last pins are usually the positive and negative terminals respectively while the middle pin(s) is the battery status indicator (BSI) pin and sometimes including the battery temperature sensor pin, BTemp.

See sample images in fig. 2.2;

Figure 2.2: Mobile Phone Battery Connectors

The Microphone

The microphone or Mic usually called 'mouth-piece' in the mobile repair industry is a device that converts sound waves (human voice signal) into electrical signal in the phone. It is usually located towards the base of the mobile phone relative to the placement of the phone between the ear (top) and the mouth (base or bottom) during a phone call. See sample images of varieties of mobile phones' microphones in fig.2.3;

Sample usage
PCB section

Figure 2.3: Mobile Phone Microphones (mouthpieces)

Speakers

The speaker in a mobile phone is also called the 'ear-piece'. It provides the user of the handset with audio output from the caller. This device is placed at a position in the mobile phone relative to the placement of the ear during a phone call which is usually at the anterior part of the motherboard. See sample images in fig. 2.4;

Figure 2.4: Mobile Phone Speakers

Ringers

Ringers provide alert to users when a call is placed to the mobile device. Some ringers actually appear similar in shape and form with speakers and some too have dual functions as speakers and ringers combined, or speaker/ringer/vibrator all in one unit.

See some samples in fig. 2.5;

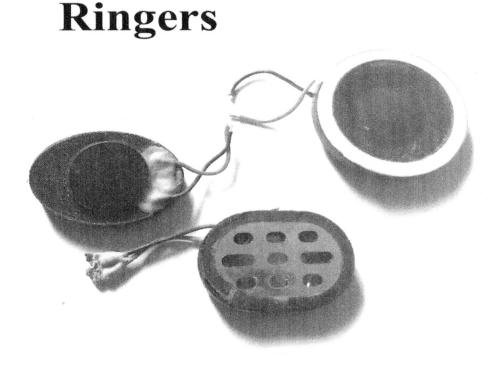

Figure 2.5: Mobile Phone Ringers

Vibrators

Vibrators also provide users with alert but in a silent manner by causing the vibration of the phone. They are made up of a D.C motor which is electromechanical in nature as electrical signal causes the rotation of the rotor within an armature.

See sample images of various vibrator types below. With the compiled images in fig. 2.6, you cannot go wrong in identifying what component is a vibrator within a mobile phone assembly.

Vibrator

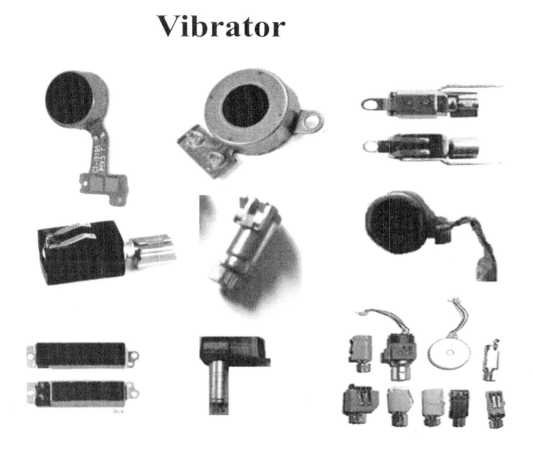

Figure 2.6: Mobile Phone Vibrators

Charging Ports

Charging ports are the connecting points for mobile phone chargers to transfer recharge voltage to the battery through the charging circuitry of the motherboard. They come in either pin-type design or modular USB data interface ports type.

See images of sample charging ports in fig. 2.7;

Figure 2.7: Mobile Phone Charging Ports

Display Units

The display unit is the mobile phone's visual/video output system for user interface. They are liquid crystal displays (LCD) and of recent were incorporated with resistive or capacitive touchscreens for user keyboard input.

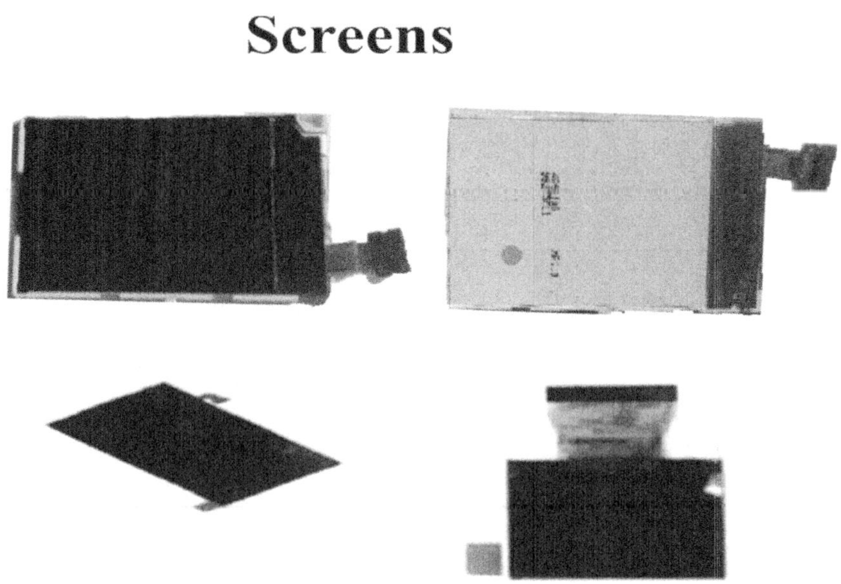

Screens

Figure 2.8: Mobile Phone LCD Screens

Display Connectors

These are socket points where the LCD displays are connected to the motherboard. There are various forms and in some cases the display is connected to the interface point through a flex connector. Note that flex connectors are not only used for connecting LCDs but also camera, keypad, volume keys, etc. See image in fig. 2.9;

Figure 2.9: Mobile Phone LCD Connectors

ON-OFF Switch

Switches are used in various forms for various functions in the mobile phone. There are physical on/off push button switches for power-on functions, side volume up/down switches, camera buttons etc. In other cases they are logical buttons that trigger a logic "1"/ "0" pulse. Below is a sample physical switch soldered to the motherboard usually hidden by more beautiful, sleek rubber or plastic buttons on the outside. See sample switch images in fig. 2.10;

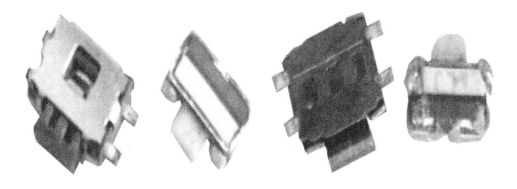

Figure 2.10: Mobile Phone Switch

Keypads

Keypads provide users with input to the mobile phone system to control its operations. Today most phones operate based on the virtual software controlled keypad system. The physical keypads were more prevalent in earlier basic and feature phone classes. Those types work as on-off logic switches which actuates when the separate concentric silver contacts are bridged together by a cylindrical metal contact.

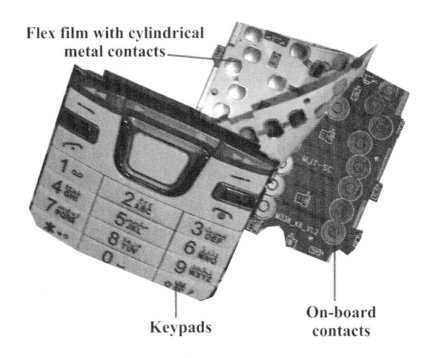

Figure 2.11: Mobile Phone Keypad System

SIM Card Connector/Carrier

SIM (which means Subscriber Identity Module) connector connects the SIM card to the motherboard of the phone. The SIM card itself is a smart memory chip supplied to the user by the chosen telecommunication carrier which contains information about that particular user, identifies him/her as a legitimate subscriber and provides access to network services.

Figure 2.12: Mobile SIM Card and SIM Connectors

Memory Card Connector

Memory cards which provide external or extended storage capacity for the mobile phone user are interfaced to the mobile device through the memory card connector embedded on the motherboard;

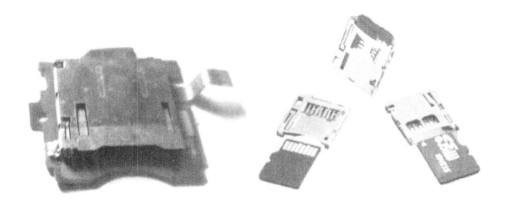

Figure 2.13: Mobile Memory Card Connectors

Camera

Mobile phones are equipped with various calibers of camera for taking pictures. They are connected to the motherboard through interface socket points.

Camera On-Board Connector

Camera

Figure 2.14: Mobile Phone Camera and Camera Connectors

Headphone Jack/Connector

This provides point of connection for external earphones or 'handsfree' cord earphones.

Figure 2.15: Mobile Phone Hands-free Ports

Antenna

The antenna couples in and out message signals to and from the mobile phone. This means that the antenna functions primarily to transmit and receive signals. The older mobile phones had their antennas sticking out from the body of the phone. Nowadays most antennas are inbuilt and only accessible when the phone is disassembled. There are various ways and forms antennas are built into the motherboard. A technician must observe to identify these representations. Example pictures below are some samples for old and new models.

Antennas

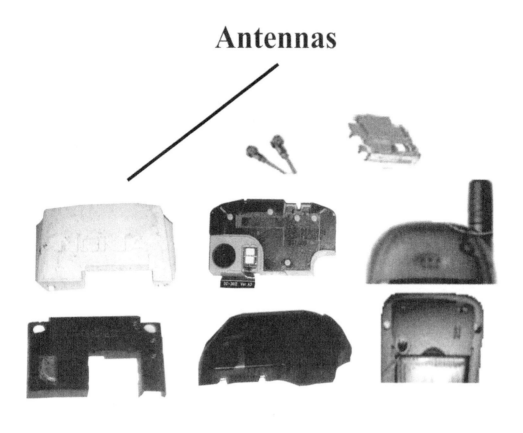

Figure 2.16: Mobile Phone Antenna System Components

Internal Electronic Components

Internal electronic components for bigger electronic/digital devices are usually of larger packages compared to the microelectronic components found in mobile phones and tablets. In the next page, snapshots of both the bigger components and their equivalent microelectronic forms as found in the mobile phones will be seen.

In chapter 6 we shall discuss in details about these electronics components.

Phone ICs

Mobile Phone ICs

BGA leads

Various Types and Sizes of Integrated Circuit Packages (ICs)

Figure 2.17

Transistors

Emitter

Base

Collector

Transistor as Seen in Mobile Phones =>

Figure 2.18: Transistors

Capacitors seen in mobile phones are in smaller form factors and specific colors.

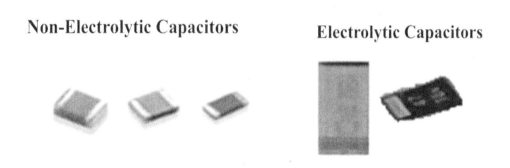

Non-Electrolytic Capacitors

Electrolytic Capacitors

Figure 2.19: Capacitors

Diodes

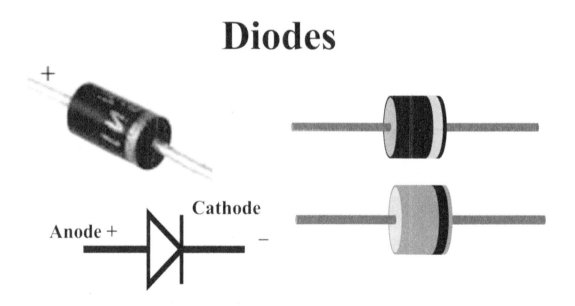

Diodes found in mobile phones are also smaller in size;

Mobile Phone PCB Diodes

Figure 2.20: Diodes

INDUCTORS

In the mobile phone, you will find inductors as shown below;

Figure 2.21: Inductors

Resistor

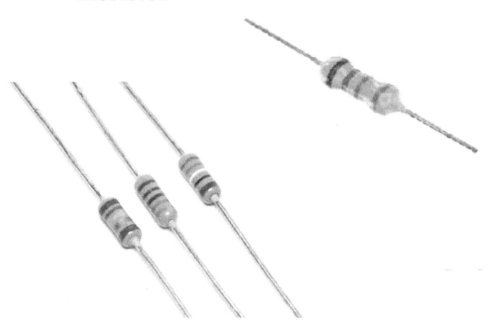

On mobile phone PCBs, you will find resistors in smaller forms as shown below;

Figure 2.22: Resistors

All the internal electronic components above are found in smaller form factors in the mobile phone as seen in the image clip below;

Sample cross-section of internal electronic components

Figure 2.23

In order to differentiate these components appropriately and diagnose faults, it is important for a technician to acquire in-depth knowledge of meter reading and circuit analysis to do electrical level troubleshooting and repairs.

Chapter 3

Introduction to Mobile Phone Hardware Repairs

With the advancements recorded thus far in the ICT sector, a great number of electronic gadgets have been introduced into the market which has made electronic communication easier. Mobile Phones or Cell phones are one such device which has made our world a global village in terms of communication. Mobile Phones are no longer a luxury but a necessity for businessmen, students and people of all profession to communicate with each other. Different classes of people can no longer afford to live or function without their phones. It is one of the most important companion or must-have item on human beings in the 21st century! This therefore is to the advantage of anyone who wants to break into the telecommunication/ICT industry as technical support personnel, or as a business person.

Market Potential

Electronic gadgets are delicate devices and tend to go out of order if handled roughly. With a larger population of humans estimated in billions possessing a mobile handset, the market potential for providing repair services and solutions is very promising.

The opportunities in providing one-to-one professional services are huge. Aside the huge profit margin in selling personal skills, it opens doors for interfacing with a whole lot of people whose appreciation of your work and expertise with a good sense of responsibility could lead to greater business possibilities.

Mobile Phone Hardware Repair Tools

The first thing an entrant to technical support should learn is about the various tools that would be required to effectively carry out his job and how to use those tools. There is a saying that "a bad workman always blames his tools". So we will start right from here so that you do not become a bad workman.

Let's go.

As a startup technician, have it in mind that there are tools that are very expensive that you may not be able to afford them at start-up. The basic tools are cheaper and easy to get and if you equip yourself with the right skill set and knowledge about Mobile Phone repairs covered in this book, the basic tools can make money for you until you are ready to make those big budget purchases. Below are the list of tools and equipment with pictures.

1. Soldering Iron and Soldering Station: Used for Soldering

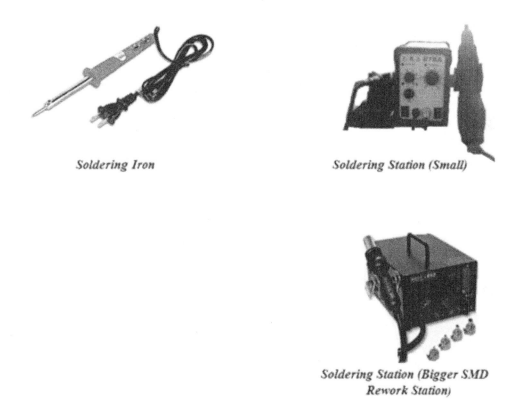

Soldering Iron   *Soldering Station (Small)*

Soldering Station (Bigger SMD Rework Station)

Figure 3.1: Soldering Iron and Rework Stations

2. Tweezers: Electronic board components are usually tiny and require the use of tweezers to pick them out or place/hold them down during soldering. They are very handy tools during the repair process.

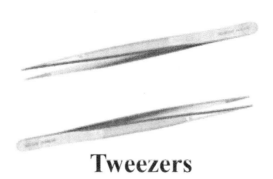

Tweezers

Figure 3.2: Tweezers

3. Soft Brush for cleaning the electronic board

Figure 3.3: Soft brush

4. Digital Pocket Multimeter: Used for checking and troubleshooting faults by measuring power supply voltage readings, connectors and motherboard wiring continuity checks etc. There are various grades of the product in the market. See image in fig. 3.4;

Figure 3.4: Digital Multimeter

5. Nose Cutter for cutting wires

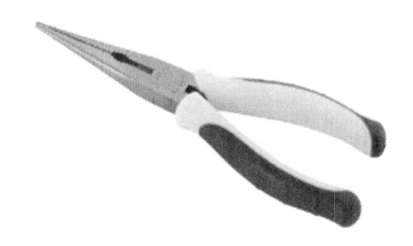

Figure 3.5: Nose Cutter

6. Screwdriver set used for mobile phone disassembly and reassembly by removing and re-tightening the screw nuts in the mobile phone. See image in fig. 3.6;

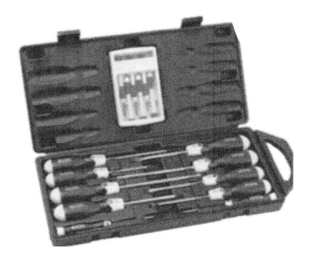

Figure 3.6: Screwdriver set

7. Soldering leads used together with the soldering iron during soldering;

Figure 3.7: Soldering lead

8. P.C.B (Printed Circuit Board) or Motherboard Clamp-Stand or Holder used for fixing the electronic board in place while carrying out repair work on it.

Figure 3.8: PCB Clamp-Stand/Holder

9. Soldering Fluxes used during the soldering process for effective heat transfer and to prevent oxidation. They come in liquid and paste forms

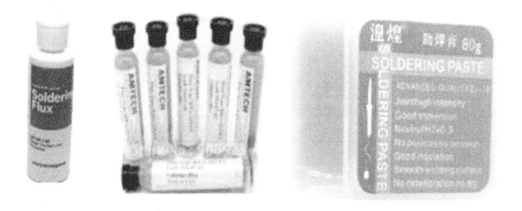

Figure 3.9: Soldering pastes

10. Magnifying Glass and Lamp are used to magnify the electronic board's view in order to see the tiny components properly.

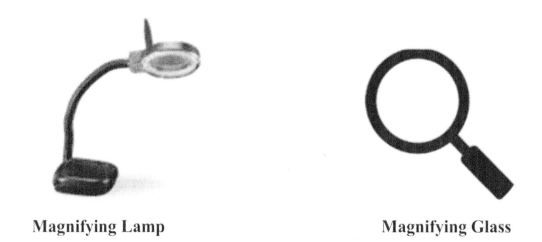

Magnifying Lamp   **Magnifying Glass**

Figure 3.10: Magnifying tools

11. Mobile Phone Casing Openers used for slicing open conjoined front and back fascia of mobile phones. They come in different forms and shapes and a technician can also improvise a means for safe disassembly.

See images on fig. 3.11;

Figure 3.11: Casing openers

12. D.C Power supply unit used for providing alternative D.C supply

Figure 3.12: D.C Power supply unit
Image Source: www.alibaba.com

13. Electronic Board Cleaning Agents are used for cleaning the P.C.B after a liquid damage or during mobile phone servicing. Many technicians use Methylated spirits. This is not a good standard board cleaning agent because it contains toxic oils. Search for and obtain from any chemical vendor, IsoPropyl Alchohol (IPA) which is a better non-oil cleaning agent for mobile phones. Thinner also serves as a good cleaning agent for PCBs. However peripheral component units must first be removed from the main board before it is applied.

14. Jumper Wires are also important. It is advisable to purchase the commercially available coated ones like in the picture below although you may get some strands off most flexible electrical wire bundles.

Figure 3.13: Roll of Jumper wires

15. LCD/Touchscreen Machine Separator is a new device made with the introduction and predominance of touchscreens in mobile phones used for separating damaged touchscreens from the LCD with ease. It is a pricey device.

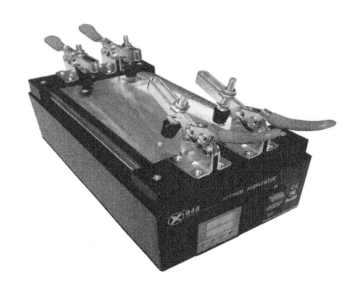

LCD/Touchscreen Separator machine
Figure 3.14

Finally, I will like to encourage a starter not to lose heart with the assumption that one must have all these tools and equipment before you can start a mobile phone repair workshop. Your most basic need is "Technical know-how". The tools required for **'Hardware Repairs'** mobile phone service operations, just like PC repairs are pretty simple and inexpensive. You can carry most of these tools in a small tool handbag or briefcase sized container with the exception of an SMD rework station and a computer (Desktop or Laptop for software repairs). The total cost of these toolkits ranges between 3000-5000 Naira ($20-30) which is very affordable. The best way to maximize use of this book to learn is to purchase these tools and try out what you learn as you go through this book.

PART 2

TECHNICAL HANDS-ON REPAIRS

Chapter 4

Technical Skill-Sets a Technician Must First Master

A good technician must master some key skills practically before he begins to apply that knowledge on technical fault correction. The major difference between a mobile phone technician or most technicians and their clients is not just the knowledge of how a system works or what to do, but actually **doing** what you know. Most times, users already 'know' what could have gone wrong and in some cases, probably what needs to be done to correct the fault BUT THEY CANNOT **DO** IT.

Doing It and ***Doing it right*** therefore is the reason you get paid by the client. For instance, a client brings to you his mobile phone and complains that people could not hear him at the other end. The client goes further to tell you his microphone or mouth-piece is bad and needs to be changed! (Maybe he picked that knowledge somewhere and maybe he is partially correct because changing it might not be the only solution). So you go thinking *'Hugh? Wait a minute why did you come to me with it then? You could as well have fixed it already!'*

The truth is, he/she cannot **Do (fix) It.** Your technical skill in the area of mobile phone disassembly and reassembly will fetch you his/her money. You know what? It is an important and so delicate a skill that other electronic technicians (for bigger devices like TV, Radio etc) still go after mobile phone technicians when their phones develop faults.

This brings us to the second skill - soldering. Most of those who work on bigger motherboards like home electronics technicians do whack jobs on tinier mobile phone motherboards. BGA and micro-electronic device soldering therefore, is another very important skill to master.

The third skill a technician cannot do without is on the use of Multimeters. Every electronic or electrical technical support personnel must be knowledgeable in this area to be distinctly more efficient. It is a skill that must be applied in the day-to-day operation as a technical solution provider especially if you understand electronic circuits and systems very well.

Understanding electronic circuits and the reading of circuit diagrams is another area that technicians must pay strict attention to. However, the lack of or level of education and probably the area of study of individuals interested in doing technical support may pose a hindrance to in-depth appreciation of this skill area. I will encourage the reader not to lose heart about this. It is not mandatory but essential for a higher level of professionalism.

In this book, I hope to provide you with the foundational knowledge required.

Mobile Phone Disassembly and Reassembly

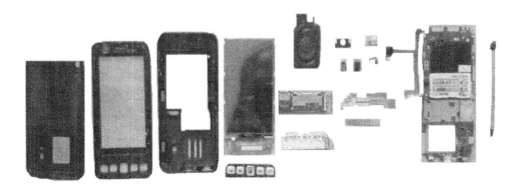

Figure 4.1: Sample Phone Disassembly

Requirement: Precision Screw driver set

Figure 4.2: Precision Screwdriver Sets

Background

Today's cell phones have more computing power than earlier computers that were larger in size. As technology advances, these handsets and their associated components become smaller and smaller. For every task of repairing a phone, you must first identify the mobile device manufacturer and model number. This is important. The information is usually written at the back label underneath the battery, sometimes on the front of the device.

Remember that everything you learn in this book applies to both mobile phones and tablets.

Procedures

Each phone or tablet is unique in the way it is coupled together and the software it runs. The following are just a general guide to follow which is applicable to all phones and tablets' disassembly.

1. Turn the mobile device off as a first step.
2. Remove the back cover of the phone you want to disassemble.
3. Remove the battery, SIM card, and if there is any, the memory card especially for models that have the card slots at the side of the device and not directly seen on the back above the battery compartment.
4. Now take a few moments to study the device design. Observe the rear side of the device carefully for screws, screw-holes, or screw-holes stuffed neatly with cylindrical rubber padding.
5. Then again observe for the slit border-line of coupling between the front and back casing of the phone. This is a sure feature on every phone as there hardly is a modular design without a demarcation slit. Now there is an exceptional case. Nokia designed such partially modular design in some models whereby the top and bottom of the phone can be removed while the PCB is eventually slid out from the module. See fig. 4.3a.
6. Then take your screw driver, observe the type of Phillips screw head used. It could be a 3-point, 4-point or 5-point star or

pentalobe. Choose the screw bit that fits and remove the screw nuts one by one, placing them carefully in a holder on your work table. Be very careful not to misplace these nuts. Usually your screw driver has an intrinsic magnetic property that holds the nuts on its body until you remove them to a safer place.

Caution: *If you are dealing with an iPhone product, carefully mark the screws and their locations as soon as you remove them. If you replace a screw into a location that is different from where it was removed from, the screen may be damaged and it will result into a blue screen condition.*

Now take a look at the pictures in fig. 4.3;

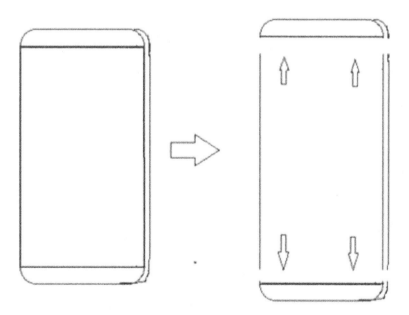

PCB slid out topwards or downwards

Fig. 4.3a

Figure 4.3b: Back cover screw holes

You can see the four screw slots above the battery and two beside it left and right, making a total of six. In some cases there may be 4 at the edges of the square section above the battery covered with a clip-fixed back cover which you must remove before you find the screws and 4 downwards. The point is; your task is to locate the screws holding the phone's casing together. Have it at the back of your mind that these screws exist, tucked away in such a way to avoid being very obvious to the untrained eye while ensuring a sleek, less mechanical design. In cases where you fail to find any screws at the rear especially for the square/rectangular section above the battery compartment, know for sure that the screws are hidden on the front chassis behind the screen or front cover casing of the device. In such cases, you have to remove the front cover casing by sliding off the clips holding it to the chassis and the back casing.

Take a look below at a sample front casing with clips to understand what they are like.

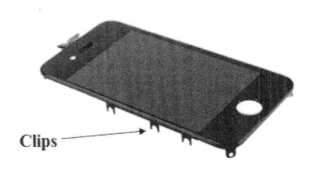

Figure 4.4: Sample casing side fixture clips

Fig. 4.5 shows some common specimens of screw heads;

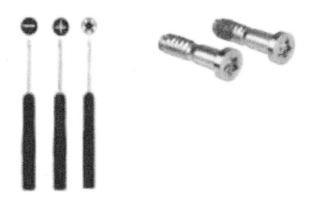

Figure 4.5: Screw heads

Observe that when holding the device, your hand should grip the sides of the phone while the other holds the screw driver. Avoid bare palm touches on the board as static electric discharge from your palms can damage the motherboard. Standard practice is to buy and use anti-static wrist straps.

7. Once you succeed in dissecting the upper or lower casing from the other/chassis, cautiously watch out for flexible cable connectors that may be stuck to the casing body; may require immediate detachment; are probably attached to side keys(for volume control, camera etc). You need to apply tact and keen observation when handling phones you've never disassembled before.

8. Carefully pick up any part (plastic or whatever) that falls off to the table and make an observatory note of where that part came off from. Like the Phillips screw-nuts, place each item carefully in a safe container.

9. Next is to take another long look at the chassis with on-board components. Are there other tightly fixed Phillips screws? Take them out sequentially, taking note of which part is being held in what position. It gets easier as you go step by step. **Do not force anything out** - you have to keenly observe and you'll figure out whatever (gum or nuts) it is that holds it in that position.

10. Note that the flex connectors that socket certain components to the cell phone motherboard are of different types. A hands-on practice with dummy phones will help to home-in on some models while you try to figure it out yourself.

The above-listed are a summary of the general steps to take in mobile phone disassembly. To reassemble the components back, you will have to follow a reverse order of actions you took in dissecting the specimen.

Recommended Action

Go to a 'scrapped phones' (there usually are) market and buy faulty or dead phones for practice. Some sell at N200-N500 ($2) a piece.

How to Use the Multimeter for Measurement

Figure 4.6: Digital Multimeter

What is a Multi-meter?

A multi-meter is a device used commonly for diagnostic tracing in electrical/electronic circuits to confirm that expected voltages and currents are present at the right points in the circuit as well as resistance across component terminals. It is therefore used for measurement of voltage, resistance and current in electronics or electrical equipment as well as to test continuity between two points to verify if there are any breaks in the circuit or line.

There are two types of multimeter;

- Analog Multimeter which has a needle style gauge.
- Digital Multimeter which has an LCD display with digital readout.

We shall rather focus on Digital multimeters especially using the specimen type in the images here. There are several other types in the market.

Meter Probes or Leads

- Probes are the handles used to hold the tip on the tested connection point. The tips are at the end of the probes and provide a connection to the test point.

- The Red meter lead is connected to Voltage/Resistance or amperage port and is considered the positive connection probe. There are usually two ports, one for lower currents and the other for high current measurements from 10A.

- The Black meter lead is always connected to the common port and is considered the negative connection probe.

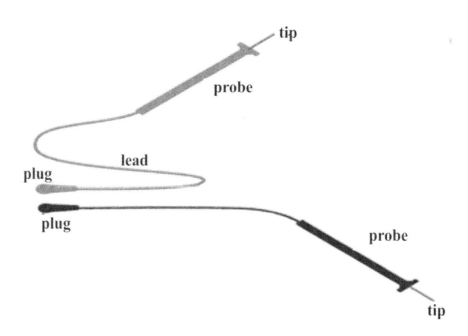

Figure 4.7: Digital Multimeter probes

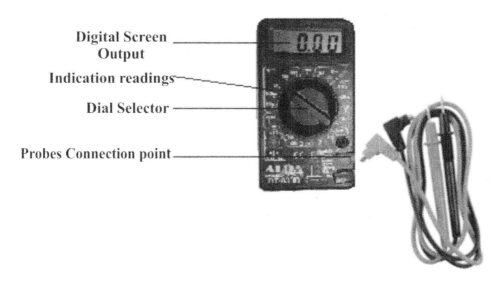

Digital Screen Output

Indication readings

Dial Selector

Probes Connection point

Understanding the Meter Calibration Parameters

Before we learn how to measure the various electrical quantities, it is important for the trainee to learn about the meaning of the numbers selected by the dial selector switch for any quantity being measured. Below is a magnified image of the calibration surface of the meter;

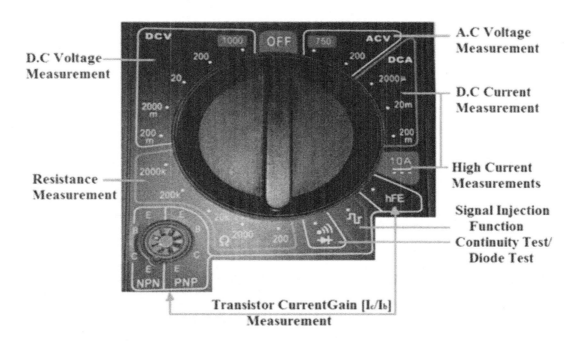

D.C Voltage Measurement

Resistance Measurement

A.C Voltage Measurement

D.C Current Measurement

High Current Measurements

Signal Injection Function

Continuity Test/ Diode Test

Transistor CurrentGain [I_c/I_b] Measurement

Each of the sections has a range of values that are similar to the prefixes used in the metric system such as **milli**-meter, **kilo**-meter etc. These prefixes are used just the same way for volts, ohms and amps – the units of measurement of electricity. Looking at the image above, you will notice the following;

m = milli

k = kilo

μ = micro

Symbols	Prefix Name	Numerical Equivalent	Mathematical Expression
m	milli	0.001	10^{-3}
μ	micro	0.000001	10^{-6}
k	kilo	1, 000	10^{3}
M	Mega	1, 000, 000	10^{6}
G	Giga	1, 000, 000, 000	10^{9}

Table 4.1: Metric system and units

There are others but let me stick to the multimeter before us. Some multimeters have an auto range feature that selects the range automatically thereby removing the mental hassle of determining the dial selector point manually. Let me explain each calibration range;

D.C Voltage Measurement: The range of values here are from 200 millivolts to 1000 volts DC comparable to a linear scale from (-x) to (0) to (+x) axis on a cartesian co-ordinate. When measuring battery voltages, the dial selector should point to this block. For accurate resolution of values, point to the value range closest to the expected value measured.

For instance, mobile phone batteries range between 3.6V to 4.2V max. The closest to this value is "20" on the multimeter DCV block. Point the dial selector to '20' in order to measure the battery voltage. Most Digital Multimeters are auto-polarity sensing devices. This means that for such types you do not have to worry about having the Red lead on the positive and the Black Lead on the Neutral or negative of the battery or other terminals. It just gives you the accurate reading.

A.C Voltage Measurement: The range of values here is between 0V to 750V AC (0-200 and 201-750). For any value between 0 – 200, there will be an output or the display will be "1" or out-of-range signified by "OL" (overload) in others. When that happens, move the dial upwards in the range (in this case to 750) and test. To measure AC voltage, we place the Red lead into the "VΩmA" port and black lead into the "COM" port. Turn the dial selector switch to ACV or V~ in some models.

If it is a manual ranging meter set it for the proper range. As an example the meter would be set to the 200V range to measure an 110V outlet and 750V range to measure a 220V AC outlet. If you have an auto-ranging meter you only need to set function to ACV. It is always a good practice to connect the black probe first, followed by the red probe.

D.C Current Measurement: This function also measures DC current and therefore is selected to measure such values. There are two ranges of values for measuring up to a maximum 200milliamps and for values up to maximum 10A. When measuring higher current values, the red probe has to be moved to port 1.

See the image in fig. 4.8;

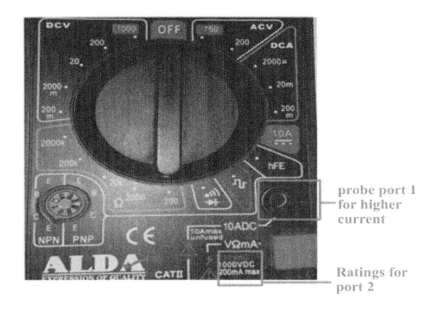

Figure 4.8: Digital Multimeter probe connection

Resistance Measurement: The resistance calibration follows a range of values from 0-200 ohms up to maximum 2,000k (2, 000, 000 ohms) or 2MΩ. K is kilo which is thousand. 2000k is equivalent to 2000 x k (1000) which is 2, 000,000. During measurement, it is advisable to begin from the lowest range and move up if the output is "1" or "OL" indicating out-of-range.

Continuity Test/Diode Test: This selection point is for continuity testing with audible alarm to aid in troubleshooting without taking your eyes off the PCB. It also doubles for testing Diodes' forward resistance.

Transistor Current Gain Testing: This function block is used to measure the current gain of a transistor which is the ratio of its output collector current I_c to the input base current I_b. On the left side are slots for inserting the three pins of a transistor, either an NPN or PNP, marked EBC (top-to-down); ECB (bottom-up) for any type of transistor test. It may therefore serve also to detect the right pin combinations or type of transistor since a gain output can only appear on the display when properly situated.

Signal Injection Function: This function when selected is used for injecting a square wave of about 2V peak at a frequency of between 30 and 40 HZ into an audio device. Mostly used for testing whether an amplifier is functioning or not. To use this function;

- Turn the dial selector to the Signal Injection Function

- Using the negative black meter probe, touch the ground of the circuit being measured.

- At the point in the circuit where the test signal is to be injected, touch the red probe tip.

Measurement of Voltage

Voltage (V) is the unit of electrical pressure force. One volt is defined as the potential difference needed to cause one amp of current to pass through one ohm of resistance. Voltage is broken up into 2 classes - AC and DC. Alternating Current (AC) is the NEPA/PHCN supply voltage (220-240Va/c) in Nigeria while Direct Current (DC) is battery voltage.

To measure;

- First, be careful not to touch any other electronic components within the equipment and do not short (bridge) the tips to each other while connected to anything else.

- To measure voltage, connect the leads in parallel between the two points where the measurement is to be made. The multi-meter provides a parallel pathway so it needs to be of a high resistance to allow as little current to flow through it as possible.

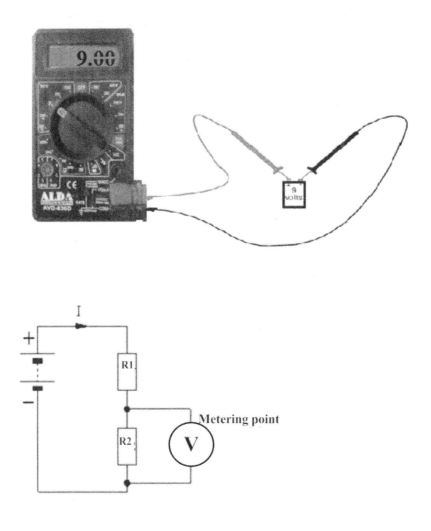

Figure 4.9: Voltage Measurement

Measurement of Resistance and Continuity

Resistance is the opposition to current flow and is measured in ohms. To carry out a resistance measurement;

- Disconnect the power source before testing.
- Remove the component or part from the system before testing.
- Measure using the lowest calibration point, if 0Ω, move to the next.

- Testing for continuity is used to verify if a circuit, wire or fuse is "closed" or "open" circuited (a break).
- Audible sound is heard if the circuit, wire, or fuse is complete (continuous end-to-end) but silent if there is a break in the circuit, wire or fuse. In analog multimeters the range is between 0 to ∞ (infinity is high resistance). "Closed" i.e 0Ω while "open" is ∞.

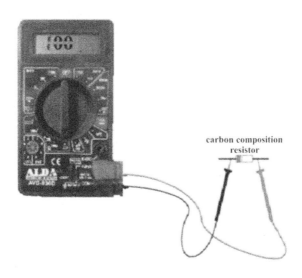

carbon composition resistor

Figure 4.10: Resistance Measurement

Measurement of Current

Current is the flow of charge through a component or conductor and the unit of measurement is the Ampere (Amps), A. To measure current;

- First disconnect the power source before measurement.
- Disconnect the completed circuit at its end.
- Place multimeter in series with the circuit.
- Reconnect the power source and turn it ON.
- Select the highest current calibration setting and work your way down.

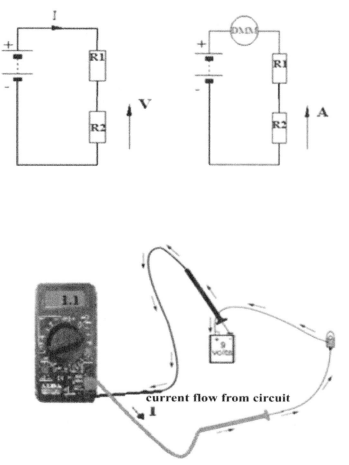

Figure 4.11: Current Measurement

Review

❖ A meter capable of checking for voltage, current, and resistance is called a *multimeter*.

❖ When measuring Voltage the multimeter must be connected to two reference points in a circuit in order to obtain a good reading. Be careful not to touch the probe's tips together while measuring voltage, as this will create short-circuits!

❖ Never carry out resistance measurement or test for continuity with a multimeter on a circuit that is energized.

❖ When measuring Current, the multimeter must be connected in a circuit in such a way that the electrons have to flow *through* the meter.

❖ Multimeters have practically no resistance between their leads. This is intended to allow electrons to flow through the meter with the least possible difficulty. If this were not the case, the meter would add extra resistance in the circuit, thereby affecting the current or values.

Symbols	Terms	Symbols	Terms
~	AC Voltage	+	Positice
▪▪▪	DC Voltage	−	Negative
Hz	Hertz	μF	MicroFarad
⏚	Ground	μ	Micro
⊣⊢	Capacitor	m	Milli
Ω	Ohms	K	Kilo
▸⊢	Diode	M	Mega
•)))	Audible Continuity	OL or "1"	Overload/Infinity

Table 4.2: Symbols and their meanings

Good Component Measurement Values

The following peripheral comp7onents attached to the motherboard of mobile phones have been proven to have a range of resistance values during their optimum performance lifecycle.

1. Microphone (Mouth Piece)   - $700 - 1700\ \Omega \pm 100$
2. Speakers (Earpiece)   - $30 - 33\ \Omega \pm 3$
3. Ringers   - $8 - 10\ \Omega \pm 1$
4. Vibrators   - $8\text{-}16\ \Omega \pm 1$

These are optimum performance values. Any value below the minimum or above the maximum would mean that the component has either failed or is depreciating to a non-functional or non-optimal level even if it is still in use and working.

How to Test Various Components

Specialized component analyzers exist for carrying out the task of testing various electronic components but the expense can be difficult to justify for the average technician especially a start-up. If you take a survey worldwide of field or bench technicians, you will discover that their most-used piece of test equipment is a Digital Multimeter (Analog multimeter for some). These versatile devices can be used to test and diagnose a wide range of circuits and components and for this book promoting technical entrepreneurship among the youths; we shall be concentrating on the use of the Digital Multimeter.

Switches

To test switches:

i. Determine what type of switch you are faced with.
ii. Put the multimeter in continuity test ("diode symbol") mode with buzzer (beep) alert.
iii. Identify the switch's PCB (Printed Circuit Board, also called the motherboard) terminals.
iv. For a 2-terminal switch in normal (OFF) state, test for continuity between both terminals. If a beep confirms continuity, replace the switch.
v. If there is no continuity in the OFF state, place the probes each on both terminals and press or operate the switch.
vi. If there is a beep (continuity indicator) when the switch is operated, the switch is ok. If there is no beep (no continuity), the switch is damaged. Change the switch.
vii. For 4-terminal switches, note that only two polarities exist in electrical supply. There are therefore only 2 test points. The extra 2 terminals are usually either for balance or due to other switch

design considerations. Identify the test point terminals (a pair is continuous with each other but separate from the other pair) and repeat procedure (iv) to (vi) above.

Microphones

To test Microphones:

i. Put the multimeter in continuity test ("diode symbol") mode with buzzer (beep) alert.
ii. Microphones are 2-terminal components. Place the positive (+) probe to the terminal connected to the PCB's positive (+) pad. It is usually marked on the PCB. Place the negative (-) probe to its negative (-) terminal too.
iii. Reading on the meter should range between $700\sim1700\Omega \pm 100$
iv. For any value below 600Ω or above 1800Ω replace.

Speakers

To test Speakers:

i. Put the multimeter in continuity test ("diode symbol") mode with buzzer (beep) alert.
ii. Speakers are 2-terminal components. Place the positive (+) probe to the terminal connected to the PCB's positive (+) pad. It is usually marked on the PCB. In some cases the terminals are PVC coated red (+) and black (-) wires. Place the negative (-) probe to its negative (-) terminal too.
iii. Reading on the meter should range between $30\sim33\Omega \pm 3$
iv. For any value below 27Ω or above 36Ω replace.

Ringers

To test Ringers:

i. Put the multimeter in continuity test ("diode testing") mode with buzzer (beep) alert.

ii. Ringers are 2-terminal components. Place the positive (+) probe to the terminal connected to the PCB's positive (+) pad. It is usually marked on the PCB. In some cases the terminals are PVC coated red (+) and black (-) wires. Place the negative (-) probe to its negative (-) terminal too.

iii. Reading on the meter should range between 9~10Ω ± 1

iv. For any value below 8Ω or above 11Ω replace.

Vibrators

To test Vibrators:

i. Put the multimeter in continuity ("diode symbol") test mode with buzzer (beep) alert.

ii. Vibrators are 2-terminal components. Place the positive (+) probe to the terminal connected to PCB's positive (+) pad. It is usually marked on the PCB. In some cases the terminals are PVC coated red (+) and black (-) wires. Place the negative (-) probe to its negative (-) terminal too.

iii. Reading on the meter should range between 9~15Ω ± 1

iv. For any value below 8Ω or above 16Ω replace.

Resistors

Resistors are passive two-terminal electrical components that implements electrical resistance as a circuit element. In an earlier section, we examined how to measure resistances.

To test Resistors:

i. Put the multimeter in Resistance test mode.

ii. There is no polarity to resistor terminals. You may place the probes either way. The PCB must be disconnected from the power supply mains.

iii.   Place the positive (+) probe on one of its terminals connected to the PCB. Place the negative (-) probe on its other terminal and take readings.

iv.   The dial selector switch should be turned to the lowest scale on the resistance calibrator before starting the measurement.

v.   Before testing a resistor, it is better to establish what an accurate reading for the specific resistor should be.

vi.   Continue to scale up until a unit value is obtained.

vii.   Test results must not be too low that the value approximates to zero ohms. That will indicate a value equivalent to a short circuit (like a jumper). Exception is for resistors used as fuses. Also if the results are too high, this may be indicative of an open circuit resistor (broken) or a resistor that has acquired a higher value. This is a possible sign of a fault.

Diodes

Diodes are electronic devices that allow current through them ONLY in one direction (anode to cathode) with ease but blocks the flow of current through them from the other direction (cathode to anode). A diode is a two-terminal electronic component. It has low resistance to the flow of current in one direction and high (or infinite) resistance in the other direction.

Semi-conductor signal diodes are the most common occurring types in mobile phone circuit-boards. Also, it is pertinent to draw the readers' attention to the difference between convention current flow and electron flow. It is explained later in Chapter 6 "Electronic fundamentals"

Convention current is the flow of current from the positive (+) terminal to the negative (-) terminal while electrons flow from the negative (-) cathode to the positive (+) anode in a diode.

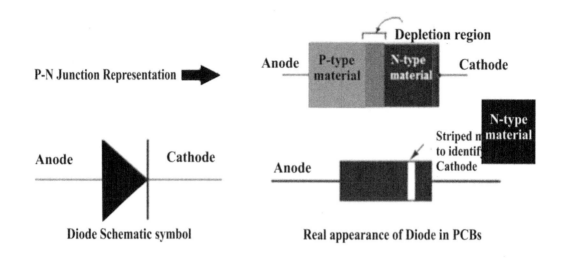

Figure 4.12: Diode Symbols

To test diodes for defect:

i. Put the multimeter in continuity test ("diode symbol") mode with buzzer (beep) alert.

ii. Place the positive (+) probe to the Anode terminal connected to the PCB pad and place the negative (-) probe to the Cathode (-) terminal marked with a stripe.

iii. **Note:** The output read on the meter display should differ for various diodes according to the diode's rated forward resistance. This test is not meant for taking value readings. It is simply a PASS/FAIL test.

iv. If there is an output value in this direction, switch the probes to the opposite terminals and there should be no reading (infinite resistance) in this state for a good diode.

v. If there are output values in both cases, the diode is shorted.

vi. If there was no reading (infinite resistance) in both cases, the diode is open.

vii. The diode should read forward resistance ONLY when the positive probe (+) is on the ANODE and the negative (-) probe is on the Cathode and no reading when the probes are reversed.

Transistors

Transistors are composed of semiconductor materials with at least three terminals for connection to an external circuit.

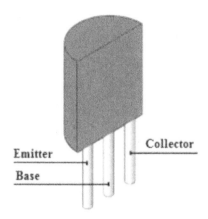

Figure 4.13: Transistor

There are two types of transistors;

- NPN Transistors
- PNP Transistors

To test transistors, we have to view the component as two back-to-back diodes connected together this way;

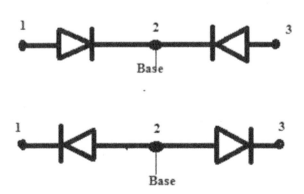

Transistor equivalent using 2 back-to-back diodes
Figure 4.14

Either of the sides could be determined to be the Collector and Emitter respectively.

Method 1

Using the digital multimeter, let us identify the 3 pins in the transistor image above with numbers 1, 2, and 3. This is for Bipolar Junction transistors;

  i.   Select continuity ("diode testing") test point on the meter with buzzer alert.

 ii.   **Note:** Reading on the meter should differ for various diodes according to the diode rated forward resistance. This test is not meant for taking reading of values. It is simply a PASS/FAIL test.

iii.   Place the positive probe (+) at pin2 of the transistor. This should not be assumed as the Base.

 iv.   Place the negative (-) probe alternately at the two side pins - 1 and 3. Any reading? If 2-1 reads and 2-3 reads, then both have forward resistance of the two back-to-back diode arms.

  v.   Alternate by replacing the positive probe on pin2 with the negative probe. Did pin 2-1 and 2-3 give any reading or infinite resistance? If both arms gave no reading, the transistor is in good condition. Next is to conclude on what type of transistor. If it gave a reading both sides while **P**ositive is at the common point (Base), then it is NPN. When **N**egative is the common (Base) pin, then it is PNP

 vi.   After checking with the positive probe at pin2, always reverse check with the negative probe on the same pin2. Pin2 will not always be the Base (common). The Base point is that pin which when used as the starting test point (+ or − probe) will give a forward resistance reading with the other probe placed alternately at the other two pins.

Method 2

Another method to test a known transistor is by voltage output reading.

Any contrary reading to the following values below would mean that the transistor being tested is bad;

i. Remove the transistor from the circuit for accurate test results.

ii. The emitter-base junction typically has a slightly higher voltage drop than the collector-base junction. This is a way to determine which is which.

iii. Start with testing the Base to Emitter junction. Place the positive probe from the multimeter to the BASE (B) of the transistor. Place the negative meter probe to the EMITTER (E) of the transistor. For a good NPN transistor, the meter should display a voltage drop between 0.45V and 0.9V. If you are testing a PNP transistor, you should see "1" (Infinite Resistance).

iv. Test the Base to Collector junction. Place the positive probe on the BASE (B) and place the negative probe on the COLLECTOR (C). For a good NPN transistor, the meter should display a voltage drop between 0.45V and 0.9V. If you are testing a PNP transistor, you should see "1" (Infinite Resistance).

v. Test the Emitter to Base junction. Place the positive probe from the multimeter to the EMITTER (E) of the transistor and the negative meter probe to the BASE (B) of the transistor. For a good NPN transistor, you should see infinite resistance. If you are testing PNP transistor, the meter should display a voltage drop between 0.45V and 0.9V.

vi. Next test the Collector to Base junction. Place the positive probe from the multimeter to the COLLECTOR (C) of the transistor and the negative meter probe to the BASE (B) of the transistor. For a good NPN transistor, you should see "1" (Infinite Resistance).If you are testing a PNP transistor, the meter should display a voltage drop between 0.45V and 0.9V.

vii. Then test the Collector to Emitter junction. Place the positive meter probe to the COLLECTOR (C) and the negative meter probe to the EMITTER (E). A good NPN or PNP transistor will display "1" (Infinite Resistance). Reverse the probes (Positive to Emitter and Negative to Collector). A good NPN or PNP transistor should read "1" or Infinite Resistance.

Capacitors

To test capacitors specifically in mobile phone PCBs, we have to first consider its property as a component that store energy as an electrostatic field. They are found in mobile devices in various colors and types as seen earlier in this book.

- Non-Electrolytic Capacitor: They are light black (dark grey), yellow or brown in color. They are non-polarized (no positive (+) or Negative (-) terminal marking).

- Electrolytic Capacitor: They are either Orange in color with brown strip at one end or black with a white strip on one end. The side with the strip is Positive (+) while the other side is Negative (-).

The reason for this description is that testing for capacitor failure includes observing the coloration that occurs when they burn out.

Capacitors become defective in two ways;

- Short circuit
- Open circuit

To carry out a test for short circuit defect;

i.   Set the multimeter to its minimum resistance scale.
ii. For **electrolytic capacitor** connect the negative (-) probe to the capacitor's positive (+) terminal and the positive (+) probe to the negative (-) terminal.
iii. If the meter reads zero ohms initially and goes to infinity ('1' in some digital multimeters) then it is not short-circuited (shorted).
iv. For **non-electrolytic capacitors** like ceramic and other capacitor types with a capacitance less than 1.0 µF, the meter reading will

remain motionless i.e. infinite resistance.

v. If it is shorted, the meter reading will tend to zero ohms.

vi. For bigger capacitors, the standard thing to do is to remove a lead from the PCB circuit. But for mobile devices, do not try it. The idea is to test the ability of the capacitor being tested to behave according to its normal operational property of charge storage. When D.C supply is applied to its terminals, the voltmeter output will simply reflect the supply voltage output after a while; if the capacitor is leaking or if the capacitor has shorted, the voltmeter reading will jump high and then drop low again although not to zero; and if the meter registers no increase in value or jump at all, then the capacitor is either open or the capacitance is too low to register a result.

vii. For mobile phone capacitors, clean the PCB to ground the capacitors and neutralize all residual charge. If the target for testing has any charge, bridge the terminals to discharge it. Then apply power for 20 seconds to the PCB. Test again to confirm that it acquires charge from the supply as in (vi) above.

Inductors

Inductors are simply made up of a coil of wire wound on an armature or soft iron core. The best test to check whether an inductor is good or not is by testing the inductor's resistance with your multimeter;

i. Set the multimeter's dial selector switch to ohmmeter (resistance) setting.

ii. Polarity does not matter with resistance measurement. Place the (+) and (-) probes each on one terminal of the inductor.

iii. The inductor should read a very low resistance across its terminals, only a few ohms. If an inductor reads a high resistance, it is defective and should be replaced in the circuit.

iv. If an inductor is reading very, very small resistance value, less than an ohm (very close to 0Ω), this may be a sign that it is shorted. Functional inductors normally read a few ohms, greater than 1Ω

and usually less than 10Ω. This is a healthy range for an inductance value. Any value outside this range is normally a sign that the inductor is bad.

Testing Integrated Circuit Packages (ICs) On Mobile Phone PCBs

The Power IC and CPU

To test these powerful chips, we use the following measurements deduced from normal values in functional mobile devices. *Note that these are deduced from years of field service experience. These are not to be construed as scientifically proven values.* Using a D.C power supply unit;

i. Adjust the voltage setting of the DC Power Supply to 4.2V D.C.
ii. Place the positive probe of the D.C Power Supply unit to the positive (+) terminal of the Battery Connector of the mobile phone and the negative Probe to the battery connector's negative (-) terminal.
iii. Check the D.C Ampere reading. If the DC Ampere is over 6A, then either the Power IC or CPU is damaged.
iv. First replace the Power IC.
v. If the problem is not solved, replace the CPU.
vi. If there is 0A reading on the display, then there could be problem with any of the following;
   • Battery Connector
   • Power Switch current supply track or
   • RF Crystal oscillator
vii. If the current on the Ammeter reading is below 2A, there may be a software problem or a dead RTC (Real Time Clock) battery.
viii. If there is a beep sound from the D.C Power Supply machine, then there exists a short-circuit problem with the mobile device.

The Soldering Process

Soldering skills is one skill you cannot do without if you want to function as a good technical support provider. One action you must take is to practice.

Practice! Practice!! Practice!!!

You have to practice until you perfect the skills.

What is Soldering?

Soldering is the process of jointing two terminals together. The necessary tools required are;

1. The soldering iron /station - Use a 25W iron for small jobs and 100W for larger jobs. The soldering station has a variable temperature iron which is safer for boards as the tip temperature is adjusted to suit the job size.
2. Soldering wire – made of Lead and Tin alloy
3. Soldering paste/flux – is an additive that facilitates the soldering process by removing and preventing oxidation thereby improving the wetting/melting characteristics of the liquid solder.
4. Tweezers or clamp – Use tweezers or clamp to hold the components during the process as the components are very small.
5. Cutter/ Needle-nosed Plier.

Take a look at some needed tools images in fig. 4.15.

SMD Rework Station

Figure 4.15: Soldering Tools

Soldering Procedure

Soldering deals with both surface mount and 'through-hole' components which are pressed into printed circuit boards (PCBs). These components have leads or wires that are either surface mounted or passed through a hole in the board, soldered to the pad of metal plating around the hole.

There are different techniques for soldering various components into the board but the general principle governing the soldering process are as follows and will suffice;

- To solder a component to the PCB, use a tweezer or tong to place or hold the component in place, which in most cases are small miniature devices. Then with one hand holding the soldering iron, place the iron's tip first on the pad (contact) while holding the solder wire on the other hand directed at the tip of the iron at the joint between the PCB and the component's terminal. This way, the hand holding the solder wire controls the amount of solder melted at the joint as it is withdrawn from the joint. See image below

- You may use a clamp to hold the board in place (recommended) or just placed on the work table while you solder the components.

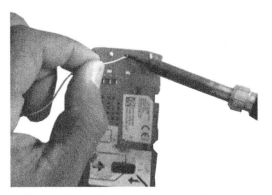 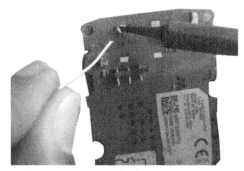

A. Feed the solder to the iron tip   B. Stop feed by withdrawing feed-hand

- Prepare the components to be soldered. For cell phone micro size packages, use the heat from the iron to moisten the terminal point with small lead and use cleaning agent to wipe the surfaces for clean soldering. For bigger components, bend the component's leads correctly and carefully to avoid damage, and fit into the PCB board's terminal position.

- Next you "tin" the solder. This is done by melting a small blob of solder on the soldering iron bit (tip). This process is called tinning the bit as it helps to improve heat flow from the iron to the lead and pad, safeguarding the board from excessive heat.
- Make solder balls with the iron and lead on the work table.
- Use the iron's tip to pick a lead ball. Place the soldering iron tip with the tiny lead blob or ball on it on the interface of the pad and lead, making sure it touches both the lead and pad.

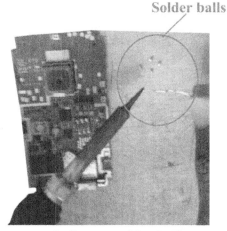

1. Create solder balls

2. Lifting a ball with iron tip

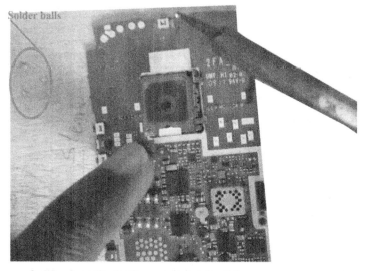

3. Placing the ball on a joint-in this case a switch terminal

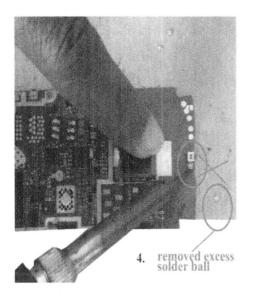

4. removed excess solder ball

5. perfect finish

- Carefully solder in the appropriate location. Remember to prop the iron in a safe standing position when not in use to avoid burns or damage to useful surrounding components.

- Feed the right quantity of solder on the interface between the PCB pad and the component's lead and allow it to cool. Remove excess solder if it is much. This should not take more than a second as the molten solder easily solidifies as heat source is removed.

- If the solder does not melt easily to the jointing area, it is due to insufficient heat transfer to the area or due to a dirty surface.

- Remember to stop feeding the solder to the jointing terminal by removing the soldering lead wire. No more than a drop of lead is necessary for a good joint though it varies with the size and type of component. But the soldering-wire feed-hand controls what quantity is fed to a joint.

- Ensure you move the iron quickly out of the jointing point as excessive heat on the surface can easily damage the pad(terminal point) on which the component is to be terminated, likewise the component may get damaged due to excessive heating. So move quickly. You may judge the level of hotness of the board by using a finger to feel the board temperature.

- A good joint will look shiny, smooth and cone shaped otherwise it may be a cold joint with dull, gravel-like, rough and frosty look. Visible indications tell if your joint is good. The solder should melt with the components' terminal point surface to form an alloy with the metal surface. The solder joint should coat the component's surface in even distribution. It should neither be too little nor too much.

- While carrying out the process you may clean the oxidation off the tip of the iron at intervals to aid heat transfer. After a good joint is made, make sure you allow the joint to cool before moving the components.

How to Use the Rework Station

A Rework station is a soldering machine used for carrying out high precision soldering jobs including removal and replacement of motherboard components. The name 'Rework' is derived from the fact that it is used to 'repeat work' (soldering) that has been done previously on-board during the manufacturing of the PCB. Rework stations have hot air guns or blowers which blow out hot air for use to either heat ICs (Chips) or to replace them. The heating process is meant to cause the solder holding the terminals of the components fixed on the motherboard to soften and cool to repair joints that have dried or broken. When ICs get disconnected from the circuit board, faults occur in the system.

Supposing for instance an IC (Integrated Circuit) serves the purpose of distributing power (Power IC) throughout the motherboard and the BGA (Ball Graphics Array) lead terminals underneath have dried, rusted or broken, it may lead to the cell phone not powering on. If the IC is related to charging, the battery will no longer be charged through the phone. SMD (Surface Mount Device) ICs also experience oxidation or rusting of their terminals but it is less prevalent and easily repaired with the soldering iron.

When using the rework station, there are two knobs of interest for optimum performance. Adjusting these knobs for the best heat transfer setting required is important. The variable temperature setting has a range of temperatures in degrees Celsius. The air pressure setting has its own calibration clockwise from low to high. There are also rework stations that have no digital display with just low to high calibrated knobs. Ensure that the blower does not function without adequate accompanying air. If you run the temperature without accompanying air, the blower filament will get damaged.

IC BGA Soldering and Repair

Adjust the temperature relative to the operation being carried out;

Reflow Soldering: BGA ICs malfunction due to wear and tear or corrosion of their mounting solder balls. Any crack in the solder that disconnects the PCB track from the IC will cause the chip to malfunction. Because of the tight packed space underneath the ICs, it is easy for liquids to get trapped and cause corrosion. Sometimes severe impact on the phone due to rough handling causes cracks in the solder ball terminals of the ICS. Therefore to repair, a hot air stream from the hot air rework station is used to molten the solder balls and as they cool, reconnect properly to both the PCB and the chip. To achieve this, controlled hot air is channeled to the IC. During the process, it is required to clean the underside of the IC by channeling cleaning fluid underneath and using air pressure from the blower to force out the fluid mixed with dirt. Repeat the process for as many times as possible until only clear fluid is expelled. Apply soldering paste and repeat the same process. During this time, the paste and heat act to repair the solder balls and at intervals, press on the chip with the thumb lightly. This will help secure the contacts and aid you to gauge the level of heating being applied. If it is excessive, your thumb will feel the heat. Ensure that cleaning fluid is used again this time to expel the soldering paste. Note that it is important to do this as soldering paste residue can cause overheating of the chip during normal operation of the phone due to normal heat energy dissipation. This procedure is to be used after a normal dry heating process does not repair an identified malfunctioning IC as well as before an outright removal, re-balling and replacement process is carried out.

For Replacing a BGA Chip(IC) On PCB: During the soldering process, heat the overall chip assembly using hot air stream. The solder balls underneath the chip have standard controlled amount of solder, and when heated during the soldering process, this solder melts. Surface tension causes the molten solder to hold the IC package in the correct alignment with the circuit board, while the solder cools and solidifies. The solder alloy composition coupled with the soldering temperature is such that the solder does not completely melt, but stays semi-liquid, allowing each ball to stay separate from its neighbors.

For Irreparably faulty component removal (ICs) and replacement with another: You could use very high temperatures with moderate air pressure in order not to blow away relevant components around the operation area. By very high temperature, it is not to suppose carelessness. It means you do not mind the component being removed getting damaged in the process of removal compared to when removing a component that is to be re-balled and reused in the motherboard. When using such very high temperatures, ensure that you do not apply heat for long durations on the circuit-board as excessive heat spreading all over the motherboard may damage components with low withstand temperature. Be snappy about the process, using a tweezer to apply an upward pull to the component. The pull should not be such as to forcefully detach the component when the solder has not melted else it will damage the ball point terminals on the motherboard.

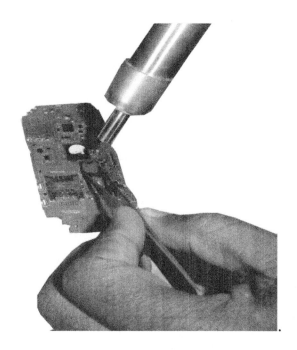

For faulty component removal (ICs), re-balling and re-use: The rework station comes with different sizes of nozzles. Choose the appropriate nozzle size depending on the location of the component within a particular surface area. For a sparsely populated (surrounding electronic components like resistors, capacitors, diodes etc) surface area and size of chip, choose a bigger nozzle while the reverse is the case for a smaller nozzle.

The faulty IC is removed with moderate temperatures balancing the need to remove the chip without damaging it with the duration of heat transfer. Applying very high temperature for a shorter duration than a moderately high temperature for a longer duration in the removal process takes a sound measure of good judgment. To aid the heat transfer process and protect the terminal pads connecting the component to the circuit-board from getting damaged as you apply the upward pull with the tweezer, apply soldering flux. You have to also apply soldering flux at the edges of the IC before heating or removing it. Remember that the air pressure applied must be commensurate with increasing temperatures as a dry heat transfer will lead to charring or burning the component. Finally, take note of the markings on the top of the IC you want to remove. A dot is usually used to serve as a guide for IC placement. It is called a Nose Point.

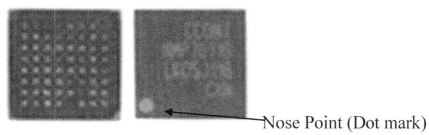

Nose Point (Dot mark)

Figure 4.16: IC

On successful de-soldering of the component, clean the underside with brush and cleaning fluid, apply flux or soldering paste. Then using your soldering iron, create tiny blobs of soldering lead and use them to re-ball the joints. Applying too much quantity of lead will muddy up the multiple grid array. Flux helps also to disjoint the spread of lead solder across the terminals bridging them. After re-balling all ball points on the underside of the IC and the equivalent ball points on the circuit-board, you may run a hot air stream over both surfaces and allow it to cool and set. Clean out the surface with brush and cleaning fluid, confirm that all the tracks are separated from each other without any solder debris joining together any two terminals.

To re-solder the component back, you apply fresh soldering flux on both surfaces - the ball points on the underside of the IC and the motherboard surface. Use the tweezer to pick up the IC and place according to the original placement mark or Nose Point and apply hot air. This time, you should be applying a downward force to stick the component in place.

CAUTION

When working on motherboard contact points (the shiny gold terminal points or pad on which a component is soldered to) do not apply excessive heat on these pads especially with fluxes. It usually flakes them out of the motherboard limiting your chance of reconnecting the component back. When that happens, the system and the repair process fail irreparably. In home electronics boards, it is easier to trace the track supply line to that contact pad by digging deep into the motherboard. With mobile phone motherboards, it is difficult and in most cases impossible.

Recommended *Action*

Search *for scrapped dead circuit boards and practice before trying on working circuit boards. Also cut tiny strands from cables and also try out cable sectioning from one component terminal to another. Desolder components too using tweezers to pull upwards while applying hot air. Practice!!!*

Chapter 5

Mobile Phone Hardware Architecture

Overview of Mobile Cell Phone Technology

Modern digital cell phones are complex computers which can process millions of calculations per second in the process of compressing and decompressing voice communication streams. It would be useful to give an overview of the cell phone technology in this chapter.

How does a cell phone work?
What makes a Mobile Cell Phone different from a regular telephone?

A mobile cell phone is basically a radio. One of the most interesting things about a cell phone is that it is actually a sophisticated complex radio. The telephone was originally invented by Alexander Graham Bell in 1876, while wireless communication can trace its roots to the invention of the radio by Nikola Tesla in the 1880s which was brought to light when Guglielmo Marconi conceived of a system that can bring about long-distance wireless radio transmission.

Before mobile cell phones were invented, there was a need for wireless communication within cities, across regions and even over vast geographical spaces far apart. But what became available was the radio telephone system. Communication within cities through this wireless means utilized radio waves by having telephones with in-built transmitters capable of transmitting to and fro a central antenna tower. The system being an analog one had the limitations of channel availability to meet user demands at about twenty five channels per tower. Its mobile capability lay in the fact that the radio telephone could be installed in any mobile transport operating within a specific radius from the central tower.

But as the mobile cellular phone system arrived, cities were segmented into cells, each cell having a base 'tower' station. In almost every city today, it is easy for you to pick out a number of cell towers dotting the cities' skylines. Each cell has a coverage radius size in square miles or kilometers as determined by the cellular communication companies who are allocated specific frequency spectrums to use.

The cellular system often represents cells as hexagons on a hexagonal grid, which by design effectively cascades the connectivity between cells thereby serving millions of users per cell through a method of frequency recycling.

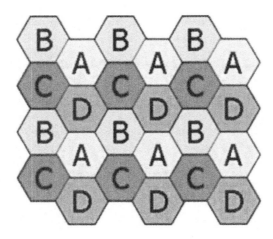

Fig. 5.1: Structure of Cellular Mobile Station

This method enables millions of people to communicate simultaneously using cell phones. There is no dormant, dedicated circuit per subscriber; rather each frequency pair for transmission and reception during a call can be assigned and reassigned to multiple users as the need arises as long as the cells are distant from each other in the hexagonal grid.

The cellular system consists of a base station subsystem, including a tower and a small building that houses the radio and switching equipment (Base Transceiver station and Base station controller). In the analog system, a single cell out of seven on a hexagonal grid is said to use one-seventh (1/7) of the available duplex voice channels with a unique set of frequencies, without collisions.

Base stations and mobile phones are both equipped with low power transmitters. This is necessary to prevent the transmissions in one cell from extending and crossing the cell boundaries. The frequency band allocated per cell are therefore retained and re-used within that cell. As for the mobile phones, low power transmitters ensures that smaller batteries can be used to power the phones, making it possible to design portable pocket-sized products. The signal strength of most cellular phones' power amplifiers are usually between 0.3 to 0.6 Watts. Each of the base stations we see spread across cities are aggregately controlled by regional master control stations known as the Mobile Service Switching Centre (MSC).

The Call Process from Cell to Cell

All mobile cell phones have special assigned codes associated with them. These codes are used to identify the phone, the subscriber and the telephone company. The various Cell Phone Codes used are as follows:

1. *Electronic Serial Number (ESN):* It is a unique 32-digit number hard-coded by manufacturers into the phone for use with CDMA phones.
2. *Mobile Subscription Identification Number (MSIN)*: A 10-digit number known also as the Mobile Station ID (MSID) which identifies the device to the telephone company. It is derived from a subscriber's telephone number.
3. *System Identification Code (SID):* A unique 15-bit number that is assigned to each mobile telephone company which identifies it to the country's communication authority. The SID in a phone listens for the carrier company's SID broadcast to register a network.

There are two types of mobile phone systems based on these connectivity codes. One kind are designed with provision for removable Subscriber Identity Module card (SIM card) while the other type does not have the option of a removable SIM card.

The Electronic Serial Number (ESN) is hardcoded into the device by the device's manufacturer at the time of production. Similar to the 15-digit IMEI (International Mobile Equipment Identifier) they are permanently embedded in the phone. But the SID and MIN are service control codes programmed by the telecommunication service providers when a subscriber purchases a service plan or in the SIM card which subscribers insert into the phone to access or utilize a particular network provider's services.

Wireless communication systems are broadcast networks in a way. They transmit or broadcast beacons which corresponding devices with similar beacons discover and pair with. It is the same concept with wireless home routers used for data connectivity. Whenever a phone is first powered ON, it also listens for an SID (System Identification number) on a programmed special frequency set by the service provider for controlled communications between its cell stations and subscribers' phones.

Communication protocols run by the routers and switchgears in the base station for voice/data etc synchronize with the protocols in the firmware run by the phone's baseband processors on this signaling frequency. Defined protocols and interfaces are determined by the GSM specification which guides the communication exchange between various system components. Similar to the Open System Interconnect (OSI) reference model used for internetworking, the GSM protocols follow a layered structure – Physical Layer, Data Link Layer and a third layer for mobility, voice call and resource coordination, which equivalent in the OSI model includes the Network layer, Transport, Session, Presentation and Application layers' functions.

If the phone fails to discover a valid SID broadcast by its home network (the company it subscribed to or that owns the SIM card), it knows it is out of coverage area and displays a "No Service" or "No Network" message. But when it receives the SID, the phone compares it to the SID programmed into the phone. If the SIDs matches, the phone recognizes the cell as its home network and transmits a registration request for network service.

The MSC maintains a database for all subscribers' cell phones per cell which comprises of a Home Location Register (HLR), Visitor Location Register (VLR) and even the Equipment Identity Register (EIR). This helps the MSC to easily triangulate and track all phones, knowing which cell a phone is in whenever it wants to connect to the phone. Once the call reaches the MSC, it searches for the phone in its database, assigns a frequency pair on lease from a pool to that phone for the period of the call. All this happens in microseconds. The phone receives the leased frequency over the control channel and once the phone and the cell tower switch to those frequencies, the call is connected.

The further away a phone moves from its cell, the lower the signal strength. The signal strength at cell boundaries is low in the hexagonal grid but the closely knit adjacent cells' overlapping signals help to ensure seamless connectivity across geographical areas. While one cell's signal diminishes, adjacent cells' signal comes into view. The base station in the cell in which the phone is moving toward detects the phone's increasing signal strength. Both base stations coordinate with hands-off/handover through the MSC. Once this is achieved, the phone continues with its communication in a new cell.

Mobile phones operate as full duplex communication devices. This means that "transmit" and "receive" signals simultaneously travel between two end devices during the duration of a call process which is the reason both users can hear (receive) and talk (transmit) at the same time like a normal face to face conversation. This is possible because during the communication process, two separate frequencies are utilized with one for talking (transmit) and the other for listening or hearing (receive) over multiple channels of the communication system.

Mobile phones operate within cells that are linked to several other millions of cells on a worldwide scale. You may observe that despite the low transmission power of both a user phone and the cell's base station which limits its frequency propagation to a small radius of operation, the network of cells scales the coverage capacity of a cellular system far beyond that of traditional analog radio telephone systems. When in motion, mobile phones switch cells, maintaining an unbroken communication through a process known as roaming.

Multi-Band vs. Multi-Mode Mobile Cell-Phones

1. *Multiple Band*: A phone that has multiple-band capability can switch from one frequency to another. For instance, a tri-band TDMA phone could use services in an 800-MHz, 900MHz or a 1900-MHz network system. Likewise a quad-band GSM phone could use GSM services in the frequency ranges at 850-MHz / 900-MHz / 1800-MHz / 1900-MHz band or 850- MHz / 900 / 1900 / 2100MHz.

2. *Multiple Mode*: In cell phones, "mode" refers to the type of transmission technology used. So, a phone that supported AMPS and TDMA could switch back and forth to GSM, HSPA, HSPA+, WCDMA or dual band CDMA Evdo etc. It's important that one of

the modes is GSM as this ensures that the mobile phone connects to analog services when in an area that does not have digital services support.

3. ***Multiple Band/Multiple Mode:*** This allows mobile phones to switch between frequency bands and transmission modes as needed. This feature can be automatic or manually enabled in the phone by the user.

Changing bands or modes is done automatically by phones that support these options. Usually the phone will have a default option set, such as 1900-MHz TDMA, and will try to connect at that frequency with that technology first. If it supports dual bands, it will switch to 800 MHz if it cannot connect at 1900 MHz. And if the phone supports more than one mode, it will first try the digital mode(s) then switch to analog. There are dual-band mode, tri-band mode and quad-band phones. This means that a phone could support two or more digital technologies, such as CDMA and TDMA, as well as analog or it can also mean that it supports one digital technology in two bands as well as offer analog support.

Mobile Phones Motherboard Components and Layout

One descriptive pictorial image will serve as a basic illustration in teaching this section. It properly captures the foundational layout in the progressive design of mobile phones from the old 'Basic phone' generation to the new 'smartphone' generation.

Generally, the mobile phone's (mobile devices) circuit board is the heart of the system and contains a number of chips and discrete electronic components like resistors, capacitors, inductors etc. The motherboard buses unlike PCs are basically printed copper wiring tracks running between the various components and System on Chips (SOC).

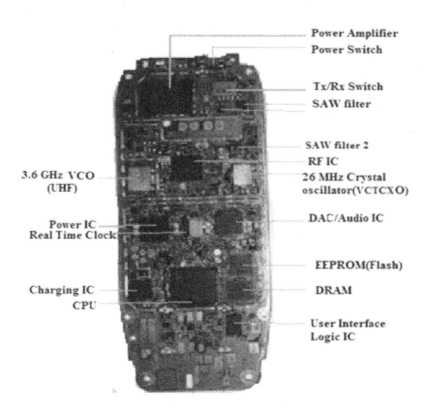

Power Amplifier
Power Switch

Tx/Rx Switch
SAW filter

SAW filter 2
RF IC
26 MHz Crystal
oscillator(VCTCXO)

DAC/Audio IC

3.6 GHz VCO
(UHF)

Power IC
Real Time Clock

EEPROM(Flash)

Charging IC
CPU

DRAM

User Interface
Logic IC

Figure 5.2: Nokia 3310 PCB

To understand the PCB layout design, one needs to first appreciate the functional description of the various function-specific integrated circuits along with their various interrelationships with each other. It is totally a blind adventure to launch into the intricate design of mobile devices as a technician without a somewhat basic knowledge and understanding of the workings of the device's functional units or electronics. Recent designs of smartphones follow the same foundational layout but with lesser discrete components, fewer but more powerful integrated circuits, multiples of processors or microcontrollers and device controllers.

In every mobile device, there are two distinct modules;

- *The RF Module and*
- *The Baseband (BB) Module(Analog BB / Digital BB)*

Before describing the interoperation of the key functional components and modules, let us first describe and define them individually.

Key Components of the Radio Frequency (RF) Module

- Radio Frequency
- Power Amplifiers (PA)
- Low Noise Amplifiers (LNA)
- TxRx Switch (or Antenna Switch)
- SAW filters
- Local Oscillators (LO)
- Voltage Controlled Oscillators (VCO)
- RF Processor or Analog Baseband Processor

Key Components of the Baseband (BB) Module

- Analogue-To- Digital converter (AD/DA)
- Microprocessors
  [*Main Control Processor*
  Baseband Processor
  Digital Signal Processor (DSP)
  Application Processor]
- Power Control IC
- SIM or USIM card

Radio Frequency: RF is short for Radio Frequency. In communication engineering, the term "RF-signals" is used to denote signals containing information (voice, text or data, video etc) in the frequency bands used for radio communication.

Power Amplifiers (PA): It is usually located in the RF module within close proximity to the antenna of the mobile device and the Tx/Rx switch (or Antenna Switch). It acts as a band pass filter as well as amplifies message carrier signals for transmission on the network.

Low Noise Amplifiers (LNA): An amplifier usually increases the power of an input signal which consists of both a message signal and noise. Low Noise Amplifiers are used in the RF circuits to amplify very low-power signals without significantly degrading their signal-to-noise ratio. They are placed close to the Tx/Rx switch in the RF module so they filter noise from the incoming message signals before they are sent to the RF processor.

TxRx Switch (or Antenna Switch): The first point of interface by an incoming RF (Radio Frequency) signal after the receiving antenna is the Tx/Rx or antenna switch. There is a PCB wire track from the antenna to the Tx/Rx switch. The switch is a kind of frequency band selector. Remember that most mobile phones are multiple band phones from the GSM 850 Mhz, 900MHz, 1800Mhz to 1900 Mhz bands extended to 2200MHz in smartphones. The TX/RX switch is normally open to two RX outlets (GSM_Rx and DCS_Rx. If it senses no control voltages at specific comparators, it will work as a duplexer (allowing bi-directional communication path over a single path) and the GSM900 signal is passed to GSM_Rx while GSM1800 signal is passed to DCS_Rx. In this duplexer mode the switch isolates the receiver and transmitter path even though they both share an antenna. The signal from GSM_Rx is then passed to the first of two or more Rx SAW filters.

SAW Filters: SAW is short for Surface Acoustic Wave. It is a type of mechanical wave motion which travels along the surface of a solid material. It has band pass filter characteristics whereby it provides out-of-band signal immunity. Their operation is based on the interference of mechanical surface waves. Input/output transducers are formed on a piezoelectric material through the conversion of electrical signals into mechanical waves and back due to the use of piezoelectric crystals in the SAW filters.

Local Oscillator: The Local Oscillator LO is an electronic device used to produce a sine wave or signal in the receiver which the RF signal processor mixes with the message signal to lower its frequency. This frequency conversion process produces separate differential (sum and difference) frequencies from the combined frequencies of the input signal and that of the local oscillator. This is what happens to the input signal from the SAW filters as they are sent for processing in the RF processor or receiver which in most cases comprises a mixer. The reduced frequency at this stage is usually called an Intermediate Frequency (IF). On a general note, mobile phones do not have separate Receiver and Transmitter but Transceivers (a combined Transmitter/Receiver).

Voltage Controlled Oscillator (VCO)*:* A voltage-controlled oscillator or VCO is an electronic oscillator whose oscillation frequency is controlled by a voltage input. The applied input voltage determines the instantaneous oscillation frequency. There is a feedback system known as Phased Locked Loop synthesizer which generates frequencies for both Rx and Tx in both frequency bands that synchronizes the VCO to the phase and frequency of an incoming signal. The VCO generates very high frequencies in the range of 3420-3840 MHz whenever the Phased Locked Loop is in operation. These frequencies are divided by 2 or 4 in the RF processor so that they can generate all channels in GSM 900MHz-1800MHz. D.C voltages between $0.7 - 3.8V$ coming from the loop filter controls the VCO frequency. Even when the PLL is not operational, frequencies between 3 and 4GHz are still found at the VCO output.

RF Processor or Analog Baseband Processor (ABP): The RF Processors usually handle analogue radio frequency signal processing in the RF module. These signals are handed down from the RF front end. Most RF processors are transceivers (both a receiver and transmitter) with in-built IQ demodulators for signal modulation and demodulation. The Analog Baseband part of a GSM modem is responsible for interface between the digital domain and the analog domain of the GSM modem. The Analog Baseband may consist of these integrated components in its IC package.

A/D and D/A section: Analog to Digital (A/D) and Digital to Analog (D/A) converters are responsible for digital to analog and analog to digital conversions.

The Control subsystem: The control subsystem acts as the controller of the input and output of any analog and digital signal.

The Charging Subsystem: A charging system is linked to the Analog Baseband which is responsible for charging mobile phone batteries.

Audio Codecs Section: Audio Codecs are responsible for the processing of analog and digital audio signals received through the microphone, speaker, headset, ringtones and the vibrator circuits. The signal output from its receiver circuitry is applied to its IQ demodulator. Here the data in the form of "In-phase" and "Quadrature" signal components are applied to the IQ demodulator and the raw data extracted for further processing by the phone.

The design of the transmit circuitry of the analog baseband is such as to maintain low power consumption and avoid battery drains. To achieve this, Gausian Minimum Shift Keying (GMSK) modulation method is used by GSM standards as it does not require the use of linear RF amplifiers but uses the more efficient non-linear RF amplifiers.

However EDGE technology which is based on Eight-Point Phase Shift Keying (8PSK) uses linear RF amplifiers. This causes power consumption and battery drain problems. To overcome this design problem, the structure of mobile phones is designed to receive phase information at an early stage of the transmitter chain while the amplitude information is added at the final stage of the transmitter chain.

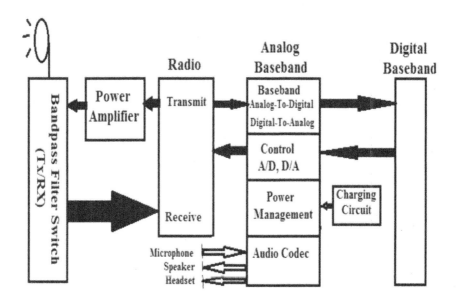

Figure 5.3: Analog Baseband Processor Operation Diagram

Analogue-To- Digital Converter (AD/DA Converters)

Analog-to-digital and digital-to-analog conversion chip translate the outgoing audio signal from analog to digital and the incoming signal from digital back to analog. It can process millions of calculations per second in order to compress and decompress the voice stream. The radio frequency module of the design uses analogue techniques.

Speech Conversion into Digital Signal

Speech produces acoustic pressure due to the motion of sound. A telephone converts electrical energy into sound and vice versa. In wireless technology, a coder inside the mobile telephone converts sound to digital impulses on the transmitting side and on the receiving side it converts these impulses back to analog sounds. This coder is also called Vocoder, a speech analyzer and synthesizer found in all digital wireless telephones as part of the Digital Signal Processor which is responsible for this conversion. During this process, sound is converted into electrical signals and transmitted on one end of the Vocoder. At the receiving end the speech synthesizer interprets the signal and produces a close match of the original sound. The sound signals vary due to the telephone circuit's resistance, while electrically representing speech as a continuous (analog) electromagnetic wave. However, digital signals remain stable throughout the length of their travel because digital signals are a numerical representation of sound in binary digits (1s and 0s). Any time you hear sound, your ears are responding to tiny, rapid changes in the pressure of the air. These changes are called sound waves. They may have a single frequency and constant amplitude or a complex mixture of waves with different frequencies and amplitudes. The normal human ear is said to perceive sound ranging in frequency from 20 to 20,000 Hz.

Microprocessor Types

In the baseband module, there may be one, two or more microprocessors depending on the level of sophistication of the mobile device. In such designs where there is more than one processor, there is usually a Master-Slave relationship. General purpose processors are usually called CPUs (Central Processing Units in PCs and Workstations). Example is Intel Pentium IV, Arm, ARM 7 etc. Earlier basic phones that processed only voice call and SMS were designed with single general purpose processors that handled everything from user interface (keypad, display), RF processing to battery management. They were also called Baseband Processors in some applications. In earlier "basic" and "feature" mobile phone technologies, Baseband processors were the primary processors for accessing cellular networks.

However, its architecture has evolved from analog to digital (2G) to 3G and then Long Term evolution, LTE. Some of these chips are not really

Microprocessors but System on Chip (SoC). System on Chip is an integrated circuit (IC) that integrates all components of a computer or other electronic system into a single chip. It may contain digital, analog, mixed-signal, and often radio-frequency functions—all on a single chip substrate. System on Chip mirrors the design of Microcontrollers than Microprocessors.

However the latest smartphones possesses such attributes like quality graphics, portable size with third party user applications support and multimode connectivity features. Smartphones incorporate the capabilities of both computing and communication devices that require a higher processing capability that is difficult to integrate into a single microprocessor. They therefore have on-board many Microprocessors and microcontrollers. The Main Microprocessors usually have busses to communicate with memory on separate chips (though often embedded within the same package) and to communicate with other devices. They also contain microcontrollers. They may be called Baseband Processors or Application Processors depending on the design. Some designs integrate all the functionalities described in one chip while in other designs there are a separation into two, three or more processors in a mobile device as mobile technology continues to evolve.

The Micro Control Unit Processor (MCU)

The Micro control processor or Microcontroller is the Main Processor at the heart of the mobile phone design. It may be part of a Baseband Processor and controls all the processes occurring in the phone from the User Interface whereby it monitors the input/output systems like keypad presses, information decoding/encoding, LCD display output, menus and other user interface functions. The Micro control processor manages the interface with the mobile network base station for registration on the network and other control information. The software required for this is known as the protocol stack contained within flash-files and it enables the phone to make, receive and terminate calls while coordinating handovers when a phone roams from one cell to the other. Additionally the software formats the data to be transmitted into the correct format with error correction codes included and monitors battery and battery charging control.

The protocols used to interact with the network are becoming increasingly complicated with the progression from 2G to 3G and now 4G LTE. Along with the increasing number of third party mobile applications, the load on the processor is increasing. To combat this, the design for this area of the phone circuitry often uses ARM processors which enable high levels of processing to be achieved for relatively low levels of current drain.

Microcontrollers contain a processor core (CPU), memory, and programmable input/output peripherals and are referred to as Socket on Chips (SoC). Earlier mobile phones like the 1G and 2G phones had only one general purpose processor which handled everything though the tasks were less compared to 3G and 4G LTE capable phones of today. Micro Control processors may be called Application Processor in some designs where the Application Processor is separated from the Baseband processor. However in other designs, they are integrated into Baseband Processors.

The Baseband Processor

A baseband processor also known as baseband radio processor (BP or BBP) is an IC or part of an IC in a network interface that manages all the radio functions in a mobile device. A baseband processor typically uses its own RAM and firmware.

Baseband processors typically run a real-time operating system (RTOS) as their firmware. A normal BBP design includes a Digital Signal Processor (DSP) for the lower half of the Physical Layer in the communication protocol stack, and a general purpose processor (MCU or Application Processor) for the upper part of the Physical Layer. DSP (Digital Signal Processor) and MCU communicate by employing a shared memory interface. This shared memory contains both actual data and control information. The actual data is processed by the application processor (MCU); whereas, control information and parameters describe the action to be taken with the respective data. The MCU instructs the DSP to perform decoding for a particular GSM burst type on the receiving side, after which the DSP receives I/Q samples from the Analog Baseband modem and performs detection / modulation /decoding. The result of the operation (including any decoded data) is reported back to the MCU.

For the transmit path, the MCU presents the transmittable data and auxiliary information to the DSP, which then takes care of encoding and sends the corresponding burst bits to the ABP (RF processor or Analog Baseband Processor). Remember that most ABP devices take care of the modulation and sometimes demodulation as well to reduce DSP load.

The Baseband Processor cores (MCU) have the typical set of peripherals of any Advanced RISC Machine (ARM 7) based microcontroller, such as RTC, UARTs for RS 232 and IrDA, SPI, I2C, SD/MMC card controller, keypad scan controller and USB device.

The additional GSM specific peripherals are: GPRS crypto unit, GSM TDMA timers and smart card reader interface for the SIM card. [8]

"Baseband processors are sometimes separated from the main processor (the Application Processor, AP) due to such considerations as radio performance, legal requirements, radio reliability, and security concerns". [9]

Digital Signal Processor (DSP)

Digital Signal Processors are Microprocessors specifically tuned to carry out signal processing for digital signals. They basically perform specialized, complex instructions, simple to moderately complex instructions and multiple operations per instruction.

Application Processor (AP)

The Application Processor (AP) is a multi-core General Purpose Processor which is used for providing user interface and running applications. The name Application Processor is more applicable to modern smartphone designs while being the replacement for MCU general purpose processors (CPU) used in basic or feature phones.

The AP is a special type of System on Chip (SoC) which supports a number of multimedia related features such as web browsing, email, multimedia entertainment and games etc produced by integrating the AP and Baseband Processor inside one physical package. When this is done, each processor is allocated isolated memory access by assigning separate portions of the integrated RAM and Flash memory to each of the two processors. Then each processor is provided access to its own memory address space.

Application processors enable smartphones to run independent operating systems and employ customized user applications. They provide additional processing capabilities for performing tasks with minimal power consumption.

In Smartphones, the Application Processor Core used is usually an Advanced RISC Machine (ARM) based processor which is specially optimized for application in minimal power consumption environments and are designed with the following assemblies;

a. The Processor Core
b. The Multimedia Modules
c. The Wireless Interfaces and
d. The Device Interfaces

The Multimedia modules are hardware implementation of one or more multimedia standards that perform multimedia related computations which are usually time consuming. Within this module are;

1. JPEG module for decoding pictures viewed on the display, and encoding pictures taken with the phone's camera.
2. MPEG module used for decoding streaming video, video on demand, and incoming video conferencing data as well as encoding video taken with the video camera.
3. Audio modules used for MP3 (music) players, or to encode and decode voice data.
4. Graphics Processing Unit (GPU) for rapidly manipulating multimedia functions. They accelerate image creation in frame buffers intended for output on a display unit. GPUs manage 2D and 3D graphics, video capture, playback, mobile gaming delivery and provide rich user interface.

Wireless Interfaces enable the smartphone to communicate with the cellular network and data network. The digital components of the Wireless Communication System are integrated into the chip as part of the application processor, while the analog section are placed off-chip as microcontrollers. The following forms part of the wireless interface;

1. Bluetooth Module which enable communication with peripherals such as headset, and other nearby mobile devices.
2. Wi-Fi module which enable communication with local 802.11 networks.
3. GSM modules or modems which enable communication with the cellular network for both voice communication and internet access.

All three modules listed above are found as separate ICs on the PCB of mobile phones and tablets.

Device Interfaces enable mobile phones (smartphones or tablets) to communicate with peripheral devices such as display LCD, keypad, Universal Serial Bus (USB), Secure Digital card (SD), Multimedia Card (MMC), and camera. Each of these peripheral devices is connected to the application processor through a separate interface. For instance, the display controller interface allow for effective communication between the display and other modules integrated with SoC. Similarly camera interface allow for interaction between the camera and other digital modules while USB interface facilitates the connection of external devices through the USB port. SD/MMC interface enables smartphones to connect external memory storage devices.

System Memories

There are various types of memory chips (ICs) used in the mobile phone, ranging from those used for earlier "basic phones" to the Flash memories used in smartphones and latest technologies. As technology keeps advancing in the area of embedded and removable memory units, so also are their implementations in mobile devices. Mobile phones use embedded memories and the higher the sophistication, complexity and software application routines the processor used is capable of handling, the higher the size of memories and storage capacity needed.

The mobile phone just like any computing device consists of a primary memory unit - the RAM and secondary memory including slots for expandable memories through memory cards.

In the next sections, I will be discussing the different types of memories that are used in details starting from the earlier systems to the latest implementations.

ROM refers to Read Only Memory chips that are permanent embedded memories in which the manufacturers store the firmware codes that control the mobile device. It is a form of data storage used to store program codes or configurations that rarely needs to be updated. These codes can only be read by the Microprocessor but cannot be written to or modified. In computer technology, original ROM's contents cannot be altered. The word "Read-Only", means that it does not permit random access writes to individual memory locations. It is a non-volatile type of memory that retains the stored information even when the device is powered OFF. The data on the ROM can be loaded into the RAM when needed; like when the device is powered ON, the program codes are loaded into RAM (Random Access Memory) which is the main working memory of a computer system for instruction execution.

The fact that ROM can never be changed is a disadvantage in some applications. Manufacturers needed a way by which a device's code can be upgraded, re-programmed or to update firmware and correct an error. Doing these has a lot of benefits as we have seen in recent times with mobile devices where a device is not permanently bricked but can be re-flashed.

Therefore in mobile devices, original Read Only Memory (ROM) on a phone (Basic, Feature or Smartphone) has not really been the practice. What we have in phones is mostly the "flash" type of EEPROMs

(Electronic Erasable Programmable Read Only Memories), similar to the technology used for BIOS (Basic Input-Output System) in PCs.

EEPROM means Electrically Erasable Programmable Read Only Memory. When researchers discovered ways by which individual bytes of ROM to be erased and reprogrammed, EEPROM was born.

EEPROMs can be programmed and erased in-circuit, by applying special programming signals. This is what flasher boxes do during flashing. Most of the older basic and feature class of phones had EEPROMs which were limited to single byte operations making them slower, but modern EEPROMs allow multi-byte page operations. Older EEPROMs had very limited life for erasing and reprogramming (write cycles), currently though still limited is approaching a million operations in modern EEPROMs. EEPROMs can be re-written a limited number of times and require special procedures which is a common language term in the mobile phone repairs community called "Flashing" just as a PC BIOS can be "Flashed".

The kind of ROMs in mobile devices is a type of NVRAM known as Flash memory, of which a portion is set by software as "Read only". Although flash memory is a kind of EEPROM, there is also technically Non-Flash type of EEPROM.

RAM means Random Access Memory. RAM in the phone is a 'temporary' memory used by a phone during its operation. It is a volatile storage unit in computing systems and one of the critical components of a phone along with processing cores and dedicated graphics. Without RAM in any kind of computing system like a smartphone, it would fail to perform basic tasks because file access would be very slow. RAM is embedded in a mobile device in addition to flash storage - NVRAM and work in sync with the Microprocessors. Operating systems, application programs and data in use at any given time by the device are loaded into RAM (working memory) so that they can be easily accessed by the Microprocessor. Data in RAM is usually lost after a mobile device is switched OFF or power-cycled with a reboot.

RAM memory is also a middle man between the file-system, which is stored on the ROM (mainly EEPROM, Flash or NVRAM) and the processing cores, passing information as quickly as possible. Critical files that are needed by the processor are stored in the RAM, waiting to be accessed by the processor. These files could be data such as operating system instructions, application data, graphics or any time critical data that needs to be accessed at very high speeds faster than other storage units can provide.

RAM that is used in smartphones could be SRAM (static RAM) or DRAM, with the D standing for dynamic. *"The structure of DRAM is such that each capacitor on the RAM board stores a bit, and the capacitors leak charge requiring constant "refreshing"; hence the dynamic nature of the RAM"*. [10] It also means that the contents of the DRAM module can be changed quickly and easily to store different files.

It is of great advantage if the RAM used is not static RAM because the storage can change to cope with whatever tasks the system is performing per time. *"RAM is also much faster than NVRAM or NAND-Flash memories which are non-volatile. But they are more expensive than Flash storage and less scalable too. They cost more per Gigabytes than NAND flash storage. RAM DIMM (Dual Inline Memory Module) DDR4 (Double Data Rate 4) boards scale to no more than between 64GB and 128GB but NAND DDR4 boards scale twice as much to 256GB. In as much as RAM is faster, its cost, less scalability factor and volatility is driving the increased use of flash storage which scales higher, is fast and cheaper in direct memory channels although they have less write-erase life cycles and does not provide random access (a requirement for processors) like RAM."* [11] But where Flash is used, code stored in flash (device firmware) is often first copied into RAM when the device is powered up before execution.

NVRAM is (Non-Volatile Random Access Memory), a kind of Flash storage device. It is essentially RAM which acts as a ROM.

Flash (NAND / NOR) Memory

Flash memory is an electronic non-volatile computer storage medium that can be electrically erased and reprogrammed. Flash memory was developed from EEPROM (electrically erasable programmable read-only memory).There are two main types of flash memory, which are named after the NAND and NOR logic gates [12]. Flash memory is a form of NVRAM (Non-volatile Random Access Memory). NOR flash is different in that it allows random access for reading data from any memory location while NAND allows only page access, reading data in blocks of memory. NAND flash is also cheaper in cost with a higher storage density than NOR flash making it more popular.

The disadvantage it has to NOR is its lower erase / writes cycle before it wears out. NAND-Flash allows its memory to be written only in blocks, which greatly simplifies the internal wiring and allows for higher densities. Memory storage density is actually the main determinant of cost in most computer memory systems, and due to this, it has evolved into one of the lowest cost solid-state memory devices available.

NAND-flash has enabled many milestones in memory storage from smartphones, tablets to digital cameras, cloud computing etc. Flash makes it possible for the basic cell phone of yesterday to now do things like streaming video, take pictures, email handling, GPS and as well make phone calls. Most modern smartphones use flash memory to store firmware which is then copied into SDRAM or SRAM when the device is powered up.

Flash file-system is used for embedded flash memories like in mobile phones that have no controllers while the removable flash memories such as USB flash drives and memory cards have controllers. A controller performs wear leveling/error correction on flash memories because of their limited write cycles. Using a specifically designed flash file-system which "writes" over the media in parallel reduces the long duration required to erase NOR-flash blocks.

NAND or NOR-flash type of memory is often used to store configuration data in numerous digital products, a task that was possible only by using EEPROMs or battery powered static RAM (CMOS batteries in older computing systems, also in older mobile phones). Flash memories are non-volatile, have fast read access times (not as fast as RAM though), highly durable with high mechanical shock resistance, withstands high temperature, pressure and immersion in water. [13]

Your understanding of these explanations will help you during flash programming especially working on Android devices.

Power Control Chip (IC)

Power management and distribution is usually controlled by dedicated chips that function in sync with the RF and Baseband processors. In some cases they are called Universal Energy Management (UEM) chips or ICs.

Power Management: The power management circuitry is responsible for the management of energy in a mobile device and consists of the power distribution, power switching and battery charging subsystems.

Power Distribution: The power distribution subsystem distributes the desired voltage and current to all other sections of a mobile device. Power supply source is usually from a 3.6 V battery which is further controlled by discrete electronic components that step it down or up to various required reference voltages at 1.6 V, 1.8V and 2.8V or 4.8V respectively.

SIM or USIM card

SIM is the acronym for Subscriber Identity Module or Universal Subscriber Identification Module (USIM). It is an integrated circuit chip used to securely store the International Mobile Subscriber Identity (IMSI) number and its related key, which identify and authenticate subscribers on mobile phones. They usually have extra memory space to store user contacts in them. SIM cards are always used on GSM phones. They were embedded in lower end CDMA phones, while the newer LTE-capable ones use SIMs.

The SIM circuit forms part of the function of a Universal Integrated Circuit Card (UICC), a physical smart card made of PVC material with embedded contacts and semiconductors. They are designed to be transferable between different mobile devices. A SIM card contains its unique serial number (ICCID), international mobile subscriber identity (IMSI) number, security authentication and ciphering information, temporary information related to the local network, a list of the services the user has access to, and two passwords: a Personal Identification Number (PIN) for ordinary use, and a personal unblocking code (PUK) for PIN unlocking.

There are a number of multi-SIM mobile devices today like the Dual-SIM mobile phones. Multi-SIM functionality is implemented in different ways. One method seen in most china mobile phones is composed of inherently different mobile phone systems implemented on the PCB in one mobile phone unit or model. What is simply done is to duplicate on-board each of the RF chips (ICs) that make up the GSM phone chipsets such as two antenna units, two RF frontends, two analog basebands, two digital basebands, and two sets of Microprocessors etc.

The relationship between the microprocessors will be that of a Master-Slave one. Only one of the two basebands (The Slave) will have a keypad or display and is connected through serial line to the other baseband processor (The Master). Other ways of achieving a multi-SIM design is by using a multiplexer to perform electronic switching between multiple SIM card slots. As a result, a mobile user can use one of the two SIMs at any time. When carrying out software repairs, it is not advisable to change the IMEI of multi-SIM phones.

The Mobile Phone System Operational Summary

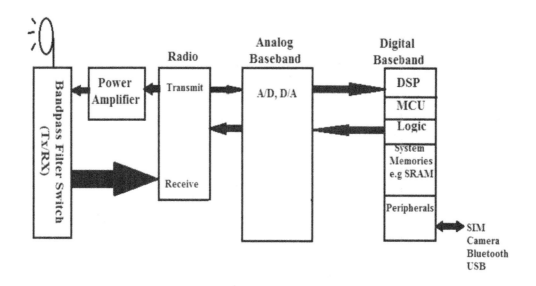

**Basic RF Front End Operation and Digital Baseband
Components Diagram
Figure 5.4**

Mobile Communication begins in the RF front end. And this is how;

In a radio receiver circuit, the RF front end is a generic term for all the circuitry between the antenna and the first intermediate frequency (IF) stage. It consists of all the components in the receiver that process the signal at the original incoming radio frequency (RF), before it is converted to a lower intermediate frequency (IF).

For most architecture, the RF front end consists of the following:

- An impedance matching circuit to match the input impedance of the receiver with the antenna, so that maximum power is transferred from the antenna.
- A Band-Pass Filter (BPF) to reduce input noise and image frequency response.
- An RF amplifier often called the low-noise amplifier (LNA) which primary responsibility is to increase the sensitivity of the receiver by amplifying weak signals without contaminating them with noise, so they are above the noise level in succeeding stages.
- The mixer which mixes the incoming signal with the signal from a local oscillator (LO) to convert the signal to the intermediate frequency (IF).

The analog-to-digital (AD) and digital-to-analog (DA) conversion chips (ICs) translate the outgoing audio signal from analog to digital and the incoming signal from digital back to analog. The Radio Frequency (RF) and power subsystem handles power management and battery recharging, including the processing and filtering of hundreds of FM channels. RF amplifiers boost the signal strength of low frequency message and control signals traveling to and from the antenna, passing them to and fro the Analog Baseband RF processors for signal encoding, decoding and modulation before sending it downstream to the digital signal processor.

The digital signal processor (DSP), a highly customized processor designed to perform signal-manipulation calculations at high speed takes over for full duplex digital processing while the Microprocessor handles all the user interface functions for the keyboard and the display; deals with command and control signaling with the base station and also coordinates all other functions on the circuit-board. The Read Only Memory (ROM) and Flash Memory chips provide storage for the phone's operating system and customizable features, such as the phone directory while the RAM aids the functioning of the Processors in their data and command fetch-execute routines by providing temporary storage to OS and user applications when in use.

It is important at this stage that the reader or technician imaginatively put together the theory and knowledge of the inter-relationships between these component units in figuring out logically the appropriate situation of a fault when the behavior of a mobile device is explained by the user or monitored by the technician. Recognizing the location and identity of these various ICs on the PCB is important for BGA reflow soldering and re-hot process during a functional failure. Remember that not all function-chips or ICs are singularly placed on the PCB but are integrated together with others into a microcontroller while in other models they may be found as single control chips.

With the descriptions and summary of the functional blocks in the mobile phone system and circuit-board above, a critical study of our introductory distinct sample PCB image of a basic phone (the Nokia 3310) compared to a Smartphone sample PCB below would provide a good aid for proper understanding of the myriads of components spread across the circuit-board especially with an organized sense of order. Higher levels of integration achieved in modern phones' design use Microcontrollers to integrate multiple processor cores into one chip, bridging the separations between modem, analog baseband, ADC/DACs and DSPs. Hence you find fewer ICs and fewer discrete components in modern phone PCBs. Armed with a sound theoretical background and a technical eye that separates the PCB into two modules; it is easier to recognize functional unit components that require attention when the mobile device is faulty. In the next chapter, further identifiable physical features of these integrated circuits shall be discussed.

At the end of this book, the reader would have gained more than average knowledge required to excel in the field. Information is useless except it is organized into purposeful knowledge and acted upon. The author expects therefore, that the information and training gained from this book should be turned into gold mines for as many as follow through with the pursuit of excellence in mobile phone technical service delivery for wealth either temporarily or permanently (because every enterprise is an investment vehicle which may change when it is necessary on the journey to wealth).

Sample Images

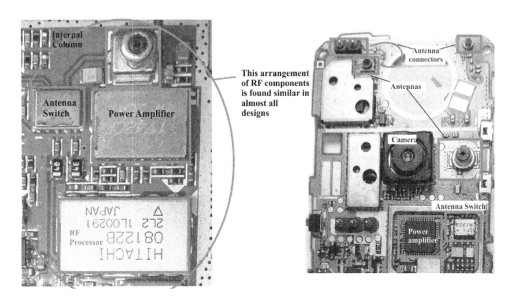

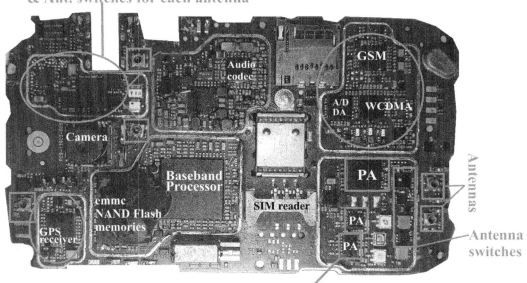

Fig. 5.5: Sample Images

Chapter 6

Electronics Fundamentals

The field of electronics birthed many of the technological products being enjoyed by mankind today. Computers for instance, owe their existence to the field of electronics. Electronics technology has its roots in the discovery of electricity; that branch of science that deals with electrical phenomena, discovered by the application of the principles of physics.

This course is very important for technicians in order to master their craft. The reason is simple. When you understand electronic components; their names, their functions and behavior in the circuit, how they fail, how to test and verify their status (functional or non-functional) and how they are interconnected with each other; then your task is easy. This is my objective in teaching this basic electronic foundational course.

Although you find a multiplicity of manufacturers/brands of mobile phones and within each brand multiple models, beneath the coverings or casings of these diverse products are the same parts. Parts manufacturers do not care about brands. While certain custom made specifications and quality ratings may differ across brand names, the parts are mostly similar and the same parts manufacturer may be supplying two or more competing mobile phone brands. For instance, the processors found in mobile phones are made by chip manufacturers like Intel, Skyworks, Qualcomm, MediaTek, SpreadTrum, Broadcom, Coolsand etc. The ICs or other chipsets made by these manufacturers could be used by any of Samsung, Nokia (Microsoft), Infinix, Tecno, LG, etc. The same applies to components like speakers, microphones, ringer etcetera. Based on their form factors and allocated PCB space, two dissimilar brands of mobile device can interchange parts with similar form factors in some cases during repairs. A Samsung microphone of the same size as the allocated space for microphone in say LG brand of phone can be used during a repair/replacement job. So on the surface, customers buy brand names.

Therefore, understanding the internal PCB electronic components is important. Let me start by inculcating perspectives in your thought process using existing simple definitions which explains the organization or structure of knowledge.

Some definitions

Physics is that branch of science concerned with the study of properties and interactions of space, time, matter and energy. At secondary or high school class, you may have undertaken this subject.

Electricity is the branch of science that deals with *electrical* phenomena which is the set of physical occurrences related to the presence and flow of electric charge.

Electrical engineering is a branch of engineering that deals with the *technology* of electricity, especially the design and application of circuitry and equipment for power generation and distribution, machine control and communications.

Technology is the study of or a collection of techniques.

Finally, *Electronics* is the study and *use* of *electrical devices* that operate by controlling the flow of electrons or other electrically charged particles. Electronics deals with the technology of utilization of electricity. After the discovery of electricity, electrical power, its generation and distribution capacity, the question one needed to ask is, to what use? How will mankind benefit from this energy flowing across conductors? In every home, office and wherever man is found today, aside the incandescent bulb invented by the great Thomas Edison, there is no much use for electricity without electronic devices and products powered by electrical energy.

In this section we shall discuss basic electronic theories and practices needed as a foundation for the task of becoming a field electronic technician in the specialized microelectronic device area - mobile phones category.

Principles and Concepts of Electricity

Centuries ago, a number of scientists became interested in the observation of some natural phenomenon about the electric charge. Some particular substances were observed to exhibit attraction to each other when brought close to each other. For some substances, this was observed after being rubbed together.

This observation became known as static electricity. For instance, when a glass rod is rubbed on silk for a period of time, the silk and glass would tend to stick together. There was an observable attractive force pulling both materials towards each other demonstrated when the two materials were separated. Other materials that behaved in a similar manner were wax and wool pair.

However, further investigation of this phenomenon exposed the fact that the invincible force of attraction between the two substances after being rubbed together also acted in opposite direction when like objects were placed together. This resulted in the conclusion about the existence of two forces;

- Attraction Force
- Repulsion Force

Furthermore, it was postulated from the fact of observation of these materials that;

Like objects repel each other while,

Unlike objects attract each other

One of the hypothetical conclusions drawn from the scientific observation of these objects and their behavior when rubbed together was that more than one kind of change occurred whenever these materials were rubbed together;

- That invisible "fluids" known as "charges" were being transferred from one object to another during the rubbing process and
- That these fluids had the capacity to exert a physical force over a distance.

Benjamin Franklin later came up with the conclusion that there was only one "fluid" exchange taking place between rubbed objects and that the two different "charges" of the fluids were nothing more than either an **excess** or a **deficiency** of that one fluid! After further experiments, following Benjamin Franklin's speculation of the wool rubbing off of the wax, the type of charge associated with 'rubbed' wax became known as "negative" (due to <u>assumed</u> deficiency of fluid) while that associated with 'rubbing' wool became known as "positive" (due to its <u>assumed</u> gain of excess fluid).

Later discoveries exposed the fact that the "fluid" comprised of extremely small bits of matter called *Electrons*. These extended experiments revealed that all objects are made up of extremely small building blocks known as "Atoms". Atoms are in turn composed of particles which further comprise of three smaller fundamental particles known as *Protons, Neutrons* and *Electrons*.

The branch of natural science that deals with the composition and constitution of substances and the changes that they undergo as a consequence of their molecules is known as Chemistry. The student who would like to delve further into this study is free to do so as for the purposes of this book, we will go no further than the basics required for technical proficiency. However our focus is on the behavior and properties of the electrons which is a subatomic component of matter.

Protons and the neutrons are contained in the nucleus of an atom. The tightly knit combination of neutrons and protons in an atom provides stability and differs from the spaced out electrons that are more mobile and orbiting around the nucleus of an atom. So even though each atom in a piece of material tends to hold together as a unit, there is actually a whole lot of empty space between the orbiting electrons and the cluster of protons and neutrons in the center of the atom.

Electrons are so free to move about that they can even be knocked out of their respective positions in the atom or entirely out of the atom by very negligible energy compared to what is required to knock out particles in the nucleus. When this happens, although the atom retains its chemical identity, an imbalance occurs.

There exists a force of attraction between the orbital electrons and the protons in the nucleus of an atom. It is this attraction force that makes it possible for electrons in the atom of an object to travel a distance to reside around atoms of another object.

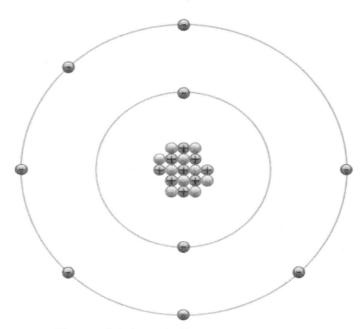

Figure 6.1 Atomic Structure
Image source: https://commons.wikimedia.org/wiki/File:Atombau_fluor.png

Electrons and protons are of opposite polarity to each other, hence are attracted to each other in an atom. Protons however are held bound in the nucleus of an atom due to another force called Nuclear force.

In every atom, there are equal and opposite number of these particles such that their attraction/repulsion forces cancel out. Remember that like charges repel while unlike charges attract each other. Each electron has a negative charge, while each proton has a positive charge. Being of equal numbers within an atom, they counteract each other's presence so that the net charge within the atom is zero. If electrons leave or extra electrons arrive, the atom's net electric charge will be imbalanced, leaving the atom "charged" as a whole, causing it to interact with charged particles and other charged atoms nearby.

The Neutrons are electrically neutral as they do not attract or repel electrons or protons or even similar neutrons. They have no charge altogether. The process of electrons arriving or leaving is exactly what happens when certain combinations of materials are rubbed together; electrons from the atoms of one material are forced by the rubbing to leave their respective atoms and transfer over to the atoms of the other material.

In other words, electrons are made up of the "fluid" hypothesized by Benjamin Franklin. The result of an imbalance in this "fluid" (electrons) between objects is called "static" electricity because the displaced electrons tend to remain <u>static</u> after being moved from one insulating material to another.

In the case of rubbing wax and wool together, further experimentation revealed that electrons in the wool actually transferred to the atoms in the wax, which is exactly opposite of Benjamin Franklin's hypothesis! But in his honor for designating the wax's charge as being "negative" and the wool's charge as "positive," electrons are said to have a "negative" charge. ***Thus, an object whose atoms have received an excess of electrons is said to be negatively charged, while an object whose atoms are deficient of electrons is said to be positively charged.***

In 1832, Michael Faraday proved that static electricity was the same as the electricity produced by a battery or a generator. On PCBs, static electricity causes damage to sensitive semiconductor circuitry, the reason technicians are required to wear anti-static wrist straps.

An electric current is therefore a flow of electric charge. In electric circuits this charge is often carried by moving electrons in a wire. It can also be carried by ions in an electrolyte, or by both ions and electrons. Electrical current flows through an electrical conductor from one end to the other. The principles and concepts of electricity gave rise to a number of electrical quantities such as Current, Voltage, Resistance, Power etc.

When a conductive path is created to allow free electrons to continuously move in order to achieve a specific purpose, an electric circuit is formed. This continuous movement of free electrons through the conductors of a circuit is referred to as current, and it is often referenced in terms of "flow," just like the flow of a liquid through a hollow pipe.

In order to motivate the electrons to "flow" in a circuit, there is a force called voltage. Voltage is a measure of potential energy <u>relative</u> to two points in a circuit. The presence of voltage at a point in a circuit is a measure of the amount of potential energy available to move electrons from one reference point (A) in that circuit to another reference point (B).The free electrons in the orbit of atoms tend to move through conductors with a certain level or amount of friction, or opposition to motion. This opposition to motion is called resistance.

Difference between Convention Current and Electron Flow

Benjamin Franklin's statement regarding the direction of charge flow (from the wax to the wool instead of wool to wax), determined the use of the electrical notation of current flowing from positive to negative direction despite the fact that it is clear that electrons are the constituent units of charge, and that they are displaced from the wool to the wax—not from the wax to the wool—when the two substances are rubbed together. This is why electrons are said to have a negative charge; because Benjamin Franklin assumed ***in error*** that electric charge moved in the opposite direction than it actually does, therefore what he called "negative" (representing a deficiency of charge) in reality was an excess of electrons.

Eventually, when the true direction of electron flow was discovered, the notation of "positive" and "negative" had become well grounded among scientists. It became accepted and therefore became known as *conventional flow or current.* But if charge flow is designated according to the actual direction of movement of electrons in a circuit, it is known as *electron flow notation.*

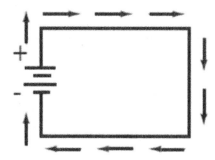

Figure 6.2a: Conventional flow from positive to negative terminal

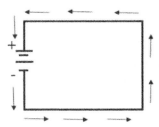

Figure 6.2b: Electron flow from negative to positive terminal

In conventional flow notation, we show the motion of charge according to the labels of (+) and (-) although this, technically speaking, is not the true direction of motion. This way the labels make sense, but the direction of charge flow is incorrect. In electron flow notation, we follow the actual direction of motion of electrons in the circuit, but the (+) and (-) labels are in the reverse. Any notation chosen will lead to equal success as you analyze circuits, either as an imaginary conventional flow of current or the real electron flow direction.

Conductors and Insulators

The electrons of different types of atoms have different degrees of freedom to move around which depends mainly on the types of materials. Metals for instance have their outermost electrons very loosely bound in their atoms that they move freely in the space between the atoms of their material just by the influence of heat energy.

Because these loose electrons are free to leave their respective atoms and move around in the space between adjacent atoms, they are called free electrons.

But for materials like rubber or glass, the electrons in their atoms have very little freedom for motion. While external forces such as heat energy or physical rubbing can force some of these electrons to leave their respective atoms and transfer to the atoms of other materials, they do not move between atoms within that material very easily.

This ability of electrons to move about within a material is known as electric conductivity. Conductivity is determined by the types of atoms in a material (the number of protons in each atom's nucleus, determining

117

its chemical identity) and how the atoms are linked together with one another. Materials with large free electrons are called **conductors**, while materials with small or no free electrons are called **insulators.**

Examples of conductors include silver, copper, gold, aluminum, iron and steel while insulators include materials like plastic, wood, rubber, leader etc. Just as there are differences between conductors and insulators, different materials also have varying degrees of either conductivity or insulation property.

While the normal motion of "free" electrons in a conductor is random, with no particular direction or speed, electrons can be influenced to move in a uniform manner through a conductive material. This uniform motion of electrons is what we call *electricity*, or *electric current.* Just like water flows through hollow pipes to supply water from a tank, so also electrons flow through the hollow of conductors.

Electrical Continuity

For a strip of conductive metal to allow electron flow in a continuous manner end- to-end, there must be a source and a destination.

A continuous piece of conductor

To get electrons to flow in this conductor or piece of wire, we have to add source and destination.

Electron source   **Electron destination**

With the Electron Source pushing new electrons into the wire on the left-hand side, electron- flow through the wire can occur (as indicated by the arrows pointing from left to right). However, the flow will be interrupted if the conductive path formed by the wire is broken as shown below;

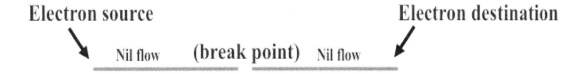

Electron source

Nil flow **(break point)** Nil flow

Electron destination

Once there is a break in the conductor, electron flow stops. The solution to situations of this nature is to create a jump wire across the break point. This is what technicians do to correct such faults in electrical circuits. See the image below;

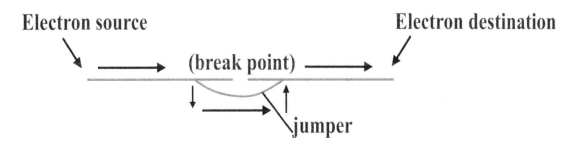

Electron source **Electron destination**

(break point)

jumper

The "jumper" re-routes the electron flow around the break point after a jumper is introduced creating a continuous path to the destination. Conductors do have negligible intrinsic resistance present in their constituent materials. Due to frictional resistance encountered by moving electrons, the conductors may experience increase in temperature.

Electrical Quantities and Their Relationships

As a prelude to exploring the world of electricity and electronics, it is vital to start by understanding the three basic electrical quantities which are the three basic building blocks required to manipulate and utilize electricity namely voltage, current and resistance. In any circuit, the amount of current flowing depends on the amount of voltage available to motivate the electrons, and also the amount of resistance in the circuit to oppose electron flow. Just like voltage, resistance is a quantity relative to two points.

Units of Measurement

Voltage (V): The unit of measurement of Voltage, symbolized by the alphabet "V" is Volt in honor of the Italian physicist Alessandro Volta (1745–1827), who invented the voltaic pile, possibly the first chemical battery. One volt (1V) is defined as the difference in electric potential between two points of a conducting wire when an electric current of one ampere dissipates one watt of power between those points.

Current: The unit of measurement of current, symbolized by the alphabet "I" is Ampere, named after André-Marie Ampère (1775–1836), French mathematician and physicist, considered the father of electrodynamics. The ampere is a unit of current, which is the amount of charge transiting per unit time, while the coulomb is a unit of charge. The ampere is defined as the constant current that will produce an attractive force of 2 × 10−7 Newtons per metre of length between two straight, parallel conductors of infinite length and negligible circular cross section placed one meter apart in a vacuum.

Resistance: The unit of measurement of resistance symbolized by "R" is the Ohm named after German physicist Georg Simon Ohm. It is defined as an electrical resistance between two points of a conductor when a constant potential difference of 1 volt, applied to these points, produces in the conductor a current of 1 ampere, the conductor not being the seat of any electromotive force. The abbreviation for the value of the resistance quantity is expressed with the symbol Ω, a Greek alphabet.

As we explore the various relationships between these quantities, these symbols and units are important.

OHM's Law

The first and most important relationship between Current, Voltage, and Resistance is known as Ohm's Law, discovered by Georg Simon Ohm and published in his 1827 paper, The Galvanic Circuit Investigated Mathematically. Ohm's main discovery was that the amount of electric current through a metal conductor in a circuit is directly proportional to the voltage across it, for any given temperature.

Ohm used a simple equation to describe the inter-relationships between voltage, current, and resistance.

Ohm's Law describes the relationship between voltage and current in an ideal conductor. It states that: "The potential difference (voltage) across an ideal conductor is proportional to the current through it". The constant of proportionality is called the "resistance", R.

$$V \alpha I$$

And since Resistance is a constant quantity on every metallic conductor, mathematically expressed as the constant of proportionality;

$$V = I \times R$$

Using algebraic equations, we can derive two other variations of this formula for I and R as the subject of the formula thus;

$$I = V/R \text{ and } R = V/I$$

Practically, these equations are very relevant for both designing and analyzing electrical circuits. Let us see some examples below;

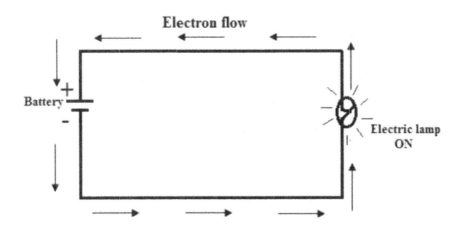

Figure 6.3a: Simple light bulb circuit

The light bulb circuit above presents us with a sample example. It has one source of voltage supply, the battery and one load- the light bulb- which is a resistance point for current flow in the circuit. When the value of any two of the three electrical quantities of voltage, current and resistance are known, Ohm's law can be used to determine the other missing value just like "find x" in algebra.

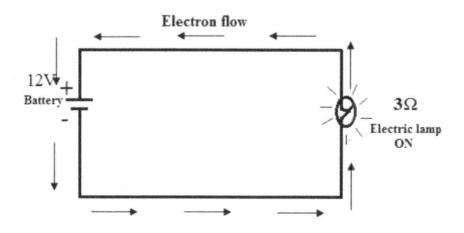

Figure 6.3b: Simple light bulb circuit

Supposing the source supply voltage is 12V and the resistance of the lamp is 3Ω,

Then using the formula V = IR;

Therefore 12V = I x 3Ω

$\qquad$ I = 12/3

$\qquad$ I = 4A

The amount of current flowing in this circuit is 4A.

Likewise if we have a battery source of voltage, 16V and the current produced by the battery is 2A, then the resistance of the lamp that will serve as the load will be;

$\qquad$ R = V/I

$\qquad$ R = 16/2

$\qquad$ R = 8Ω

And so on. Ohm's law is a very simple and useful tool for circuit analysis that it is important as a technician that one masters its use.

Voltage

Voltage is defined as the difference in electric potential energy between two points per unit electric charge. The voltage between these two points is equivalent to the work done per unit of charge against a static electric field to move that charge between two points and is measured in units of volts (a joule per coulomb).

Voltage can be created by either a static electric field, electric current passing through a magnetic field, by time-varying magnetic fields, or some combination of these three processes.

When voltage is applied between two points, one point has the presence of more charge than the other. In order to explain the concept of voltage, let us use the analogy of transferring water between two water cans.

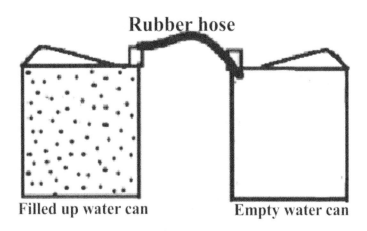

Figure 6.4a: Voltage Illustration

Let;

Water = Charge (measured in Coulombs)
Pressure = Voltage (measured in Volts)
Flow = Current (measured in Amperes, or "Amps" for short)
Pipe Width = Resistance

In fig. 6.4a above, when the water in the can is sucked into the pipe and transferred to the empty can, a pressure difference between the two ends drive the flow of water along the pipe into the empty can. However, with both cans placed at the same ground or surface level, there will be no sustained flow. Therefore to create a potential difference between both cans, the can with water (source of charge) is placed at a higher elevation as seen in fig. 6.4b.

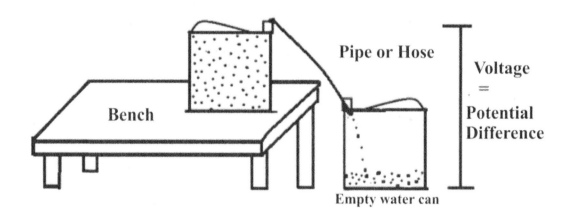

Figure 6.4b: Voltage Illustration

The pressure at the base of the pipe in the empty water may represent voltage. The water in the tank represents charge. The more water there is in the filled can, the higher the charge and the more the pressure measured at the base of the pipe in the empty can as water flows down.

We can think of the full water can as a battery source where a certain amount of energy is stored and then released. If we drain the full can by a certain amount, the pressure created at the base of the pipe in the empty can goes down. We may think of this as decrease in voltage. There is also a decrease in the amount of water that will flow through the pipe. A lesser pressure would mean that less water will flow.

Voltage is defined so that negatively charged objects are pulled towards higher voltages, while positively charged objects are pulled towards lower voltages. Therefore, the "conventional current" in a wire or resistor always flow from higher voltage to lower voltage. More than just a continuous path (circuit) therefore is needed before a continuous flow of electrons will occur in a circuit. Some means is required to push electrons around the circuit and this is the very function of voltage in a circuit. With electrons, the influencing force for their directional flow around a circuit is the same force at work in static electricity which is produced by an imbalance of electric charge. That imbalance is similar to what happened in the example of the two water cans above.

Current

Going back to our example using two water cans, we can think of the amount of water flowing through the pipe from the full can as current. As the pressure increases, water flow increases as well and vice-versa. With water, we would measure the volume flowing through the pipe over a certain period of time. But with electricity, we measure the amount of charge flowing through the circuit over a period of time.

Current therefore is defined as the rate of charge flow past a given point in an electric circuit, measured in Coulombs/second or Amperes. In electric circuits this charge is often carried by moving electrons in a wire. It can also be carried by ions in an electrolyte, or by both ions and electrons as seen in batteries. Electric current may be alternating (AC) or direct type of current (DC).

Alternating Current (AC): Alternating current is the movement of electric charge in such a way that the charged electrons periodically reverse direction. AC is the type of electric current used for supply of electric energy to consumer premises.

Direct Current (DC): Direct current however is the flow of electric charge in a uniform direction. Direct current is produced by sources such as batteries, thermocouples, solar cells etc. Direct current may flow in a conductor such as a wire, but can also flow through semiconductors, insulators, or even through a vacuum as in electron or ion beams. The electric charge flows in a constant direction, which is different from alternating current AC.

Resistance

A measure of the opposition to the flow of electrical charge or the degree to which a conductor opposes an electric current through that conductor is what is known as electrical resistance. The opposite is electrical conductance.

Electric circuits are designed to maximally utilize the energy injected into it by a voltage source without harm to the circuit components. If there is no resistance to current flow from a source to the circuit, the magnitude of current may be destructive to components of the circuit if a high quantum of energy is released, especially in the form of heat. The resistance serves to limit the amount of current through the circuit with a given amount of voltage supplied by the battery or other voltage source.

Conductors are materials that have very low resistance while insulators are materials which possess very high or infinite resistance.

Resistance is measured in ohms represented by the symbol Ω. According to ohm's law;

Resistance;

$R = V/I$

Power

Power is a measure of the work done in a given amount of time. It is a measure of the speed at which a standard amount of work is done. Beside voltage, current and resistance, power is a derived quantity as a result of the combination of voltage and current. In electric circuits, power is derived as a function of both voltage and current expressed as;

$P = EI$ or $P = VI$

Where P = Power, E (or V) = Potential difference, Electromotive force or Voltage and I = Current.

The unit of measurement of power is Watts (W).

Voltage is the specific work (or potential energy) per unit charge, while current is the rate at which electric charges move through a conductor. Together as a product (multiplication), voltage (work) and current (rate) constitute power as an output. A circuit with high voltage and low current may be dissipating the same amount of power as a circuit with low voltage and high current. Neither the amount of voltage alone nor the amount of current alone indicates the amount of power in an electric circuit.

For instance, if a circuit is an open circuit, voltage would be present between the terminals of the source while current is zero; hence the power output will be zero. There would be no power dissipated, no matter how great that voltage may be.

Since **P= I x E and I = 0, any value x 0 = 0**

Therefore, the power dissipated in any open circuit must be zero.
Similarly, if we have a short circuit created with a pure metallic conductor cable (with absolutely zero resistance); there will be current in the loop with zero voltage, so likewise no power would be dissipated.

Since **P=IE** and **E=0, any value multiplied by 0 = 0**

Therefore, the power dissipated in a superconducting loop must be zero.

The formula for calculating power can further be derived into;

P = VI, since from ohms' law **V = IR**
P = (IR) x I; so **P = I^{2}R**
Or since I = V/R
P = V x (V/R); so **P = V^2/ R**

Electronic Components, Functions and Uses

There are various discrete electronic components. They are used in almost all implementations of electronic circuitry that constitutes the many electronic devices like radio, TV, computers, mobile phones, telecommunication equipments etc. used in all fields of human endeavor. These utility devices and equipment all share a common anatomy in internal circuit-board composition. The difference between one electronic device, gadget or equipment from another is in the circuit-board design (arrangement of the discrete electronic components) tailored towards a specific purpose. Therefore the purpose of a device determines its circuit-board design.

What this means for a technician is that a sound foundational understanding of electronics technology at a basic level is a key element in expert level performance in the field. While an engineer studies at a deeper level and produces complex electrical or electronic designs, a technician defined as someone who studies, or practices technology should implement designs, maintain designs, and correct faults in the design whenever it occurs.

Discrete electronic components are the opposite of their counterparts in the circuit-board - the integrated circuits (ICs). They are individual, separate electronic components.

Description of Discrete Electronic Components

The following basic components are found on the PCB of all electronic devices, including the mobile phones which are our primary focus in this book;

    a. Resistors
    b. Capacitors
    c. Inductors
    d. Transistors
    e. Diodes

Whenever I teach basic electronics particularly for resistors and capacitors, I try to use an analogy about a farmer using a plot of land for mixed product farming and borehole for irrigation. The same manner is a plate of circuit-board used for electronic product design. Such example may not be a perfect one that captures all the actions happening in a circuit-board but it will help your understanding a bit I hope.

The water supply from a borehole serves to represent the power source for current flow to all components in the circuit-board. Pipes are laid for water to flow to each section of the farm just like the wire tracks on the printed circuit board.

Assuming the farmer segmented the farm into sections for Rice farming, Animal husbandry (Horses, Sheep and goats, cows and maybe poultry), corn and millet section etc, so also is a motherboard of a phone or other electronic board sectionalized into final sub-circuits for display unit, speaker, ringer, microphone, etc. Each of these final sub-circuits are compartments with similar discrete electronic components like the others, different only in the purposeful design(arrangement of the components) based on the current and voltage requirements of associated components. Sometimes a final sub-circuit would be integrated into a whole chip (integrated circuit, IC) aggregating the functions of the discrete electronic components in one whole.

Assume also that for the purposes of this illustration, the main focus is how to get water circulated and shared to each section of the farm according to need. For instance, the water requirements for the rice section would be much more compared to the requirement for maize. The water requirement for goats and poultry will definitely be small compared to that of the horses or cows, as well as the frequency and timing of supply to each section. The same way it is with an electronic circuit.

Resistors serve to limit the flow of current and even set voltages at specific points in the circuit. If you relate it to our farm, an irrigation farmer who turns on the water at a central point in the farm with pipes circulating to the various sections will have to install various pipe dimensions according to need as well as stop corks at the entry point closer to each section. The bigger the pipe (low resistance), the higher the volume of water supplied to a section and vice versa. Stop corks (representing variable resistance) may also serve to further regulate flow to areas where it is needed to flow slowly, faster or stopped completely. These can be equated to the resistor's ability to regulate and control flow of current in a circuit.

Another component of importance is the capacitor. In DC circuits, capacitors act to store charges albeit temporarily and also discharge the stored charges, block DC current, pass or filter AC currents etc. The main purpose of a capacitor in DC circuits is to filter out the AC component that enters in to the system by providing a low impedance path and as well, act as a reservoir of energy by maintaining almost a constant DC voltage across its plates. The AC components may be noise; ripples, unwanted radio frequency signals and any alternating signal which a combination of components on the circuit-board may create that may corrupt the needed pure DC signals. It all depends on how these components are combined in the circuit. For instance, if you connect a capacitor in series with a parallel resistor, it will pass AC signals but a resistor connected in series with a parallel capacitor to ground connection will filter the AC component out of the circuit.

Going back to our farm, a farmer can place storage cans in each section of the farm or some sections like for the cows, poultry, horses etc for times when the central tap is not supplying water. Equate it to our DC circuit; we have such distributed temporary storage across every electronic circuit. Capacitors are used on circuit boards to serve as local store of energy for most of the very high frequency devices. As you know there are many devices on a motherboard just like the farm, trying to draw power from the power supply. This will not be energy efficient just as it will be a burden, always going to turn on the water just for poultry or just because water in one section of a farm has exhausted. With the capacitors in every final sub-circuit, energy is therefore drawn from the capacitor located right at that device's sub-circuit just like each section's storage water cans placed by the farmer.

If we relate other applications of capacitors such as filtering unwanted signals, remember that waste cans or filtration cans do exist also in farms or water distribution systems.

So high frequency components' immediate power requirements are drawn from the capacitors. The capacitors replenish their charge store from the power supply and other capacitors too. The main power supply is the battery for mobile phones and the power supply units of other electronic devices, while the main local storage capacitors found in DC circuits are the electrolytic capacitors. Electrolytic capacitors are polarized capacitors found in electronic circuits. It means their terminals have polarity (marked + and -). They are unidirectional with high impedance and therefore not used for high frequency current scenarios. Other non-electrolytic capacitors used in circuits are bidirectional with low impedance which is suitable for high frequency components application.

Let us look at these components individually in the sections below.

Resistors

Resistors are the most fundamental and commonly used of all the discrete electronic components. The principal job of a resistor within an electrical or electronic circuit is to "resist" (from which the name, "Resistor" was derived). So primarily, a resistor does the following;

- Regulates the flow of electrons or current;

- Impedes or sets the flow of electrons or current through a particular path;

- Impose a voltage reduction in an electrical circuit.

Resistors are referred to as "Passive Devices" which means that they have no intrinsic source of power or amplification but only reduce the voltage or current signal passing through them. Passive devices also have linear characteristics as they experience voltage drops across them when current flows through their terminals. The reduction process results in loss of electrical energy in the form of heat as the resistor resists the flow of electrons through it. Therefore, for current to pass through its terminals from an external power source, a potential difference is required between the two terminals of a resistor.
This potential difference balances out the energy lost. When it is used in DC circuits a voltage drop is measured across the terminals as the circuit current flows through the resistor.

In obedience to Ohm's Law, different values of resistance produce different values of current or voltage.

This makes resistors very useful in electronic circuits where they control or reduce either the current flow or voltage produced across them. Resistors may also be either "Fixed or Variable" resistors. Fixed resistors have one single value of resistance only. A 10Ω resistor is an example of a fixed resistor because it has a fixed value of 10. Variable resistors (potentiometers) on the other hand can provide an infinite number of resistance values between zero and a maximum value.

There are many different types of resistors available for the electronics design engineer to choose from. There are the very small surface mount chip resistors and as well large wire-wound power resistors. Sizes and applications may differ.

Surface mount resistors are the resistor types used in mobile phones. Typically this type of resistor is manufactured using thin film technology. Surface mount resistors are rectangular in shape, having metalized edges at either end of the body through which they make contact with the printed circuit board using solder. They are made by depositing a metal oxide film on a ceramic substrate. The resistance property is determined by the thickness and the length of the metal oxide film.

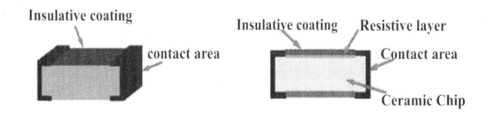

Figure 6.5:Surface Mount Resistor design structure
Source: http://www.radioelectronics.com/info/data/resistor/smd_resistor/smd_resistor.php

The surface mount resistor terminations (the metalized edges) are very important especially during soldering. They need to make a good reliable contact with the resistive element of the chip resistor. If it gets broken off or corroded, it will not function.

Temperature Coefficient: When working on these types of resistors especially using hot air stations or soldering irons, care must be taken as regards their temperature coefficient characteristics. Temperature coefficient is a coefficient expressing the relation between a change in their physical property and the change in temperature that causes it.
The use of metal oxide film enables these SMD resistors to provide a good temperature coefficient with values ranging from 25, 50 up to 100 ppm/°C in use.

Symbols: The symbol used in schematic and electrical drawings for a Resistor can either be a rectangular box or a "zig-zag" type line.

Figure 6.6a: Schematic symbol of Resistors

Resistors Circuit Connections

Resistors are connected within electrical or electronic circuits either in "Series" or in "Parallel" or the combination of both.

Resistors in Series

Resistors are connected in "Series" when they are daisy-chained together in a single line. Series-connected resistors have a common current flowing through them.

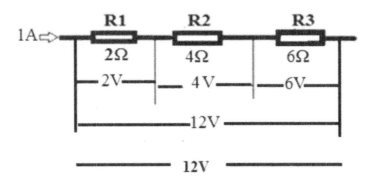

Fig. 6.6b: Resistors in Series

Mathematically, this can be represented as;

$I_T = I_1 = I_2 = I_3....I_n$ where I_T is the total current, while the total circuit resistance of series resistors is;

$R_T = R_1 + R_2 + R_3...+ R_n$ where R_T is the total circuit resistance of the series resistors.

The total voltage is also the sum of the individual voltage drops across each resistor;

$V_T = V_1 + V_2 + V_3 ... + V_n$ where V_T is the total voltage drop.

The value in ohms of the total resistance of a series connected circuit will always be greater than the resistor of highest value within the series.

From the diagram above, we see that the combined resistance of the three resistors is 12Ω. It means that all three resistors can be changed with a single 12 Ω resistor.

The Voltage Divider Circuit

We can see from the above example that, if we assume that the supply voltage is 12 volts, different voltages or voltage drops (I x R) appear across each resistor within the series network. When resistors are connected in series this way, across a single DC supply the main advantage is that different reference voltage values appear across each resistor producing a kind of circuit known as the Voltage Divider Network.

This simple circuit shares the supply voltage proportionally across each resistor in the series link with the amount of voltage drop being determined by the resistors' value and as we have learnt, the current through a series resistor circuit is common to all resistors present. So a higher value resistance will have a higher voltage drop across it, while a smaller value resistance will have a smaller voltage drop across it.

The series resistive circuit shown above forms a simple voltage divider network where three voltages 2V, 4V and 6V are produced from a single 12V supply. Kirchhoff's Voltage Law states that *"the supply voltage in a closed circuit is equal to the sum of all the voltage drops (IR) around the circuit"* and this can be used to good effect.

The Voltage Divider Rule, allows the design engineer to use the effects of resistance proportionality to calculate the potential difference across each resistor regardless of the current flowing through the series circuit.

A typical "voltage divider circuit" is shown below.

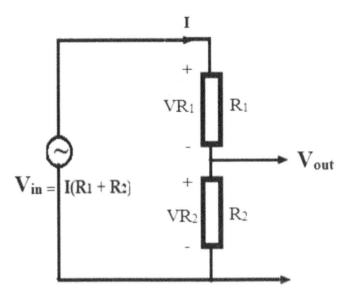

Fig. 6.6c: Resistor as Voltage Divider Circuit

In the circuit shown above two resistors, R1 and R2 are connected together in series across the supply voltage **Vin**. One side of the power supply voltage is connected to resistor, R1 and the voltage output, **Vout** is taken from across resistor **R2**. The value of this output voltage is given by the formula below.

$$V_{out} = V_{in} \left(\frac{R_2}{R_1 + R_2} \right)$$

Assuming more resistors are connected in series to the circuit, then different voltages will be present across each resistor according to their individual resistance R values providing different but smaller voltage points from one single supply in obedience to Ohms Law where;

$$V = I \times R$$

So if we had three or more resistances in the series chain, we can still use our now familiar potential divider formula to find the voltage drop across each one. Consider the circuit below.

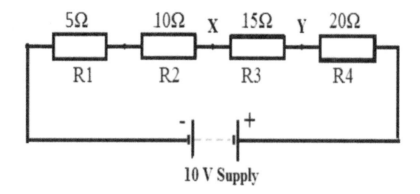

Example 6.1: Resistor as Voltage Divider calculation

To calculate the voltage across point X and Y (i.e. resistor R3), we use the same potential divider (or voltage divider) formula;

$$V_{XY} = VR3 = V_{supply} \times \frac{R3}{R1+R2+R3+R4}$$

$$V_{XY} = 10 \times \frac{15}{5+10+15+20}$$

$$= 10 \times 0.3$$

$$V_{XY} = VR3 = 3V$$

Let us evaluate another circuit to drive home the various ways a series resistor circuit can impact an electronic design. Look at this diagram below;

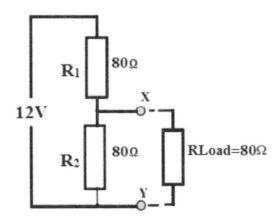

Example 6.2: Resistor as Voltage Divider calculation

Assuming we have an existing circuit like the voltage divider circuit above and a component, say a speaker (RLoad) is tapping power from this circuit with a load resistance (or impedance) of 80Ω. The circuit is designed to supply an input voltage to this speaker not exceeding 6V. Potential divider circuits like this enabled a design like this that produces a smaller voltage (in this case 6V) from a larger supply voltage (in this case 12V).

With a 12V DC supply as in the circuit above;

The voltage drops across X and Y;

  i.   Without the speaker (RLoad) connected
  ii. With speaker (RLoad) connected

are calculated thus;

For (i): where R(x-y) = 80Ω; Output Voltage Vo; Input Voltage Vi;

$$V_0 = V_{in} \times \frac{R_2}{R_1 + R_2}$$

$$Vo = 12 \text{ x } \frac{80}{80 + 80}$$

Vo = 6V across R2 when no load is connected in parallel to R2.

When the load (Speaker) is connected however, the combined parallel load at x-y will become 40Ω.

$$\frac{80 \text{ x } 80}{80 + 80} = 40 \, \Omega$$

Therefore, the reference circuit output supply voltage to the speaker will be;

$$Vo = 12 \text{ x } \frac{40}{80 + 40}$$

Vo = 12 x 0.33

Vo = 4V.

Testing the terminals of the speaker should give you this value.

The example also shows that connecting two equal value resistors, of say 80Ω each together as a potential divider network across the 12V produced a reduced lower voltage of 6Veffectively until we connected the load circuit to the network. The effect of resistor RLoad connected in parallel across R2 changes the ratio of the two series resistances thereby altering their voltage drop.

We can therefore see that a loaded voltage divider network changes its output voltage as a result of this loading effect, since the output voltage Vout is determined by the ratio of R1 to R2. In cases where the load is a variable resistor, as the load resistance, RL increases towards infinity (∞) this loading effect reduces and the voltage ratio of Vout/Vs will not be affected by additional load on the output. Therefore the higher the load impedance, the lower the loading effect on the output.

With this knowledge, a technician can troubleshoot final sub-circuits of peripheral components by checking reference voltage test points.

Resistors in Parallel

When resistors are connected in such a way that they have both of their respective terminals connected to each terminal of another resistor or resistors, they are said to be connected in parallel.

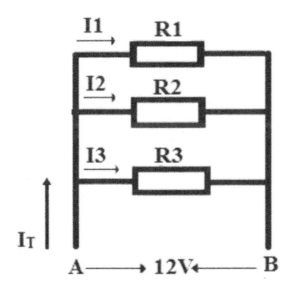

Figure 6.6d: Resistors in Parallel

The total resistance of a parallel circuit is mathematically represented below and the total resistance of a parallel circuit will always be less than the value of the smallest resistor. Unlike the series resistors, the sum of the reciprocal of parallel resistors gives the equivalent total resistor value;

$$\frac{1}{R_T} = \frac{1}{R_1} + \frac{1}{R_2} + \frac{1}{R_3} + \frac{1}{R_n}$$

But where the two resistances (or impedances) in parallel are equal and of the same value, then the total or equivalent resistance, R_T is equal to half the value of one resistor i.e;

R/2 for two resistors; R/3 for three equal resistors in parallel etcetera

Parallel resistors have a common voltage across them where total supply voltage is;

$$V_s = V_1 = V_2 = V_3 .... = V_n$$

Total circuit current flow is equal to the sum of all the individual branch currents added together as below;

$$I_T = I_1 + I_2 + I_3 ... + I_n$$

Other ways resistors can be connected in parallel are as shown below;

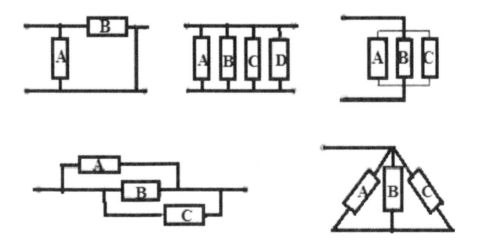

Figure 6.6e: Other Resistors in Parallel circuits

Let us do a little calculation with the following diagram below

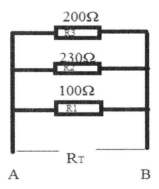

Example 6.3: Parallel Circuit calculation

To calculate R_T, the total equivalent resistance of the three parallel resistors;

$1/R_T = 1/R1 + 1/R2 + 1/R3$
$1/R_T = 1/100 + 1/230 + 1/200$
$1/R_T = 0.01 + 0.004 + 1/0.005$
$1/R_T = 0.019$
$R_T = 1/0.019$
$R_T = 52.63\Omega$

This method above applies to any number of resistors connected in parallel.

The formula for calculating **two** resistors in parallel is;

$$R_T = \frac{R1 \times R2}{R1 + R2}$$

Current in Parallel Resistors

The total current, I_T in a parallel resistor circuit is the sum of the individual currents flowing in all branches of the parallel circuit. The amount of current flowing in each parallel branch is not necessarily the same. This is because the value of the resistance in each branch determines the current within that branch. For example, although the parallel combination has the same constant voltage across it, the resistances could be of different values; hence the current flowing through each resistor would definitely be different based on Ohms Law.

Consider the three resistors in parallel above. The current that flows through each of the resistors (I_{R1}, I_{R2} and I_{R3}) connected together in parallel is not necessarily the same value as it depends upon the resistive value of the resistor. However, we do know that the current that enters the circuit at point A must also exit the circuit at point B.

Remember that Kirchhoff's Current Law states that: *"the total current leaving a circuit is equal to that entering the circuit – no current is lost"*. Thus, the total current flowing in the circuit is given as:

$$I_T = I_{R1} + I_{R2} + I_{R3}$$

Then by using Ohm's Law, where $V = IR$

And V_S = Supply voltage = 12V

I_{Rx}, the current flowing through each resistor of the above diagram can be calculated as:

The Current flowing through R1, $I_{R1} = V_S \div R1$
$I_{R1} = 12V \div 100\Omega = 0.12A$

The Current flowing through R2, $I_{R2} = V_S \div R2$

$I_{R2} = 12V \div 230\Omega = 0.05A$ and

The Current flowing through R3, $I_{R3} = V_S \div R3$

$I_{R3} = 12V \div 200\Omega = 0.06A$
Thus giving us a total current I_T flowing around the circuit as:

$I_T = 0.12A + 0.05A + 0.06A = $ **0.23A**
This result can also be verified directly using Ohm's Law as:

$I_T = V_S \div R_T = 12 \div 52.63\Omega = 0.228$ approximately **0.23A** (the same)

The equation given for calculating the total current flowing in a parallel resistor circuit which is the sum of all the individual currents added together is given as:

$$I_T = I_1 + I_2 + I_3... + I_n$$

Also, parallel resistor networks can be thought of as "current dividers" because the supply current divides between the various parallel branches. So a parallel resistor circuit having 'N' number of resistive networks will have N-different current paths while maintaining a common voltage across itself. Parallel resistors can also be interchanged with each other without changing the total resistance or the total circuit current.

Resistors in AC Circuits

In the previous sections on the behavior and design calculations for resistors in series and parallel circuits, the assumption was that both the voltage and current had a constant polarity, flow and direction. This is the nature of DC current or circuits and applicable to mobile phone circuits. In this section however, we shall briefly examine the other type of electricity supply known as AC or Alternating current.

AC voltages switches polarity from positive to negative and back again over time and the current with respect to the voltage swings back and forth. The oscillating shape of an AC supply follows that of the mathematical form of a "sine wave" which is commonly called a Sinusoidal Waveform. Therefore, a sinusoidal voltage can be defined mathematically thus;

$$V(t) = Vmax \sin \omega t.$$

The usual Ohm's law and Kirchoff's laws for calculating voltage, current and power quantities apply when a resistive DC circuit is designed with pure resistors that possess negligible presence of inductance and capacitance. But when dealing with AC circuits, peak-to-peak values of these quantities or their root mean square are considered in the calculations. So when using resistors in AC circuits the term Impedance, symbol Z is the generally used alphabet and we can say that;

$$DC \text{ resistance} = AC \text{ impedance, } R = Z.$$

Resistors are "passive" devices because they do not produce or consume any electrical energy, but convert electrical energy into heat. In AC circuits factors such as the frequency and phase difference or phase angle (φ) of the supply voltage affects the application of Ohms' law calculation for R. A resistor will always have the same resistive value no matter what the supply frequency is, from low to very high frequencies unlike capacitors and inductors. When resistors are used in AC circuits the direction of the current flowing through them has no effect on the behavior of the resistor so it will rise and fall as the voltage rises and falls. The current and voltage reaches maximum, fall through zero and reach minimum at exactly the same time. This means that they rise and fall simultaneously and are said to be "in-phase".

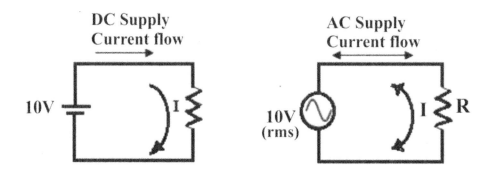

Figure 6.7: Current flow direction in DC and AC circuits

Phase Relationship Diagram for Voltage and Current in AC circuits

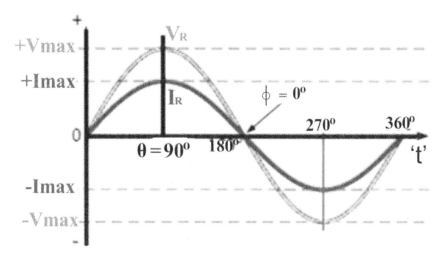

Graph 6.1: V-I Phase Relationship

On a Cartesian coordinate, representation of a sinusoid depicts its cyclic nature and explains the phase relationship between current and voltage. From the diagram above, at any point along the horizontal x-axis the instantaneous voltage and current are both in-phase because the current and the voltage reach their maximum values at the same time when their phase angle θ is 0o. Then these instantaneous values of voltage and current can be compared to give the value of the resistance in ohms by using Ohm's law.

Capacitors

A capacitor is a passive two-terminal electrical component used to store electrical energy temporarily in an electric field. In a way, a capacitor is a little like a battery. Although they work in completely different ways, capacitors and batteries both store electrical energy. Whenever an electric voltage exists between two parallel separated conductors, an electric field becomes present within the space between those conductors. Electric Fields are invisible electromagnetic forces surrounding an area which influences the properties of materials that exist within that area.

A Capacitor is basically made of two or more parallel conductive (metal) plates which are not connected to each other, but are electrically separated either by air or by what is called a dielectric. Dielectrics used can be insulating materials such as waxed paper, mica, ceramic, plastic or a liquid gel as used in electrolytic capacitors.

Figure 6.8a: Symbol of a Capacitor

There are different kinds of capacitors available. They are usually named according to the material used in making them. No matter the type of capacitor used in a circuit, they all store electric charge. The conductive metal plates of a capacitor may take the form of a square, circle or rectangle. Also the general shape, size and construction of a parallel plate capacitor depend on its application and voltage rating.

When capacitors are used in a DC circuit, they charge up to the source supply voltage while blocking the flow of current through them. This is due to the dielectric of a capacitor which is non-conductive and basically an insulator. But when a capacitor is connected to an AC circuit, current flows through the capacitor with little or no resistance to the flow.

When voltage is applied to the plates of a capacitor, the plates are charged up and the charges continue to build up at the plates until the voltage across the plates are equal to that of the supply voltage.

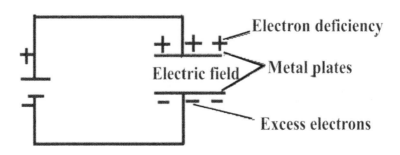

Effect of voltage across the parallel plates of a Capacitor

Figure 6.8b

The Capacitance of a Capacitor

Capacitance is an electrical property of a capacitor and is the measure of a capacitor's ability to store an electrical charge on its two plates with the unit of capacitance being the Farad (F), named after the British physicist Michael Faraday.

A capacitor has the capacitance of One Farad when a charge of One Coulomb is stored on the plates by a voltage of One volt. Capacitance, C is always positive and has no negative units. Capacitors do eventually lose their stored charges due to internal leakage paths for electrons to flow from one plate to the other. Depending on the specific type of capacitor, the time it takes for a stored charge voltage to discharge can be a long time.

When the voltage across a capacitor is increased from low to higher levels, it is said to be charging because there is an increasing amount of energy being stored in its electric field. Therefore it draws current from the rest of the circuit, acting as a power load. In this condition the direction of flow of electrons with regard to the voltage polarity is from the negative to the positive terminal.

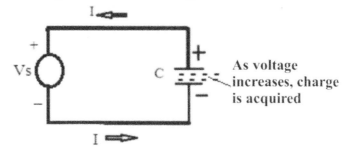

Figure 6.8c: When the capacitor is charging

The reverse is the case when the voltage across a capacitor is decreased, the capacitor supplies current to the rest of the circuit, acting as a power source. In this condition the capacitor is said to be *discharging*. Its store of energy (held in the electric field) is decreasing as energy is released to the rest of the circuit.

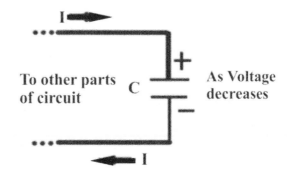

Figure 6.8d: When the Capacitor is discharging

Both scenarios above serve to illustrate the behavior of capacitors in the circuit. If a source of voltage is suddenly applied to an uncharged capacitor (which implies a sudden increase in voltage), the capacitor would draw current from that source, absorbing energy from it, until the capacitor's voltage equals that of the source. But once the capacitor voltage reaches a fully charged state, its stored charge will decay to zero.

On the other hand, if a load resistance is connected to a charged capacitor, the capacitor would supply current to that load until all its stored energy is released and its voltage decays to zero. Once the capacitor voltage is completely discharged, its current decays to zero. Because of this inherent ability to be charged and then discharged, capacitors can be thought of as acting somewhat like batteries.

Capacitors in Series

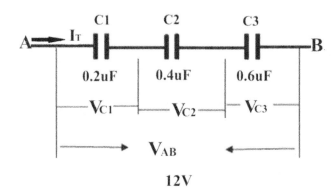

Figure 6.8e: Capacitors in Series

When capacitors are connected together in a daisy-chain with its second terminal (plate) connected to the first terminal (plate) of another capacitor, it is considered to be in series. This series connection means that in a DC connected circuit, capacitor C2 is effectively isolated from the circuit, sandwiched between C1 and C3.

The outcome of this is that the effective plate area decreases to the smallest individual capacitance connected in the series chain. The voltage drop across each capacitor therefore will be different depending upon the values of the individual capacitances. If we apply Kirchhoff's Voltage Law, to the circuit above;

$V_{AB} = V_{C1} + V_{C2} + V_{C3} = 12V$

Where Q_T = total charge

$V_{C1} = Q_T / C1$, $V_{C2} = Q_T / C2$ and $V_{C3} = Q_T / C3$

$V_{AB} = Q_T / C_T = Q_T / C1 + Q_T / C2 + Q_T / C3$

If we divide each term by Q we have;

$1/ C_T = 1/C_1 + 1/C_2 + 1/C_3 + ... 1/C_n$ as the series capacitor equation.

To calculate the total capacitance for two capacitors in series however, we use;

$$C_T = \frac{C_1 \times C_2}{C_1 + C_2}$$

With series-connected resistors, the sum of all the voltage drops across the series circuit will be equal to the applied voltage V_S (Kirchhoff's Voltage Law). This is true about capacitors in series as well.

With series-connected capacitors, the capacitive reactance of the capacitor acts as impedance due to the frequency of the supply. This capacitive reactance produces a voltage drop across each capacitor, therefore series connected capacitors act as a capacitive voltage divider network like their resistor counterparts.

The result is that the voltage divider formula applied to resistors can also be used to find the individual voltages for two capacitors in series.
Where C_X is the capacitance of the capacitor in question, V_S is the supply voltage across the series chain and V_{CX} is the voltage drop across the target capacitor, then;

$$V_{CX} = \frac{V_S \times C_T}{C_X}$$

Capacitors in Parallel

When capacitors are connected in parallel, they have a common voltage supply across them.

$$V_{AB} = V_S = V_1 = V_2 = V_3 = 12V$$

C1, C2 and C3 are all connected together in a parallel branch between points A and B as shown below;

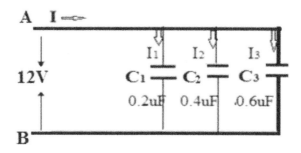

Example 6.4: Capacitors in Parallel calculation

When Capacitors are connected together in parallel the total or equivalent capacitance, C_T in the circuit is equal to the sum of all the individual capacitors added together.

$$C_T = C_1 + C_2 + C_3 + ...C_n$$

$$C_T = 0.2uF + 0.4uF + 0.6uF$$

$$C_T = 1.2uF \text{ (microfarad)}$$

One important point to remember about parallel connected capacitor circuits is; the total capacitance (C_T) of any two or more capacitors connected together in parallel will always be GREATER than the value of the largest capacitor in the group. This is because we are adding together values.

When three, four or more capacitors are connected together the total capacitance of the circuit C_T would still be the sum of all the individual capacitors added together. This is because the total surface area of the plates has been increased. If we connect two identical capacitors, the surface areas of the plates will double thereby doubling the capacitance of the combination.

Capacitors in AC Circuits

When we apply an alternating current or AC supply across the plates of a capacitor, the capacitor will alternately charge and discharge at a rate determined by the frequency of the supply. The Capacitance of a capacitor in AC circuits change as the supply frequency changes while the capacitor is being constantly charged and discharged. This is unlike in DC circuits where they become charged to the value of the source voltage behaving like temporary storage devices and maintain the charge indefinitely as long as the supply voltage is present.

The flow of electrons onto the plates of a Capacitor is directly proportional to the rate of change of the voltage across those plates. Capacitors in AC circuits pass current through them when the voltage across its plates is constantly changing with respect to time (sinusoidal AC signals), but they block current flow through them when the voltage is a constant DC signals. Therefore, Capacitance in AC circuits varies with frequency as the capacitor is being constantly charged and discharged.

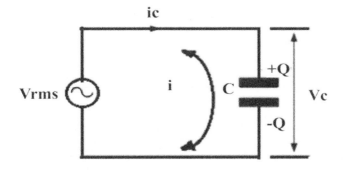

Figure 6.8f: Capacitor in AC circuit

In the circuit above, the capacitor is connected directly across the AC supply voltage. This example is a purely capacitive circuit with zero effects of any other connected components. As the supply voltage increases and decreases, the capacitor charges and discharges respectively with changing voltage. Since the charging current is directly proportional to the rate of change of the voltage across the plates of the capacitor, this rate of change is at its greatest as the supply voltage crosses over from its positive half cycle to its negative half cycle or vice versa at points $0°$ and $180°$ along the sine wave when plotted on a graph.

The smallest change in voltage occurs when the AC sine wave crosses over at its maximum or minimum peak voltage level, (Vm). At these positions in the cycle the maximum or minimum currents are flowing through the capacitor circuit and this is shown in the graph below.

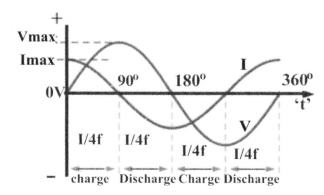

Graph 6.2: Capacitor Phasor diagram for AC circuits

Capacitive Reactance

Capacitive Reactance in a purely capacitive circuit is the opposition to current flow only in AC circuits. Like resistance, reactance is also measured in Ohms but is given the symbol X to distinguish it from a purely resistive value. Since reactance is a quantity that can also be applied to Inductors as well as Capacitors, when used with capacitors it is more commonly known as Capacitive Reactance.

For capacitors in AC circuits, capacitive reactance is given the symbol Xc. Therefore, capacitive reactance is defined as a capacitor's resistive value that varies with frequency.

Finally Capacitors, like all electrical components, have certain limitations which must be respected for the sake of reliability and proper circuit operation. For instance, capacitors are made of two conductors separated by an insulator (the dielectric), so its maximum voltage must not be exceeded. If excessive voltage is applied, the "breakdown" rating of the dielectric material may be exceeded, resulting in the capacitor internally short-circuiting. Also, some capacitors are manufactured in such a way that they can tolerate applied voltage in one polarity but not the other due to their construction.

Inductors

An Inductor, also called a coil is a passive two-terminal electrical component which resists changes in electric current passing through it. It consists of a conductor such as a wire, usually wound into a coil. Energy is stored in a magnetic field in the coil as long as current flows.

An inductor's opposition to AC current is based specifically on inductive reaction to changes in current, unlike in resistors which are based on friction. When alternating current flows through the windings of an inductor, the current flow represents increase in current through its windings so the inductor reacts to this increase by opposing it and when the current flow is decreasing, the inductor reverses polarity and reacts to oppose the decrease in current. So it actually reacts to changes in the current flow.

However, inductors are not quite pure in their reactive behavior. Firstly, they are made of wire conductors which mean that they possess intrinsic resistance property.

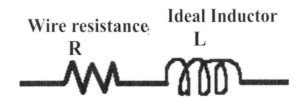

Figure 6.9: Schematic Symbol of Inductors

The in-built resistance acts as though it were connected in series with a perfect inductance of the coil. Therefore, the impedance of any real inductor will always be that of a combined resistance and inductive reactance where inductive reactance is the opposition that an inductor offers to alternating current due to its storage and release of energy in its magnetic field.

An inductor's opposition to change in current translates to an opposition to alternating current (AC) generally, which is by definition always changing in instantaneous magnitude and direction. This opposition to alternating current can be compared to that of resistance, but different in that it always results in a phase shift between current and voltage, and it dissipates zero power. Because of the differences, it has a different name – *reactance* symbolized by the capital letter "X" but measured in ohms just like resistance (R).

Since inductors drop voltage in proportion to the rate of current change, they will drop more voltage for faster-changing current, and less voltage for slower-changing current therefore reactance in ohms for any inductor is directly proportional to the frequency of the alternating current.

Diodes

Diodes are basic unidirectional Semiconductor Devices that will only allow current to flow through them in one direction. The Signal Diode is the most basic active component in electronic circuits. Unlike resistors which are passive devices, a diode does not act in a linear manner with respect to the applied voltage as it has an exponential Current-Voltage relationship. This makes it difficult to analyze diodes using Ohm's law as is done for resistors.

Before we continue, let us understand the basic theory of semi-conductors of which diodes, transistors and even integrated circuit chips are made of.

Semi-conductors Basics

Semiconductor materials from Chemistry- the periodic table - such as silicon (Si) and germanium (Ge) have electrical properties between the properties of a "conductor" and an "insulator". They are neither good conductors nor good insulators hence their name "semi-conductors". The amount of "free electrons" in their atoms is closely grouped together in a crystalline pattern called a "crystal lattice".

However, the ability of semi-conductors to conduct electricity can be greatly improved by either replacing or adding certain donor or acceptor atoms to this crystalline structure in order to produce more free electrons (-) than holes (+) or vice versa. This is achieved by adding a small percentage of another element to the base material, either silicon or germanium.

Silicon and Germanium are classified as intrinsic semiconductors individually. This means that they are chemically pure, containing nothing but semi-conductive material. But if the amount of impurities added to this intrinsic semiconductor material is controlled, then its conductivity property can also be controlled. Various impurities known as donors or acceptors can be added to this intrinsic material to produce free electrons or holes respectively. This process of adding donor or acceptor atoms to semiconductor atoms is known as *Doping*. When you "dope" Silicon, it loses its purity to become impure. This is because, any donor and acceptor atoms from another element is referred to as an "impurity", so by doping these silicon material with a sufficient number of impurities, we can turn it into a semi-conductor, likewise Germanium etc.

Silicon is the most commonly used semiconductor basic material. That is the reason a place like the Southern California San Francisco Bay area is nick-named "Silicon Valley" because the word "silicon" originally referred to the large number of silicon chip innovators and manufacturers in the region. Silicon has four valence electrons in its outermost shell which it shares with its neighboring silicon atoms to fully form eight orbital electrons. The structure of the bond between the two silicon atoms is such that each atom shares one electron with its neighbor to stabilize the atomic bond. The arrangement of Silicon atoms is symmetrical in pattern making them a crystalline solid structure. Pure silica is generally an intrinsic crystal since it has no impurities, hence has no free electrons in its atomic structure. In order to extract electric current from a silicon crystal, we create a positive and a negative pole within the silicon allowing electrons to flow out of the silicon. This is achieved by doping. There are two types of semi-conductor materials:

N-type Semi-conductor

These are materials which have 5 valence electron-impurity atoms (Donors) added to them and conduct current by "electron" motion. They are therefore regarded as N-type Semiconductors.

A semiconductor material is classified as N-type when it has more electrons than holes (positive ions) making one of its poles a negative pole. In N-type semiconductors, the "donors" are positively charged with a large number of free electrons. The holes are smaller in number relative to the number of free electrons. When doping is applied, we have positively charged donors and negatively charged free electrons. But when you apply voltage across the terminals of the "doped" semiconductor in a way referred to as *biasing,* we have negatively charged free electrons and positively charged holes.

In order for a silicon crystal to conduct electricity, an impurity atom such as Antimony, Arsenic or Phosphorus has to be added into the crystalline structure making it extrinsic (impurities are added). These donor atoms have five outer electrons in their outermost orbital which they share with neighboring atoms. This is why they are commonly called "Pentavalent" impurities - ("Penta" equals to 5). Four out of the five orbital electrons will therefore bond with their neighboring silicon atoms leaving one "free electron" un-bonded. This free electron becomes mobile once an electrical voltage is applied, leading to electron flow. Antimony which is usually used is symbolized by Sb in the periodic table.

Since each impurity atom "donates" one electron, pentavalent atoms are generally known as "donors".

P-type Semiconductor

These are materials which have 3 valence electron-impurity atoms (Acceptors) added and conduct electric current by "hole" motion. They are therefore called P-type Semiconductors.

In P-type semi-conductor materials the "Acceptors" are negatively charged electrons and there are a large number of holes compared to small number of free electrons. When "doping" (addition of impurities) is applied, we have negatively charged acceptors and positively charged holes. When voltage is applied to its terminals after doping, we have positively charged holes and negatively charged free electrons.

Supposing a "Trivalent" (3-electron) impurity is added into the crystalline structure, such as Boron, Aluminium or Indium, which have only three valence electrons available in their outermost orbital, the fourth closed bond cannot be formed. Therefore, a complete connection is not possible, giving the semiconductor material an abundance of positively charged carriers known as "holes" in the structure of the crystal where electrons are effectively missing.

With the presence of a hole in the silicon crystal, a neighboring electron will be attracted to that hole such that it will try to fill it. By moving from its location to fill up the hole, the electron leaves another hole behind it. Another electron becomes attracted to the new hole, leaves to fill it and by so doing creates another hole behind it. This goes on indefinitely in cycles making it look like a "holes movement", this time as a positive charge through the crystal structure. This movement of holes results in a shortage of electrons in the silicon, turning the entire doped crystal into a positive pole. Since each impurity atom generates a hole, trivalent impurities are generally known as "Acceptors" as they are continually "accepting" extra electrons.

P and N-type semiconductors are in general electrically neutral individually. Antimony (Sb) and Boron (B) are two of the most commonly used doping agents since they are more freely available compared to other types of materials. There are other chemical elements that can also be used as doping agents to a base material of either Silicon (S) or Germanium (Ge) to produce different types of basic semiconductor materials for use in electronic semiconductor components, microprocessor and solar cell applications.

Diodes Continued...

Diodes are semiconductors which consist of both N-type and P-type materials. There are two types of diodes based on their size;

- The Signal Diode and
- The Power Diode.

The Signal Diode is a very small sized non-linear semiconductor device generally used in electronic circuits where small currents or high frequencies are involved such as in radio, television and digital logic circuits.

The Power Diode however is a bigger sized semiconductor device with larger forward-bias currents or higher reverse-bias blocking voltages. The PN junction of a small signal diode would eventually overheat and melt if used where higher voltages are involved so larger Power Diodes are used instead.

The power semiconductor diode, known simply as the Power Diode, has a much larger PN junction area compared to the smaller signal diode, resulting in a high forward current capability and a high reverse blocking voltage. The electronic symbol given for any type of diode is that of an arrow with a bar or line at its end as shown below;

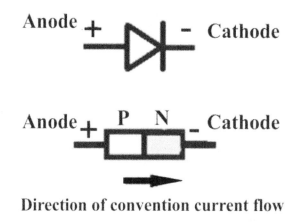

Direction of convention current flow

Figure 6.10a: Schematic Symbol of Diodes

Electron-flow direction as we have learnt from basic electricity principles is in the opposite direction to conventional current from cathode to anode. The arrow always points in the direction of conventional current flow through the diode, which suggests that the diode will only conduct if a positive supply is connected to the Anode terminal and a negative supply is connected to the Cathode terminal thus only allowing current to flow through it in one direction only. This is what is referred to as the Forward Biased condition.

However, if an external energy source is connected in the reverse direction, the diode will block any current from flowing through it and instead will act like an open switch. This is referred to as the Reversed Biased condition.

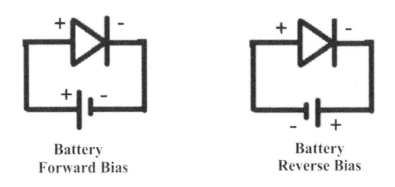

Figure 6.10b: Biasing of Diodes

To understand the concept of biasing a diode, let us also discuss the fact that a diode is also regarded as a P-N junction diode. If a suitable positive voltage (forward bias) is applied between the two ends of the PN junction, it can supply free electrons and holes with the extra energy they require to cross the junction as the width of the depletion layer around the PN junction is decreased.

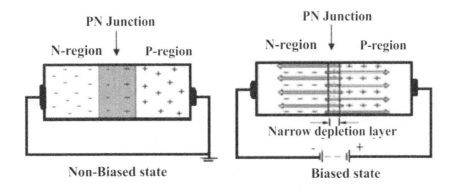

Figure 6.10c: Electrons and Holes movement in Diodes

By applying a negative voltage (reverse bias), free charges are being pulled away from the junction resulting in the depletion layer becoming widened, thereby increasing or decreasing the effective resistance of the junction by allowing or blocking current flow through the diode.

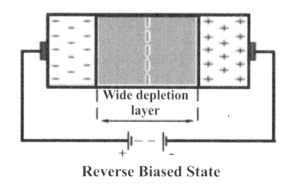

Wide depletion layer

Reverse Biased State

Figure 6.10d: Electrons and Holes movement in Diodes

The depletion layer widens with an increase in the application of a reverse voltage and narrows with an increase in the application of a forward voltage. This is due to the differences in the electrical properties on the two sides of the PN junction resulting in physical changes taking place.

Diodes are manufactured in a range of voltage and current ratings and care must be taken when choosing a diode for a certain application or when applying heat during soldering. The following are rated features;

- Peak inverse voltage which is the maximum allowable Reverse operating voltage that can be applied across the diode without reverse breakdown and damage occurring to the device.

- Maximum Forward Current which is the *maximum forward current* allowed to flow through the device. When the diode is conducting in the forward bias condition, it has a very small "ON" resistance across the PN junction and therefore, power is dissipated across this junction (according to **Ohm's Law**) in the form of heat. Therefore, exceeding its maximum forward current value will cause more heat to be generated across the junction and the diode will fail due to thermal overload, usually with destructive consequence.

- Total Power Dissipation rating which is the maximum possible power dissipation of the diode when it is forward biased (conducting). When current flows through the signal diode the biasing of the PN junction is not perfect and offers some resistance to the flow of current resulting in power being dissipated (lost) in the diode in the form of heat.

- Maximum Operating Temperature rating actually relates to the *Junction Temperature* of the diode and maximum power dissipation. It is the maximum temperature allowable before the structure of the diode deteriorates and is expressed in units of degrees centigrade per Watt, (^{o}C/W).

Power diodes provide uncontrolled rectification of power and are used in applications such as battery charging circuits and DC power supplies as well as AC rectifiers and inverters. Power diodes are designed to have a forward "ON" resistance of fractions of an Ohm while their reverse blocking resistance is in the mega-Ohms range.

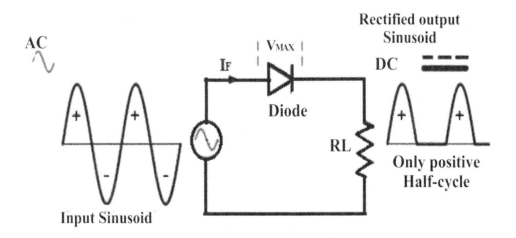

Figure 6.10e: Power diode as a rectifier

If an alternating voltage is applied across a power diode, during the positive half- cycle the diode will conduct, passing current and during the negative half cycle the diode will not conduct blocking the flow of current. Therefore, conduction through the power diode only occurs during the positive half-cycle and is unidirectional i.e. DC. This is known as rectification.

Power diodes can be used individually like in the diagram above or connected together to produce a variety of rectifier circuits such as "Half-Wave", "Full-Wave" or as "Bridge Rectifiers". Each type of rectifier circuit can be classified as uncontrolled, half-controlled or fully controlled. An uncontrolled rectifier circuit is implemented using only power diodes; a fully controlled rectifier circuit is implemented using thyristors (SCRs) while a half controlled rectifier is a mixture of both diodes and thyristors.

Half Wave Rectification

A rectifier is a circuit which converts an Alternating Current (AC) input power into a Direct Current (DC) output power as is common in AC/DC adapters. The input power supply may be either a single-phase or a multi-phase supply. The most simple configuration type among all the rectifier circuits is that of the Half-Wave Rectifier.

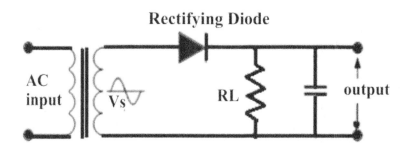

Figure 6.10f: Diode as a Half-wave Rectifier

The power diode in a half wave rectifier circuit passes just one half of each complete sine wave of the AC supply in order to convert it into a DC supply. That is where this type of circuit derived its name.

During each "positive" half-cycle of the AC sine wave, the diode is forward biased as the anode is positive with respect to the cathode resulting in current flowing through the diode. During the "negative" half cycle, the diode goes into blocking mode.

When rectification provides a (DC) power supply from an alternating (AC) source as found in most power supply units of consumer electronics, the amount of ripple voltage can be further reduced by using high capacity capacitors to smoothen the resultant output waveform. Cost and size limitations are factored into the types of smoothing capacitors used. For a given capacitor value, a greater load current will discharge the capacitor more quickly, thereby increasing the ripples output.

For a single phase, half-wave rectifier circuit using a power diode, it is not very practical to try and reduce the ripple voltage by capacitor smoothing alone. "Full-wave Rectification" is recommended.

The Full Wave Rectifier

Like the half wave circuit, a Full Wave Rectifier Circuit produces an output voltage or current which is purely DC. Full wave rectifiers have some advantages over the half wave rectifier circuit. The average DC output voltage is higher than that of half wave rectifier and the output of the full wave rectifier also has much less ripple than that of the half wave rectifier, producing a smoother output waveform.

Two diodes are used in a Full Wave Rectifier circuit, one for each half of the cycle. A multiple winding transformer with a common centre-tapped connection is used by splitting the secondary winding equally into two halves. Each diode in this design conducts in turn when its anode terminal is positive with respect to the transformer centre point "C", producing an output during both half-cycles that is twice that for the half wave rectifier. See image below;

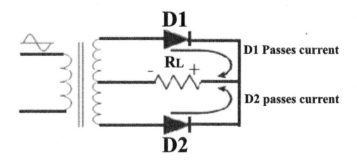

Figure 6.10g: Diode as a Full-wave Rectifier

The Diode Full Wave Bridge Rectifier

There is another diode full wave rectification design with a bridge connection which is common in most electronic devices' power supply units. It is another type of circuit that produces the same output waveform as the full wave rectifier circuit. This type of single phase rectifier uses four individual rectifying diodes connected in a closed loop "bridge" configuration to produce the desired DC output.

The main advantage of this bridge circuit is that it does not require a special centre tapped transformer, thereby reducing its size and cost. The single secondary winding of a transformer is connected to one side of the diode bridge network and the load to the other side as shown below.

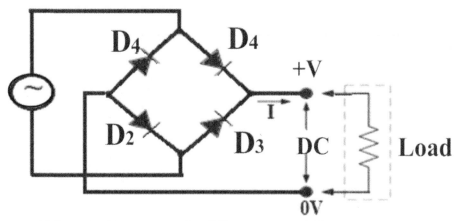

The full wave bridge rectifier

The four diodes labelled D1 to D4 are arranged in "series pairs" with only two diodes conducting current during each half-cycle. During the positive half-cycle of the supply, diodes D1 and D2 conduct in series while diodes D3 and D4 are reverse-biased and the current flows through the load. During the negative half-cycle of the supply, diodes D3 and D4 conduct in series, but diodes D1 and D2 switch "OFF" as they are now reverse- biased.

The current flowing through the load is in the same direction as before. This design is found easily in DC adapters like the travel charging adapters (chargers) of mobile phones. It is important for technicians to understand this circuit.

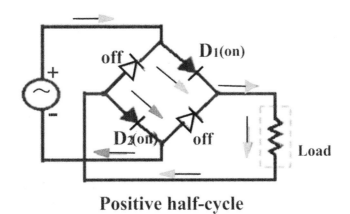

Positive half-cycle

Negative half-cycle

We can also increase the average DC output level even higher by connecting a suitable smoothing capacitor across the output of the bridge circuit as shown below;

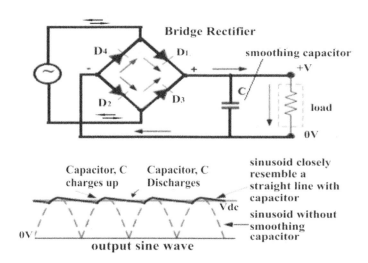

Figure 6.10h: Diode Full-wave Bridge Rectifier with smoothing capacitor

The objective of rectification is to have a current-signal output that travels through the conductors in a straight line. The smoothing capacitor converts the full-wave rippled output of the rectifier into a smooth DC output voltage. Generally for DC power supply circuits, the smoothing capacitor is an Aluminium electrolytic type that has a capacitance value of 100uF or more with repeated DC voltage pulses from the rectifier charging up the capacitor to peak voltage.

If the capacitance value is too low, the capacitor will have little effect on the output waveform. But if the smoothing capacitor is sufficiently large enough (parallel capacitors can be used) and the load current is not too large, the output voltage will be almost as smooth as pure DC.

Light Emitting Diode

A "Light Emitting Diode" or LED is a type of PN junction diode, specially made from a very thin layer of heavily doped semiconductor material. Therefore when operated in a forward-biased direction Light Emitting Diodes convert electrical energy into light energy.

In the forward-biased state, electrons from the semiconductor's conduction band recombine with holes from the valence band releasing enough energy to produce photons which emit a single colour spectrum of light. Because of this thin layer, a reasonable number of these photons can leave the junction and radiate away producing a coloured light output. Thus, the actual colour of a light emitting diode is determined by the wavelength of the light emitted, which in turn is determined by the actual semiconductor compound used in forming the PN junction during manufacture.

The light emitting diodes produces light of low heat radiation which is different compared to the heat generated by incandescent lamps which generate large amounts of heat when illuminated. They are therefore more energy efficient than the normal light bulb. Their generated energy radiates away within the visible light spectrum. They are usually small, durable and provide much longer lamp life. LEDs find application mostly as indicators like in the keypad of the mobile phones, screen lighting, dashboard of cars etc. They are usually connected in the forward bias with a limiting resistor to control the amount of current flowing to the diode.

Zener Diodes

Zener diodes are widely used as voltage reference diodes for making simple voltage regulator circuits in electronics circuits. They are used mainly as power supply regulators or to provide stable reference voltage in the circuit. They can also be used to remove peaks in waveforms that may not be required or to remove spikes that may damage a circuit or cause it to overload.

Figure 6.10i: Zener Diode symbol

Zener diodes function just like an ordinary diode in the forward-bias direction. However in the reverse biased direction their operation is rather different. For very low voltages, like a normal diode they do not conduct at all. But once a high voltage level is attained, the diode "breaks-down" allowing current to flow. They then maintain a constant voltage regardless of the current carried. You will find Zener diodes in the charging circuits of mobile phones.

Transistors

Transistors are three-terminal active devices made from different semiconductor materials that can act as either an insulator or a conductor by the application of a small signal voltage. It is a semiconductor device used to amplify or switch electronic signals and electrical power. It is the transistor's ability to change between states (insulator or conductor) that enable it to act as a "switch" (digital electronics) or "amplifier" (analogue electronics).

Transistors are the foundation of the digital revolution because without transistors, the technological products used daily like mobile phones, computers, etc. would be of larger form factors or maybe not mmanufactured at all.

Transistors were initially made from the element germanium. Pure germanium was known to be a good insulator. But adding impurities (a process called doping) changed the germanium into a weak conductor, or semiconductor. This we have discussed earlier.

Doped germanium is used to create transistors in a configuration of either P-N-P or N-P-N by connecting two layers back to back. The point of contact was called a junction. With an electrical current applied to the center layer (called the base), electrons will move from the N-type side to the P-type side. A small initial trickle current acts as a switch that allows much larger current to flow. In an electric circuit, this means that transistors are acting as both a switch and an amplifier.

When we studied diodes in the previous section, we saw that simple diodes are made from two pieces of semiconductor materials, either silicon or germanium to form a simple PN-junction. If two individual signal diodes are joined together back-to-back, this will give us two PN-junctions connected together in series that share a common P or N terminal. The fusion of these two diodes produces a three-layer, two-junction, three-terminal device forming the basis of a Bipolar Junction Transistor, or BJT for short.

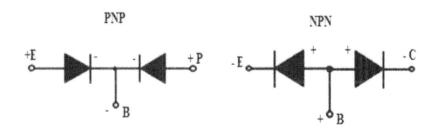

Two Diode Analogy

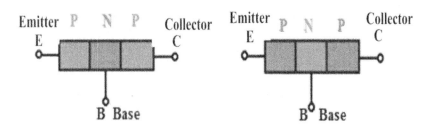

Physical Construction of Transistors

Fig. 6.11a

In electronic circuits, the circuit symbols are as shown in fig.6.11b;

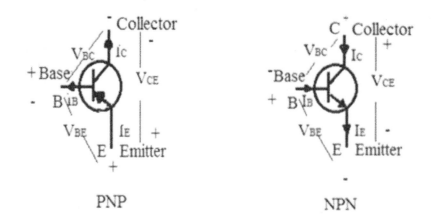

Schematic Symbols and Representation of Transistors

Figure 6.11b

The structure of the transistor is such that they have two PN junctions with a narrow base region between the two outlying areas for the collector and emitter.

During normal operation, the base-emitter junction is forward-biased while the base-collector junction is reverse-biased. When current flows through the base- emitter junction, current that is larger and proportional to the base current also flows in the collector circuit.

Take for instance an NPN transistor;

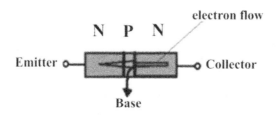

Figure 6.11c: NPN Transistor

The emitter in the n-p-n device is made of n-type material and the majority carriers in the emitter are electrons. When the base-emitter junction is forward-biased, the electrons move from the n-type region towards the p-type region and the holes move towards the n-type region. When they reach each other they combine enabling a current to flow across the junction. When the junction is reverse-biased, the holes and electrons move away from one another resulting in a depletion region between the two areas and no current flows.

When a current flows between the base and emitter, electrons leave the emitter and flow into the base. Normally, the electrons would combine when they reach this area. However, the doping level in this region is very low and the base is also very thin. This means that most of the electrons are able to travel across this region without recombining with the holes. As a result, the electrons migrate towards the collector, because they are attracted by the positive potential there. This is how electrons are able to flow across a reverse-biased junction with ease, causing current to flow in the collector circuit.

It is discovered that the collector current is significantly higher than the base current, and because the proportion of electrons combining with holes remains the same, the collector current is always proportional to the base current. In other words varying the base current varies the collector current. The ratio of the base to collector current is given by the Greek symbol β- beta which represents the Current Gain. Typically the ratio β may be between 50 and 500 for a small signal transistor. This means that collector current will be between 50 and 500 times the base current. This is amplification.

Transistors are connected within the PCB in three possible ways with one terminal being "common" to both the input and output. They are;

- Common Base Configuration (Transistor has Voltage Gain but no Current Gain).
- Common Emitter Configuration (Transistor has both Current and Voltage Gain).
- Common Collector Configuration (Transistor has Current Gain but no Voltage Gain).

The common emitter configuration is the most commonly used connection for transistors in digital electronics circuits. We shall not go into more details on these configurations. However, you may do further research and readings on transistors on your own.

Aside functioning as amplifiers as explained above, transistors also can be used in DC circuits to implement "ON / OFF" solid state switching for DC outputs. Here is how;

How Transistors Function as a Switch

The output from a transistor is usually taken from the collector. The collector current as we saw in the previous explanation is usually a multiple of that of the base current and the ratio of collector current to base current is its current gain. Therefore, since the collector current varies with the base current, a transistor can be used as a current-controlled switch between its cut-off state (OFF) and saturation (ON). The controlled current is the collector current while the controlling current (controller) is the base current.

Since we are talking about a switch, let us create a simple lighting circuit controlled by an ON-OFF switch;

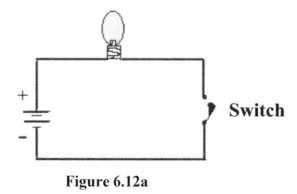

Figure 6.12a

In the diagram above the switch is open therefore, no current flows through the bulb to light it up. Assuming we replace the mechanical switch above with a transistor (NPN or PNP) to control the flow of electrons through the lamp. The controlled current is the collector current and so it must be connected in such a way that the current passes through the transistor between collector and emitter.

Therefore the current that passes through and lights the bulb must be the collector current.

See the images in fig. 6.12b;

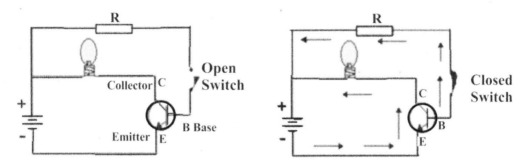

Figure 6.12b

A switch between the base and collector wires of the transistor will supply the base of the transistor with the needed base current to ensure the transistor does not remain in a cut-off state. In the open switch configuration above, the base wire of the transistor is not connected to any source so there will be no base current flow; therefore the transistor will be OFF.

When the switch is closed electrons will be able to flow from the emitter to the base of the transistor, pass through the switch up to the right side of the lamp, back to the positive side of the battery. This base current will enable a much larger flow of electrons from the emitter to the collector, thus lighting up the lamp. The transistor is said to be saturated at this point which is equivalent to being ON.

Conclusively any sufficient source of DC current could be used to turn the transistor ON. The transistor in this case was not only functioning as a switch, but as a proper amplifier by using a relatively low power signal to control a larger amount of power. Although the lighting of the bulb is as a result of energy from the battery, any small power source to the base of the transistor can serve to control the battery's ability to power up the bulb.

Integrated Circuits, ICs

"An integrated circuit (also referred to as an IC, a chip, or a microchip)

is a set of electronic circuits on one small plate ("chip") of semiconductor material, normally silicon. Any circuit in which all or some of the circuit elements are inseparably associated and electrically interconnected so that it is considered to be indivisible for the purposes of construction and commerce is an Integrated Circuit" [14]. I like this definition above from Wikipedia. It properly captures the concept and description of an IC.

The design of ICs is such that they are lightweight, small – as small as a thumbnail. They are constructed to be energy efficient, made up of several billions of transistors and other discrete electronic components in a single chip. Integrated circuits are used in almost all electronic equipment today and have revolutionized the world of electronics. Computers, mobile phones, and other digital consumer appliances are now inextricable parts of the structure of modern societies made possible by the low cost of and use of integrated circuits in their PCBs.

Integrated circuits can be classified into;

- Analog
- Digital and
- Mixed signal (both analog and digital on the same chip).

Analog ICs includes sensors, power management circuits, and operational amplifiers. They operate by processing sinusoidal analog signals and perform functions like amplification, active filtering, demodulation, and signal-mixing. With Analog ICs, circuit designers do not have to be bordered about designing a difficult analog circuit from start to finish as analog circuits are expertly designed and sold off the shelf.

Digital integrated circuit packages can contain anywhere from one to millions of logic gates, flip-flops, multiplexers, and other circuits in thumbnail sized material. Because of the small size of these circuits, their properties include high speed, low power dissipation, and reduced manufacturing cost contrasted with circuit-board-level integration.

Digital ICs such as microprocessors, DSPs, and microcontrollers, operate using binary mathematics to process "1s" and "0s" signals.

ICs can also *"combine analog and digital circuits on a single chip to create functions such as A/D converters and D/A converters. Such mixed-signal circuits' offer smaller size and lower cost, but must carefully account for signal interference."* [15]

IC Packaging has evolved over the years. The various packages are listed below. But for the purposes of our interest in this study in mobile phones' IC chips, we shall only discuss further on the BGA chips package.

The following IC packages are in existence;

- *Dual in Line (DIP) as seen in earlier home electronics gadgets.*
- *Pin Grid Array (PGA) as seen in computer Microprocessors.*
- *Leadless Chip Carrier (LCC) as seen in computer Microprocessors also called "pin-less chip" in local parlance.*
- *Plastic Quad Flat Pack (PQFP).*
- *Thin Small Outline Pack (TSOP).*
- *Ball Grid Array (BGA) or the Flip-Chip Ball Grid Array (FCBGA) as seen in mobile phone PCBs.* [16]

Surface Mount Technology (SMT) and Ball Grid Arrays (BGA)

A Ball Grid Array (BGA) package is a form of surface mount technology, or SMT package that is being used increasingly for integrated circuits. Necessity they say is the mother of invention. Integrated circuits with large number of pins necessitated that a more robust and convenient package be developed. As more and more components were being packed into IC chips, the number of pins also increased with some integrated circuits having more than 100 pins.

The BGA design was therefore developed to improve on the arrangement and surface area space for IC mounting. The BGA uses the underside of the package, where there is a considerable area for the connections. The pins are placed in a grid pattern on the under-surface of the chip carrier which is the reason it is called Ball Grid Array. The "Ball"(s) is solder ball joints.

Rather than using pins to provide the connectivity, pads with balls of solder are used as the method of connection. On the printed circuit board PCB, onto which the BGA device is to be fitted, there is a matching set of copper pads to provide the required connectivity.

BGA Chips

Figure 6.13

Sensors, Transducers and Automation

Every electronic system or circuit is designed to perform a specific function. This means that a circuit, sub-circuit or whole system unit is built to do something. In order for circuits to achieve their purpose, they must be capable of sensing an input of any kind. For instance, for a device to power ON or OFF it must sense an input signal from a source that commands the system to either ON or OFF. Likewise if the device should produce an output on the display or screen like in mobile phones, a signal must activate that output.

Electrical Transducers are used for converting one form of energy into energy of another kind. For instance, a microphone in a mobile device (input device) converts sound waves (voice) into electrical signals for the amplifier to amplify (a process), and a loudspeaker (output device) converts these electrical signals back into sound waves.

Sensors on the other hand sense a wide range of different energy forms such as movement, electrical signals, radiant energy, thermal or magnetic energy etc. They "sense" a physical change in some characteristic that changes in response to some excitation.

The type of input or output transducer used in a system will depend on the type of signal or process being "Sensed" or "Controlled".

Sensors are input-type transducers which produce a voltage or signal output response that is proportional to the change in the quantity being

176

measured. The type or amount of the output signal depends on the type of sensor being used. There are sensors which function only when a signal like current or voltage is applied to it from any external source.

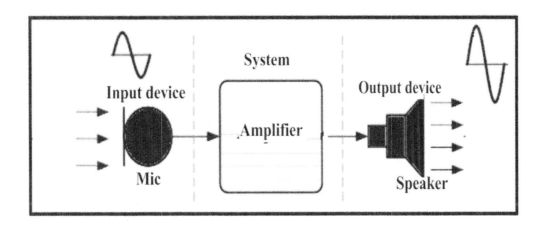

Figure 6.14: Sample sound system transducers

This applied signal will alter the internal properties of the sensor thereby making it to produce an output response.

Other types of sensors however do not need any external signal source. Rather, physical, environmental or natural stimuli affect their behavior and make them to generate an electric signal in response to such external stimulus. A photo-diode for example lights up as a result of light energy stimuli. You find these kinds of diode on the LCD of mobile phone screens where the level of light on the screen modulates with exposure to light. Proximity sensors are built into smartphones which react when it detects the presence of nearby objects without physical contact of any sort. It is usually implemented based on the target object to be sensed. So the proximity sensor could be electromagnetic as found in infrared sensors on the front of mobile phones; capacitive, inductive or photoelectric sensors if the target object is plastic or metal object respectively. These kinds of sensors change their physical properties, such as resistance, capacitance or inductance etc when they sense an external stimulus.

The output produced by any type of these sensors may be analogue or digital. If Digital, they produce a discrete output represented as binary digits such as a logic level "0" or a logic level "1".

Analogue Sensors measure physical quantities such as Temperature, Speed, Pressure, Displacement (like accelerometers in smartphones which help to maintain image orientation in an upright position by detecting the device position), Strain etc and produce a sinusoidal (AC) output signal or voltage which is usually proportional to the quantity being measured which are very small in value ranging from a few micro-volts to several milli-volts (mV). They usually undergo the process of amplification and then converted into digital signals for processing in the micro-controller systems using analogue-to-digital converters (AD/DA converters).

Finally, it is clear that Sensors and transducers aid in automating processes and system functions. To fix mobile phones, you need to recognize the in-built features, the sensors controlling such features and how they work in order to be effective.

Component Failure Analysis

Now that you have read this chapter up to this section, it is important to add to your skill set, the application of your basic electronics knowledge in analyzing circuits in order to fix faults in PCBs. In this section, some general methods for analysis of electrical circuits will be taught. The job of a technician often entails "troubleshooting", a process for locating and correcting a problem in malfunctioning circuits. Troubleshooting is a demanding and rewarding effort which requires;

- A thorough understanding of the basic concepts of the technology;
- The ability to mentally formulate assumptions and explanations of an effect;
- The ability to critically evaluate the outcome of various assumptions based on the possibility of one particular cause over another and;
- A high sense of creativity in applying a solution to rectify the problem.

It is pertinent to note that while it takes some years of experience to master the art of troubleshooting, it is also very important that a technician can easily and intuitively understand how a faulty component could affect circuits in different designs. This necessitated the writing of this chapter with all the concepts, principles and component information.

Understanding and Analyzing Basic Circuit Diagrams

There are a number of tools used for analyzing very small electrical/electronic circuits. For instance when faced with a small electrical/electronic circuit, a good technician should do any or all of the following among other physical checks and actions;

- Identify resistor combinations to ascertain if they are either series or parallel connections.
- Identify voltage or current sources so that you can apply Thevenin or Norton theorems' equivalent.
- Identify embedded voltage dividers in the circuit.
- Identify electrical continuities, links between components tracing a map of the circuit.
- Identify and isolate the affected final sub-circuit that demands attention and repair.

To further establish the causes of failure, there are two general methods used:

- The method of analyzing node voltages and
- The loop equation method

Before we continue, let us review and explain some current/voltage laws you may or may not have seen while reading this chapter. They are;

- Kirchhoff's Circuit Laws (Current and Voltage laws)
- Ohm's laws (We have treated Ohm's law earlier)
- Thevenin's Theorem
- Norton's Theorem

Kirchhoff's circuit laws are two equalities that define the current and voltage in the lumped element model of electrical circuits. They were first described in 1845 by German physicist Gustav Kirchhoff and widely used in electrical engineering, called Kirchhoff's laws. Kirchhoff's current law combined with Ohm's Law is used in nodal analysis.

Kirchhoff's first law states that:

"At any node (junction) in an electrical circuit, the sum of currents flowing into that node is equal to the sum of currents flowing out of that node"

Or equivalently;

"The algebraic sum of currents in a network of conductors meeting at a point is zero."

This Kirchhoff's current law above is represented mathematically as;

$$\sum_{K=1}^{n} I_k = 0$$

Where n is the total number of branches with currents flowing towards or away from the node and I = current.

Kirchhoff's voltage law (KVL) also called Kirchhoff's second law states that;

"The sum of all the voltages around a loop is equal to zero."

The principle of conservation of energy implies that the directed sum of the electrical voltage around any closed network is zero, or:

"The sum of the EMFs (Electromotive Force) in any closed loop is equivalent to the sum of the potential drops in that loop" or:

"The algebraic sum of the products of the resistances of the conductors and the currents in them (remember V= I x R) in a closed loop is equal to the total EMF available in that loop" represented mathematically as;

$$\sum_{K=1}^{n} V_k = 0$$

Thevenin's Theorem on the other hand states that any combination of batteries and resistances with two terminals can be replaced by a single voltage source "e" and a single series resistor "r". The value of e is the open circuit voltage at the terminals, and the value of r is e divided by the current with the terminals short circuited.

While **Norton's Theorem** states that *"any collection of batteries and resistances with two terminals is electrically equivalent to an ideal current source, i in parallel with a single resistor, r."*

The value of r is the same as that in the Thevenin equivalent and the current i can be found by dividing the open circuit voltage by r.

Analyzing Node Voltages

Assuming we have a simple circuit as shown below;

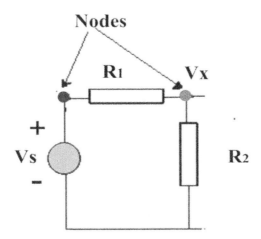

To begin analyzing this circuit, we write the KCL equations for the nodes in the circuit. The equations are written in terms of **node** voltages (although the Current Law is used, the variables are in voltages).

The circuit above is a voltage divider circuit. Two nodes exist in the circuit marked "blue" color and "red" color respectively. Each **node** is different from the other.

I. The voltage at the blue **node** is equal to the voltage at the source, if Vs - the source voltage – is known (for instance a 12V battery source).
II. The voltage at the red **node** can only be found through calculation.

Consequently, let us assume that; since there is only one node with unknown voltage, there's going to be one equation and the equation we need to write is KCL at the node with the unknown voltage!

i. First, define the unknown voltage as V**x**. Define the two currents flowing to and from the nodes (see figure below).
ii. Then we write KCL (Kirchhoff's Current Law) at the node where Vx appears.
iii. Finally, we solve whatever equation results from writing KCL.

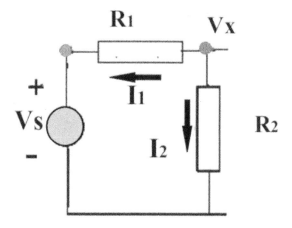

Then, according to KCL;

$$I_1 + I_2 = 0 \quad \text{since both currents are leaving the red node.}$$

To calculate the value for I_1 and I_2, we apply Ohm's law;

$$V = IR \text{ and so } \mathbf{I = V/R}$$

Where V_S = Source voltage and V_X = Unknown voltage

$$I_1 = (V_X - V_S) / R_1$$
$$I_2 = (V_X - 0) / R_2$$

In both cases the voltage across the resistor causing the current to flow in the indicated direction is:

= Voltage at the node V_X - Voltage across each of the other resistor end.

Note that one end of R_2 is connected to ground, so it records a zero voltage.

Explanation: To understand how each current is calculated, and the exact formula for the current.

The current, I, through a resistor, R, connected to a node is:

$$I = \frac{\text{(Voltage at the node - Voltage at the other resistor end)}}{R}$$

Since:
$$I_1 = (V_X - V_S) / R_1 \text{ and}$$
$$I_2 = (V_X - 0) / R_2$$

We can write the complete KCL equation thus; Ia + Ib = 0.

So, we have: $[(V_X - V_S) / R_1] + [(V_X - 0) / R_2] = 0$

Now, remember the algorithm for using node voltages.
Solve whatever equation results from writing KCL.

The result is:

$$V_X = V_S * \frac{R_1}{(R_1 + R_2)}$$

The simultaneous equation above and the result can at best be said to be simplistic compared to the numerous complex circuits encountered in the real world in consumer electronics products.

In this book, there is no motivation or persuasion to bore the reader with complex mathematical equations. It is just to spur your mind to relate with the reality of problem resolutions through knowledge which is available and acquired in regular educational institutions. There is no denying the fact that most people tend to see electronics and its wonders as some form of magic at work.

As a technician, aspiring technician or engineer, graduate technician or engineer; whatever category of reader you may be; you have been challenged. This chapter had me trying to review as much information as possible; to transfer enough perspective and background information as possible; to motivate any reader to become the best kind of technical support provider and my hope is that the reader has gained enough information for the task ahead or has been challenged enough to seek further knowledge and clarifications from several knowledge sources that abound. Before we wrap up this chapter, let us see a few samples of mobile phones' final sub-circuits in reality.

Mobile Phone Battery Charging System

The charging adapter is usually called a "charger" by both users and technicians alike. In reality, it is just an Analog-to-Digital converter used to supply direct current (D.C) input to the battery charging circuit (the actual charger) in the motherboard of the mobile device. They come as single-pin type or multi-pin type.

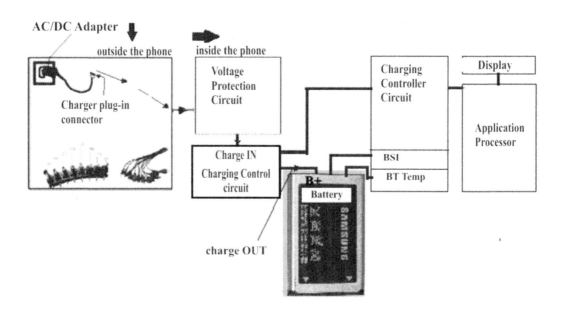

Figure 6.15a: The charging system

Battery charger technologies vary from the simple trickle-charge, timer-based ones to the intelligent, fast, pulse, inductive, USB based chargers. Others are solar chargers, wireless chargers and motion powered chargers.

Figure 6.15b: USB Pinout diagram

Most chargers manufactured in recent times are USB based systems. From the image above, the USB plug consists of four wires of different colors. The green and white wires are for data while the red and black are for positive and negative polarity charging current. This should aid you in tracing the circuit. See how, in the section "Battery Charging Faults" in chapter 7.

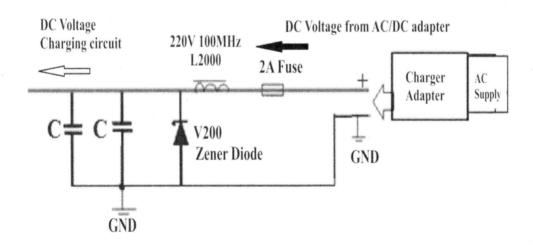

Figure 6.15c: Sample charging circuit A

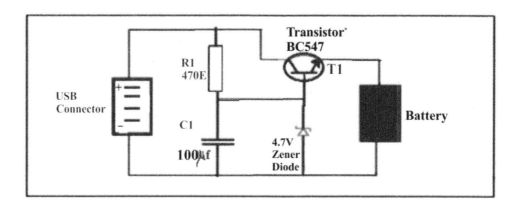

Figure 6.15d: Sample charging circuit B

Circuit Operation: Home electrical power systems supply between 110V AC in some countries and 220-240V AC in other countries. This energy supply in socket outlets is tapped by charger adapters which convert the AC voltage to a desired DC voltage between 5 to 5.5 volts DC. Electronic devices utilize only DC voltage and current. The DC voltage outputs of chargers are rectified "impure" DC voltages and through the charger pin that connects to the phone charging connector are fed as input to the phone.

Mobile phone's charging circuit is usually composed of a Fuse, Inductor, Diode (usually a Zener diode voltage regulator) and filtering Capacitors. The protection elements in this section of the circuit are the fuse and the Zener diode. Before the DC voltage reaches the charging voltage control circuits, this protection circuit controls and maintains the voltage at a fixed rating determined by the Zener diode.

Assuming the desired amount of DC voltage is only 5.0 volts, when the incoming voltage exceeds 5.0V DC the diode will then cut off or become shorted, current will flow to ground and the fuse will cut-out totally disconnecting the voltage line. The inductor's role is to filter unwanted voltage saturation by rejecting abnormal voltage modulation.

At the Charger Voltage Control Circuit, the DC voltage and current is then stabilized, regulated and other voltage purification process is carried out before it is fed to the battery. All the while, the charging process is monitored by a Charging Control Circuit which shares the information with either the Analog baseband CPU or the application processor - depending on the type of phone - to start or stop the charging process.

This is part of the Power Management circuit within the POWER IC (Universal Energy Manager, UEM in Nokia).

What happens is that a signal from the voltage control circuit sends data to the charging control circuit. This data informs the charging control circuit that a charger voltage is being sensed. The charging control circuit will then analyze and convert that data into digital signal before transmitting it to the Application processor.

Mobile Phones' Audio circuits

Audio codec circuit controls sound signals in a mobile device. It is a kind of audio amplifier, an audio mixer or a sound booster. During transmission and reception of phone calls, voice message signal is converted into radio frequency signal while incoming radio frequency signal is converted into sound signals. Its circuit therefore operates for both microphones and speakers of the mobile device as the microphone's sound signal is being amplified and then converted to radio frequency before transmission to the network. The reverse happens for the speaker.

Here is a typical block diagram of audio interfaces interconnection with the audio codec circuit.

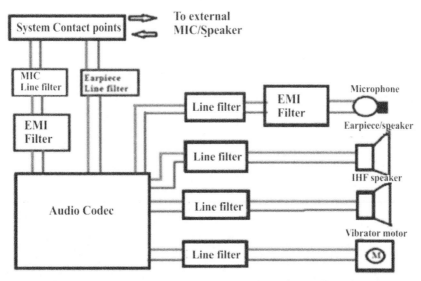

Block diagram of audio interfaces interconnection with audio codec chip

Figure 6.16a

The block diagrams and the following sample schematic circuit diagrams for mobile phone's microphone, speaker, ringer and vibrator circuits are for the reader to appreciate the interconnections between these components' sub-circuits on the PCB; the various relationships and interdependencies between them and their controlling chips. This will serve as an aid during troubleshooting, in deciding where the fault lies with a non-functional component - which IC requires reflow soldering when the component and its associated discrete electronic components are determined to be in good condition, but fail to function in the system - and also possible track trace paths.

From the audio block diagram above, the line filters are filtering capacitors for noise (noise is an analog signal (AC), so it is filtered through capacitors to ground) reduction and of course you will find resistors and inductors too. The earpiece circuit below is being filtered by an inductor coil to reduce sound saturation caused by any radio frequency interruption. It is expected that your study of discrete electronic components should become handy during troubleshooting and fault correction.

Note: *The circuits are not exactly as shown in all mobile phones in the market. While the concept remains the same, manufacturers and design configurations may change.*

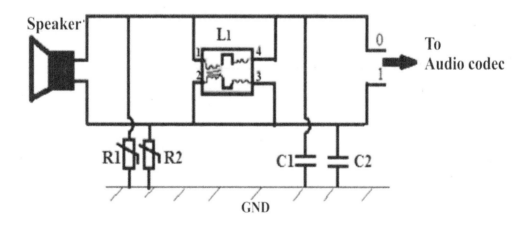

Figure 6.16b: Sample Circuit Diagram for Speakers

Observe that in the audio block diagram above, the Microphone circuit is being protected by an EMI - Filter (Electromagnetic Interference filter) to prevent audio interruptions before the audio codec circuit receives the voice signal. It may or may not be incorporated into a circuit based on the design. The microphone signal is being filtered by two capacitors after being passed-by from an EMI-Filter in order to remove the DC current coming from the EMI-filter.

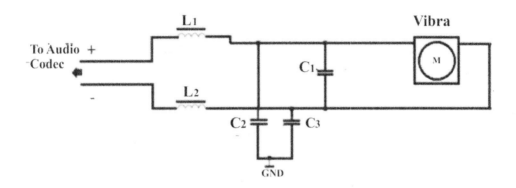

Figure 6.16c: Sample Vibrator circuit
***This is just an illustrative image**

SIM Card Circuits

A SIM Card is a Smart Card that can store data for and from a cellular phone. Such data includes network authorization, authentication and encryption, subscriber identification number, personal security keys, user contact lists and stored text messages. It has six contact pads that correspond to six PCB SIM connector pins, although one of the pins has no connection linked to it. They are;

SIM DATA: This is for digital data stored on a SIM memory

SIM Clock: This is for synchronization.

SIM Reset: This is for sending a frequency signal that triggers or reset all synchronization process.

VSIM B+ Supply Voltage: This pin provides the power supply voltage used to activate the SIM circuit.

SIM Ground pin: This pin is for ground line voltage.

One of the pins is not connected (NC).

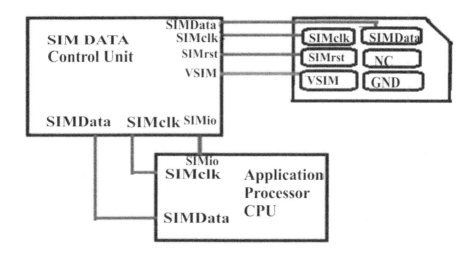

Figure 6.17: Block diagram of SIM Circuitry

From the pictorial image in fig. 6.16, it is easier to match the pin configurations of the SIM connector when fixing a SIM fault. This helps to trace the tracks to reference discrete components. For instance, looking at the block diagram above, one can confirm the reference voltage supply to the SIM by taking measurement between VSIM and GND pins. Without SIM inserted, as soon as the phone is switched ON, the BSI line grounded by a resistor, all SIM interfaces rises first to 3V and then 5V. If you are not getting any of either voltage at those pins, then the SIM control unit (usually a separate glass chip controller in some phones or integrated into the microprocessor in others) could be the cause. The solder balls underneath either of the ICs may have disconnected and reflow soldering can correct the fault in most cases.

Touchscreen System

Touchscreens are field replaceable units which are usually not repaired but replaced. It may help to have just a basic understanding of what they are like. They are a separate transparent glass or screen overlay on mobile device LCDs that are used to provide keyboard and user control command input to the system through simple or multi-touch gestures using one or more fingers or a pen/stylus. With touchscreens in mobile devices, users interact directly with the LCD display output rather than using keyboard buttons. This technology has become the predominant input system for smartphones and tablets.

Two types of touchscreens have been implemented in mobile phones so far: The Resistive type and The Capacitive type touchscreens.

Resistive Touchscreens

Resistive Touchscreen technologies are analog, require moving parts and electrical resistance to sense touch while Capacitive Touchscreen technology is digital, require solid state components and the presence of electrical capacitance to sense touch.

The images in fig. 6.17a illustrate the concept of resistive touchscreens. The design is such that two electrically conductive layers bend to touch one another, with the panel layers calculating the value of resistance that produces changes in current through them at the point touched.

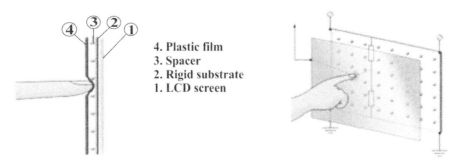

4. Plastic film
3. Spacer
2. Rigid substrate
1. LCD screen

Fig. 618a: Resistive Touchscreen illustration

Advantages: They are durable, inexpensive, and respond to other sources of touch than the finger.
Disadvantages: They are single-touch and therefore cannot perform multi-touch functions. Low visual clarity is also a drawback.

Capacitive Touchscreens

Capacitive touchscreens may either be surface types or projective types. They are the industry standard at the moment as most mobile devices come equipped with capacitive touchscreens. Surface type capacitive touchscreens have sensors embedded at the corners and a thin evenly distributed film across the surface whereas the projective capacitive type uses a grid of rows and columns with a separate chip used for sensing touch. Both types are designed based on the conductive property of the human skin.

Advantages: Better screen clarity, higher sensitivity to touch and multi touch capabilities are some of the main advantages.
Disadvantages: They are susceptible to electrical noise, more expensive, consume more processing power, and only limited to touch from conductive surfaces.

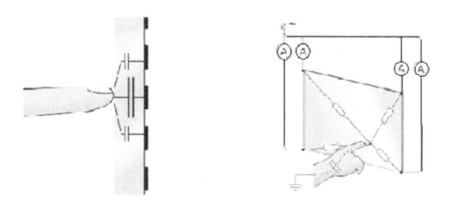

Fig. 6.18b: Capacitive Touchscreen illustration

Keypad System

It is also important to understand at basic level how the matrix keypad system works. This will be of immense benefit for troubleshooting keypad related faults.

How Basic Standard 12 Button Keypad Matrix Works

It is important to understand how a device works in order to fix it. Let me briefly explain therefore, how a keypad matrix works.

Given a standard basic mobile phone with a 4x3 keypad, which have the numbers 0-9, * and #, each square with a number or letter on the hex pad is pushed to make contact forming a switch, which connects the horizontal wires (rows) with the vertical wires (columns).

When button '*' is pressed for instance, it will connect COL1 with ROW4, or if button '6' is pressed it will connect COL3 with ROW2.

Description: The keypad matrix is divided into Rows and Columns. They are an interface technique used to interface inputs like the Mobile Phone keypads, PC keyboard keys, and also to control multiple outputs like LEDs.

Figure 6.19a: 3 x 4 Keypad Buttons and Keypad PCB

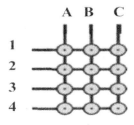

3 x 4 Keypad matrix

Figure 6.19b

The vertical lines are the columns while the horizontal lines are the rows. These rows and columns intersect at 12 points or joints although the columns and the rows are NOT in contact. They are electrically separate but can only be joined together as a switch when the finger presses down the keypad. Then the concave disc contacts merge with the dual concentric gold contacts. The naming scheme for the buttons follow the convention - 'Column: Row' according to their point of intersection. For instance, the top-left button is named A1 and the bottom left is named A4 and so on.

Operation: The matrix is controlled by a microcontroller. For the 12-button 3x4 matrix above, 7 pins of the micro controller will be used. The first 3 pins will be OUTPUTS and will be connected to the COLUMN wires, while the other 4 pins will be INPUTS and will be connected to the ROW wires. The OUTPUTS of the microcontroller IC will NOT be powered simultaneously. The outputs will go 'high' (logic '1') one after the other in cycles. This is repeated many times per second.

The microcontroller monitors the inputs for a signal. When all inputs are LOW, the microcontroller will take no action. But if a user presses button 2B for instance, it connects the matrix column B with row 2. When the "B" output of the microcontroller goes HIGH, the signal arrives also at the input 2 of the microcontroller, through the pressed (input) button.

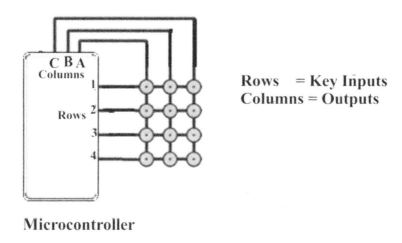

Rows = Key Inputs
Columns = Outputs

Microcontroller

Figure 6.19c

The microcontroller usually loops its outputs and monitors the input lines so that it detects when a specific output like "B" in this case is high, with a corresponding HIGH signal at the input line 2. This means therefore that the input B2 has been pressed.

Multiple simultaneous button press on a matrix will either produce no output on the display or the first key pressed is displayed. There are situations where the matrix operates normally, but not always. It is for such reasons diodes are introduced in the circuit to stop current from flowing backwards. In mobile devices, the diodes add additional needed functionality of providing keypad lighting by using LEDs (Light Emitting Diodes) in traditional keypads.

Switches

A switch is a device used to direct the flow of electric current across two joints in a circuit. It could be a mechanical, manual operated type or an automatic electronic type of switch.

When used at a power supply line input to a system, they are called power switch-types which are used to switch a device ON or OFF. There are several applications for switches. However, in all applications they are used for controlling one or more of the various electrical quantities in a circuit such as AC/DC current, resistance, voltage etc.

Primarily a switch is used to 'close' a circuit at a point in the circuit which by design is deliberately kept 'open'. Switches are either completely ON or completely OFF. In this section, we shall be examining the various manual operated switches with physical buttons for user interface control in a mobile device.

They include;

- Power ON/OFF switch
- Side Volume control switches
- Camera ON/OFF switches

Common types of switches used in Mobile device to control the above listed user interface buttons are;
   a. Push button switch-type
   b. Toggle switches
   c. Joystick switches
   d. Variable resistance potentiometer switch-type
   e. Digital logic switch-type

How the Push Button Switch-type Works

The push button switch-type has two contact terminals inside with a push bar from the top. When pressed down, the top bar with a dual position spring-load (top and bottom) closes the two terminals and maintains that position while current is passed across its terminals. When pressed again, the spring load releases the top bar and the circuit opens again. If used as a power switch, it controls two states: ON and OFF.

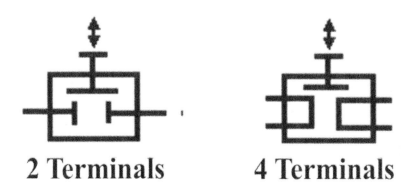

2 Terminals   4 Terminals

Figure 6.20a

How the Toggle Switch-type Works

Toggle switches are actuated by a lever angled in one of two or more positions. The common light switch used in household wiring is an example of a toggle switch. Most toggle switches will come to rest in any of their lever positions, while others have an internal spring mechanism, returning the lever to a certain normal position that allow for what is called "momentary" operation.

Toggle switch

Figure 6.20c

How the Joystick Switch Type Works

Joystick switches are actuated by a lever designed to freely move in more than one axis of motion. The particular way the lever is pushed or how far it is pushed actuates one or more of several switch contact terminals. The direction of the joystick's lever motion required to actuate the contact may be clockwise or anticlockwise. Joystick hand switches were used in earlier versions of smartphones.

Joystick switch

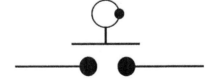

Figure 6.20d

How the Potentiometer Switch Type Works

Potentiometer switches are electronic components that function as variable resistors. The main component within the device is a resistor, illustrated between terminals A and B below. There is a third terminal 'C' that slides along the resistance, selecting a value between the highest and lowest quantity. As the slider moves, the resistance between it and the ends of the resistor change, allowing specific current value to pass.

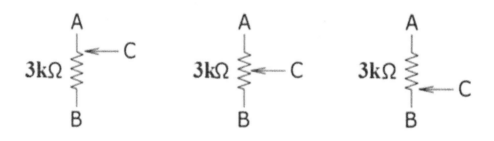

Figure 6.20e: How variable resistors work

In the illustration above, when the movable slider is at the topmost end of the resistor, there will be very little resistance between terminals A and C, with 3KΩ between B and C. In the middle image, the slider is at the center of the resistor, so we'll have 1.5KΩ from terminal C to both A and B. Finally, the moving terminal is at the far end of the resistor, with 3KΩ from A to C, and 0Ω from B to C. Switches based on this design come in various forms and sizes.

Recommendation

I would advise the reader to go through this chapter one more time before delving into the repair procedures in the next chapter. Understanding is important to mastering the repair process.

Chapter 7

Hardware Faults, Fault Detection and Repair Procedures

The job description of a technician is to diagnose faults and carry out corrective repairs. Mobile phones, Tablets, PDAs, and iPads etc just like every other electronic device or machine generally may experience failures in their hardware components during their lifecycle. In this chapter, we are going to cover the various common faults experienced by mobile devices and generally applicable repair procedures required to effectively solve such technical problems.

Every step and procedure described would be applicable to all mobile devices in the market today and in future. This is why this book and course has been designed to transfer skills and information in a way that equips the reader to act based upon knowledge and skills gained rather than enunciating quick fix solution descriptions.

The Technician's Mindset

I like to start teaching in this chapter by addressing this phenomenon briefly. A technician is someone who studies, professes or practices technology according to dictionary definition (http:wiktionary.org). I will take it further by adding that a technician is trained technically in the art of fault detection and correction through the application of hands-on practical skills in technology.

The purpose of this book is to provide training in mobile devices technology for mobile device repair technicians. The mobile phone technician should possess an attitude of a solution provider who understands that EVERY faulty device brought in for repairs *was once a working system unit*. For any such device to be faulty, any one of the following causative factors listed below must have occurred. Therefore to correct the fault he must think in line with the concept of *'cause and effect'*.

Faults are introduced into a mobile device's system by any one of the following;

- Water or moisture

- Dust
- Wear and tear of Component parts
- Excessive heat to the system board
- Forceful impact on hard surfaces resulting in component removal or damage
- Short circuit within the system board (motherboard) wiring
- Open circuit within the system board (motherboard) wiring
- Voltage spikes during charging process
- Virus or Malware
- Corrupted Operating System software
- Incompatible third party applications
- System Settings user tampering or alteration
- And a host of other user related careless handling actions

Determining before-hand the possible cause(s) of a fault in the system either through interrogation of the client or technical intuition is an effective skill for speedy and efficient resolution of faults. Medical Doctors use this method too and it's important in any field of diagnostics to first try to determine the root cause(s) of an occurrence.

Common Faults in Mobile Phones and Tablets

- *Power-On Failure: When a mobile device fails to Switch-On, it is referred to as a dead phone.*

- *Automatic Power- Off /Restart Fault: The mobile device switches off automatically without the user initiating it, or during/after a call or the mobile device reboots itself.*

- *Microphone Failure: When calls by a user to other users are successful but the other end cannot hear any sound while the user can hear them.*

- **Speaker Failure**: *When calls by a user to other users are successful but the user cannot hear a sound from the other end while being heard at the other end.*

- **Ringer Failure**: *When calls to the mobile device user produces no alert sound or ring tone.*

- **Display Faults**: *The mobile device's LCD is physically seen to be broken, shows ink blots or shows no graphics.*

- **Touchscreen Failure**: *When the Touchscreen input system fails to function.*

- **Vibrator Failure**: *When calls to the mobile device produces no alert vibration when vibrator alert option is set in the device settings.*

- **Charging Faults**: *Failure in charging the device's battery and it manifests in several forms.*

- **Fast Battery Drain Fault**: *The device's battery gets fully charged but also gets drained very quickly.*

- **Network Problem**: *When there is no network signal in the phone or poor network signal (limited network). It manifests in various ways.*

- **SIM Card Faults**: *When the SIM card fails to be recognized by the mobile device.*

- **Hanging/ Freezing Faults**: *The mobile device freezes frequently interrupting user operations and sometimes followed by a restart/reboot.*

- ✦ **Keypad Faults**: *Keypad input to the device ceases to function or some buttons do not function. Side volume buttons, Camera or Home button refuses to function.*

- ✦ **Automatic Call-Drop Faults**: *When calls to or from the device gets disconnected intermittently.*

- ✦ **Bluetooth Failure**: *When the device's Bluetooth does not function.*

- ✦ **Camera Failure**: *When the device's camera fails to function.*
- ✦ **Radio Functionality Failure**: *When the FM Radio does not function for devices with such features.*

- ✦ **Illumination Failure**: *When the LEDs for LCD display or Keyboard for older models (basic/feature phones) fail to light up.*

- ✦ **Memory Card Reader Faults**: *When the device fails to detect memory cards.*

- ✦ **Internet Connectivity Failure**: *When the mobile device cannot gain access to the internet or Wi-Fi access but can initiate and receive calls.*

- ✦ **Incomplete Power-On Failure**: *This is when a device switches on but is stuck on the appearance of logo or a blank display.*

- ✦ **Hands-free Jack Faults**: *When the external earphone connection to the mobile device is not functioning or leads to the failure of the entire audio system.*

The list above is not an exhaustive one as mobile phones exhibit various other vague mutations or combinations of the above listed common faults. However, no matter the nature of the fault or combination of faulty behavior exhibited by a mobile device, be confident enough to first dismantle the device and gain access to the motherboard.

All brands and models of mobile devices in the market today or in the future are basically electronic devices. The technical knowledge gained in this teaching is applicable to all. The general structure of all mobile device systems and device components are similar, only differentiated by manufacturing brand names.

How to Repair Various Categories of Faults

Power-On failure

Every device must first be powered-On (switched-On) before its function can be utilized. When the mobile phone fails to switch-On, it is what is commonly called 'dead phone' in local parlance to mean that the client brought the device in an unresponsive state.

Dead phone actually means that the phone could not take current when the power switch is pressed or the CPU-watchdog disable pin is grounded. Nominal supply voltage to the phone is usually 3.6V (Vbatt voltage); if it is below 3.1v, the phone is prevented by the power IC from powering up.

Dead phone could result from any of the following causes;

- A. Dead battery.
- B. Corrupted initialization/boot sector files due to virus or improper usage.
- C. Damaged Operating System software.
- D. Failed Power switch.
- E. Damaged battery terminals.
- F. Water/ moisture on the motherboard.
- G. Open circuit/short circuit of motherboard components.
- H. Damaged Power IC or Microprocessor chip.

Testing, Troubleshooting & Repair Action Steps

To begin the process of repairing a dead mobile phone, carry out the following investigations and actions;

i.   Let us assume you have a work bench, uncluttered with your set of precision screw driver set, cleaning solution like IPA or ultrasonic cleaner, brush, digital multimeter, soldering-iron /station and computer system with mobile phone software repair tools.

ii.   Remove the battery of the device and test for voltage with your digital multimeter. Expected voltage range is between 3.6V and 3.8V D.C or 4.2V max for some Chinese models. If it meets the expected range, then battery is ruled out as the cause. If the battery voltage however is 3.1V or below, the mobile device may not power-on.

iii. Next, use a similar battery for the same model of the device that is fully charged and try to power ON the device. If successful, then the client's battery is the cause of the failure. Boost the battery voltage if normal charging with charger fails to shoot up the battery voltage.

iv.   But if there is no success even with a good battery, connect the device to the computer, run the mobile repair software application and check if the software can read data from the device.

Note: *Not all mobile repair software applications have this feature. While it is the requisite standard procedure, if you do not have the software tools for the device or the software application does not have this feature to check communication with the device you may skip this step. The problem with skipping this step is that most times, technicians who focus only on hardware repair procedures neglect the fact that the problem may be software related, and then go to extreme measures fiddling with the hardware to the extent of damage to the motherboard chips (ICs). When as a last resort they later try software repair or the client eventually takes the device to a software equipped technician, the Microprocessor or Flash chip may have been damaged by their actions thereby denying the client of the possibility of a successful resuscitation of their device unknowingly.*
If you therefore skip this step for any reason, be tactfully careful when working or carrying out any repair procedure on the hardware ICs in order not to damage them.

v.   If there is communication with the device through software, it is not a guarantee that formatting the boot sector or a full flash programming will resuscitate the device. It however confirms that both the power IC and Microprocessor are in good condition. The software process may run successfully but yet the device remains unresponsive to the power-On switch. While that is a good first step before returning to hardware checks, the disadvantage of 'full flashing' is to the client. If the final solution lies in correcting a hardware failure, formatting or flashing the device would have resulted in the loss of important data from the device by that operation although in most cases, restoring the device back to operation may be of paramount concern to the technician and maybe, the client.

vi.   Make a decision between flashing the device immediately and carrying out further basic hardware checks.

vii. Disassemble the device using your precision screwdriver set.

viii. Activate three of your five senses and be alert when dismantling any device - the sense of sight (for keen observation looking out for components that may fall out from the device or missing components from any termination point, any charred part of the device motherboard for burnt components, water or other liquid spill, dirty or rusty PCB or any form of technical abnormality), the sense of smell (for burnt out part odor), sense of feeling (for excessively hot components/ICs).

ix.   Carry out a thorough cleaning service on the motherboard. Be sure to remove sensitive peripheral components attached to the motherboard interfaces like camera, the LCD, microphones, speakers etc. Clean their contact point connectors and sockets too. Do this manually or using an ultrasonic cleaner. Also ensure that the cleaning solution flows into the underside of the ICs to wash out any foreign particles underneath.

x.   Dry the motherboard completely. IPA (Isopropyl Alcohol) and other recommended electronic board cleaning solvents dry as quickly as you apply them without leaving any residual deposits. Sunlight will take a very long time while an ultrasonic cleaner, hair drier or the blower from your hot air soldering station can dry the motherboard very quickly.

xi.   After drying the board, connect the LCD and battery and attempt power-On again. There should be success in most cases where the cause of failure is due to a liquid spill or moisture on the motherboard. Water causes oxidation which is corrosion or the degradation of metals. Resistance between the circuits drop due to the shorting (short-circuit connections whereby component's leads that are not by design meant to be joined together are joined together bridging the positive and negative supply lines) of terminals from rust deposits on deteriorating solder joints.

xii.   If the phone does not power-On, check the power switch. There are various types of switches used in mobile devices. Read the section on repairing switch faults for details.

xiii.   If the Power-On switch is ok, check the battery terminals by re-soldering its base terminal connected to the motherboard. Using your multimeter for continuity or resistance test, check that the positive and negative terminals (VBat+ and VBat-) are not shorted. Check also that the BSI (Battery Status Indicator) line is not short-circuited to either of the terminals. Check the continuity between the battery connector pins that make contact with the battery and its base on the motherboard.

xiv.   Attempt power-On if all the above tests are ok. If no success, carry out a general hot air re-soldering process at moderate temperatures across the entire motherboard. This will reconnect surface mounted electronic components whose lead terminals may have deteriorated and which perhaps created open circuit connections in the circuit board.

xv.   If there is no success too, specific re-hot procedure described in details in the section "Soldering" is carried out on two major ICs; the power IC first and if there is no success, the Microprocessor IC secondly. You do not need to do this step if you confirmed the status of these two ICs with software check in step IV above.

xvi.   If these procedures fail, and having effectively worked on the processor chip and power IC, you may retry the use of software. This is because an initial trial with software as described in step

(iv) may not have succeeded with the device communicating with the software and the computer. When that happens, step (xv) is usually carried out as any failure with those specific motherboard system chips will result in the inability of the software repair procedure succeeding. So at this juncture, carry out Flash Programming on the device with the relevant software repair tools.

xvii. If there is no success yet, IC BGA re-ball procedure is carried out for either the power IC, Microprocessor or any other IC in cases where there is an IC that is observed to be overheating. This is the case also if the motherboard has a history of water or liquid spillage as either observed by the technician or revealed by the user client.

xviii. Should this fail after an attempt to power-On the device, then the internal wiring of the motherboard may have short-circuited or open circuited. This will require a critical study of the circuit-board diagram. Read the section "PCB/Motherboard Faults" for details on removing short circuit.

How to Boost a Battery

When a mobile phone battery is low, it requires normal charging to raise the voltage. However, when the battery voltage is almost or completely depleted with the voltage ranging between 0 to 2.0V DC, a normal charging process using the recommended charger may not bring the battery up to nominal rating of 3.6V to power the device. Certain conditions like cold weather conditions may affect the behavior of a battery. When this happens, a user may report a 'dead phone' or 'no charging' fault condition. To boost the battery, take either of the following simple steps;

1. Use a battery booster machine sold in the market OR
2. Use any charger adapter that is functioning but no longer in use. They all have a DC output of about 5.0V. Cut out the charging pin and expose the positive and negative flexible cords within the outer PVC covering. Several color combinations are usually used to denote positive and negative polarity.

a. Black is usually for negative if combined with red which is positive.
b. Black is negative if combined with white streaked with black stripes which is positive.
c. Blue is negative if combined with either red or white which is for positive.
d. Brown is negative if combined with either red or white as positive.

If in doubt about the color combinations and polarity, use your multimeter to check. Plug the adapter into a wall socket outlet. With the probes on each of the wires, expect a positive value if the polarity matches with the red and black probes touching each wire. If the polarity is reversed, a negative value of DC voltage will be displayed. Be sure the adapter output ranges between 5V-5.5V DC.

Having determined the positive (+) and (-) wire from the charger adapter, identify the positive (+) and (-) battery pins as well. On the battery body, it is usually marked.

You may also determine with your multimeter the same way you did for the adapter wires. Once that is settled, plug the charger adapter to a live wall socket outlet, connect;

Positive adapter wire TO Positive battery pin
Negative adapter wire TO **Negative** battery pin

Hold this in place for about 10 to 15 minutes. If the charge on the battery reaches about 3.5V DC, you may now use the normal recommended charger to charge through the mobile phone. At 3.5V, the battery can power the device but will display "low battery".

Battery Charging Faults

Charging Systems are used for restoring charge voltage to batteries which are the primary source of power to mobile phones. The charging system comprises of the following components;

- The External Charging Adapter
- The Internal Charging Port

- The Motherboard Charging Sub-circuit
- The Battery

Each of these component units may fail to function resulting into a user client complaint of a failed charging process. The mobile device may fail to charge its battery due to the following reasons;

A. The external charging adapter has completely malfunctioned
B. The contact pins in the charger's cable connector has broken, bent or lost connection with its electrical supply cords from the adapter.
C. The charger's D.C output supply to the mobile device is either below 5V D.C. or above 5V D.C.
D. The contact pins in the charging system port on the motherboard has broken, bent or lost contact with the motherboard.
E. The internal motherboard charging sub-circuit has one or more malfunctioning electronic components either as open circuit or short circuit or damaged due to water/ moisture on the motherboard.
F. The battery may be damaged, empty or dead.

Testing, Troubleshooting & Repair Action Steps

To begin the process of repairing a charging fault, carry out the following investigations and actions;

i. First, you need to connect the phone to a charger, connect to a live power supply socket and observe the behavior of the mobile device.
ii. The next thing to do is to connect another functional charging adapter that is compatible with that particular mobile device to confirm if the fault is from the client's charging adapter. In some cases, this basic confirmation may have been done already by the client but it is still safe to do so. If it happens to be the case, advise the client to buy a recommended charging adapter. Let me add that if your service centre is engaged in sales, this presents opportunity to profit from sales.

iii.   If charging adapter is not the problem, next you check the battery. Make sure the battery is a healthy one. If the problem is the battery, change it.

iv.   If battery is not the problem, turn OFF and disassemble the mobile device to gain access to the charging port. There are two types of charging ports: The Pin-type charger male port and The Multi-Pin USB charger port unit. Ensure that in either case, the pin or pins are in good condition within their respective housing assemblies.

v.   If the external facing pin or pins that mate with the charger cable are in good shape, check the inner motherboard contact pins and ensure none is bent, broken or detached from the motherboard. In the case of detachment from the PCB, visual inspection is hardly enough because they are very tiny and the solder underneath each pin may deteriorate without being visible.

vi.   If the charging port is damaged, replace by de-soldering and re-soldering a new one. They are sold in phone parts shops. Some earlier single-pin ports were not soldered to the PCB and some newer smart phones have detachable charging sub-circuit boards that are not soldered to the motherboard. These are easier to replace than repair. An example is the Samsung Galaxy S4.

vii.   Use PCB cleaner to clean the charging port contacts thoroughly.

viii. Switch On the soldering station and using your blower, run hot air on the charging port connection pins. In the absence of a rework station, use a sharp tip soldering iron to re-solder each pin one after the other. Do not add extra soldering lead to the terminals. This will muddy up and bridge the terminals. Instead rub a very slight quantity of flux on the pins before heating.

Caution: *Excessive heating and movement of soldering iron on a contact point especially when flux is applied may damage the motherboard contact pad that links the internal PCB wiring to connect with surface components.*

ix.   Test the device by connecting the battery and a charger to it. Is it ok? If the problem persists, next…

x. Check the fuse. There is usually a fuse (see section "Charging Circuits" in Chapter 6) with continuity test. If there is no buzzer sound, change or bridge with a strand of flexible wire. If there is a buzzer sound, it is fine. Continue electrical level troubleshooting with a multimeter to check and replace discrete electronic components such as Zener diode regulator or transistor etc. or repairing motherboard ICs (in this case charging IC). Apply the knowledge gained in Chapter 6 "Electronics Fundamentals" and the section "IC BGA Soldering and Repair" in chapter 4.

This is how to do a simple charging circuit trace;

The USB charging ports have four pins. From the plug-in direction facing the charging port, the positive (+) pin is on the extreme left while the negative (-) pin is on the extreme right

After disassembling the phone, a look at the port from the inside will change in direction with the positive charging port pin on the right while the negative pin will be on the left from that inside view angle. Usually at close proximity to the charging port are collocated discrete electronic control components (capacitors, resistors, diode etc) just as you find in fig. 6.12c and fig. 6.14d. In a real PCB they will appear like below;

Discrete electronic components

To trace the circuit, begin with locating and testing the fuse. A fuse is a low value resistor, usually about 1KΩ.

i. Using a multimeter at the continuity diode test buzzer point to test the fuse will produce a beep (continuous) if it is unbroken (in good condition) and no beep if it has broken.

ii. Place one probe of the multimeter on the positive pin of the charging port and trace by touching the second probe on each edge terminal of the discrete components. The fuse is usually black like other resistors on the PCB or colored (sky-blue, milky-white or other unusual color different from most other components on the PCB).

iii. Any indication of continuity (beep) by the second probe touching both sides (edge terminals) of a resistor indicates a working fuse. You will identify a faulty fuse if the trace from the first probe on the positive pin to one edge terminal of a resistor is continuous while touching the other edge terminal of the same resistor produces no beep.

iv. If however the fuse tests 'OK', check the status of the zener diode, capacitors or transistors as the case may be. If they all test 'OK', identify the glass charging control chip and re-hot. If re-hot fails, replace the chip.

Common charging faults error messages/behaviors

a. Not Charging (Nokia)
b. Charger Not Supported (Nokia)
c. Charging paused Battery temp too low (Samsung)
d. Charging paused Battery temp too high (Samsung)
e. 'X' Stop charging
f. Charging error stop charging
g. Self charging Mobile Phone
h. Phone only charge with PC and not chargers

For several thousands of mobile phone models in the market designed with differences in PCB component layout despite a similarity in their charging system sub-circuit (wiring diagram), there are so many pictorial cable-sectioning solutions. This applies to other mobile phone faults and so as a mobile device technician, you have two options when faced with an electrical/electronic level problem.

1. Download the PCB diagram for each phone under repair and trace the circuit using your multimeter.
2. Use the internet library through Google images to search for each specific device's pictorial cable-section (PCB wiring track) traced by other professionals who have studied the circuit diagram of the phone.

In either of these cases, your application of the key skills covered in Part 2 - Chapter 4 "Technical skill-set a Technician Must First Master" and "Electronics Fundamentals" must come to play. My hope is that you join in adding, advancing and improving the global GSM community by utilizing the skills gained in this book to discover solutions through PCB track tracing and reading circuit diagrams. If not, the shortcut is using Google images to search pictorial solutions uploaded by other technicians to the GSM phone support online community. For a better understanding of what these pictorial diagrams look like, I will share a few here to serve ONLY as illustrated examples.

Not Charging: When a phone displays "Not Charging" as soon as a charger is plugged in, it means it would not charge the battery despite sensing a charging voltage. This problem occurs when a required current or voltage is not enough to boost up and charge the mobile phone's battery. One reason for this problem is a faulty BSI Line (Battery Status Indicator) that tells the charging control circuit about the battery's operating status. A faulty resistor, capacitor, voltage regulator or broken track also can be the cause. If you have done basic repair procedure as listed above, then carry out a PCB trace to either replace a component or use a jumper cable to correct an open circuit.

Caution/Disclaimer: *These example images are only meant to show the reader what is obtainable when accessed through online searches. The solutions shown are not being endorsed by this book due to this posting here. The image differs for each product model. Using images sourced online are at the technician's discretion!*

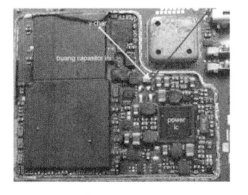 

Source: Google images from http://forum.gsmhosting.com

Figure 7.1a

Charger Not Supported: when you encounter this fault, after the basic steps above has been exhausted, apply same as in 'Not Charging' above. Charger Not Supported problem is caused by a faulty BTEMP thermistor component or broken track. BTEMP stands for Battery Temperature. It is a battery pin used to monitor the battery temperature status during charging.

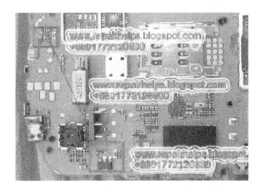 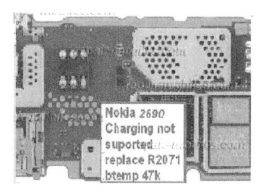

Source: Google Images from http://forum.gsmhosting.com

Figure 7.1b

Charging paused Battery temp too low or high: when a mobile device displays something similar to the image below;

Figure 7.1c

If the phone's charger is ok and only the cell phone is heating up it may be due to heavy application usage or malware activity in the background. Mobile phones have certain ICs or component units that dissipate more heat during multiple application processing. They include;

a. The processor - when an application that utilizes heavy CPU processing is running.
b. The video/graphics chip - when your app uses OpenGL.
c. The display when lit over a long time (depending also on the brightness setting).
d. The battery (when charged continuously or drained quickly).
e. The modem also needs rather much power for 3G/4G/LTE data transfers.

There is a safety mechanism built-in to monitor battery temperatures through the BTemp battery connector pins. This safety mechanism will react with such a display output for high battery temperatures as a result of overheating if any of these components get excessively hot. In most cases, it is most likely a mix of all the above listed. Applications that are corrupted might also cause overheating in which case you have to eliminate such applications. When in doubt about which application could be the cause, a hard reset of the mobile phone or software flash programming becomes an option.

Take the following initial steps before attempting hardware repair;

   i.   Lower the screen brightness.

  ii.   Uninstall any third party App that may have been recently downloaded into the device.

 iii.   Switch to 2G only in the mobile networks settings: Go to Settings>Wireless & Networks>More>Mobile Networks>Use only 2G networks (saves battery juice). This is because when a mobile device is in an area where 3G network is absent; the radio will be searching consistently, overworking the modem thereby generating heat.

 iv.   If all else fails including hardware repair steps, Use software repair procedures as covered in later chapters.

For electrical/ electronic level repairs, apply hardware track trace using the recommendations above. See track trace jumper samples below.

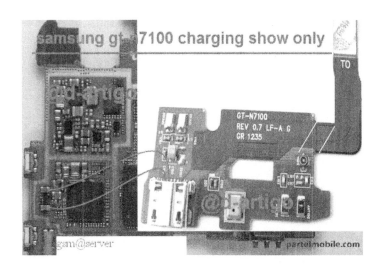

Source: Google Images from http://forum.gsmhosting.com

Figure 7.1d

Charging paused Battery temp too high:

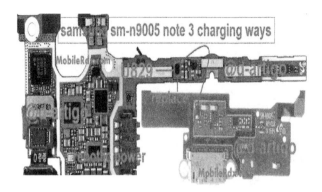

Source: Google Images from http://forum.gsmhosting.com
Figure 7.1e

Automatic Self-charging Mobile Phone: when a mobile phone behaves this way, it is symptomatic of a loopback current from the phone's battery to the charging circuit or IC. A simple solution is in cleaning the charging port contacts and the entire PCB because a short-circuit condition is existing. However when that fails, in which case the short-circuit condition is not existing on the PCB surface mount; next is to carry out a PCB trace for a faulty capacitor or charge sensor chip.

Audio and Alert Faults

The audio systems present in mobile devices consist of the Microphone system, the Speaker, the Ringer, and the external Hands- free jack. We shall be discussing about each system one after the other.

Speaker Faults

The speaker or earpiece is the device responsible for hearing voice messages during a phone call. When they become faulty, it is signified by the following behaviors;

- The user of the mobile device will not hear from the other end of the conversation completely.
- The user can barely hear the caller's voice from the other end.

- The voice signal from the other end will be cranky, stifled by noisy interference.

Testing, Troubleshooting & Repair Action Steps

To repair speaker faults, follow the steps below;

i.   First of all, confirm the behavior of the mobile device by initiating a call. If you do not want to make a complete call, make a toll-free emergency call by dialing 112 or as applicable in your home country and listen. Once the call connects and is active, increase the side volume-up button. For mobile phones without side volume keys, check the home central four-directional key (for left, right, up, down cursor directions) and press the right or up keys. Whichever one is for volume-up, a slider will pop up on the LCD display indicating an increment. If the slider is already at maximum and no audio from the other side, then the fault is within the system.

ii. Next, turn OFF and disassemble the mobile device.

iii. Locate the speaker and detach/disconnect it from the motherboard.

iv. Observe the PCB contact pads for the speaker contacts (2 pins or cords for positive [+] and negative [-] electrical supply) for dirt, oxidation or corrosion.

v.   Clean the PCB contact pads thoroughly whether you observed the presence of dirt, oxidation, and corrosion or not.

vi. Use your multimeter to take readings from the speaker. Resistance values for a good one ranges between 30~33Ω ±3. If the speaker also serves as ringer, the value is between 7-8Ω.

vii. Connect back the speaker if the values are good or replace with an alternate good one and test. If ok, end.

viii. If it is not ok, use cleaning fluid and brush and thoroughly clean the entire motherboard with focus on the electronic components surrounding the speaker contact pads vicinity. Most times by design, the control components are directly on the reverse side of the PCB parallel to the same spot with the speaker or peripheral component being controlled. This helps to remove any surface short-circuit agent like rust between surface mounted components.

ix.   Then, turn ON the rework station and run a moderate temperature stream of hot air on the PCB with focus on control electronic elements around the speaker vicinity. This is to correct open-circuit connections for deteriorated solder joints between the components and the motherboard.

x.   Test the speaker again by powering ON the device. If ok, end.
      If it is still not ok, power ON the motherboard and test for the presence of voltage at the contact pads for the speaker. Begin components and motherboard IC (in this case audio IC) troubleshooting and repair procedures as learned in chapter 6 "Electronics Fundamentals" and the section "IC BGA Soldering and Repair" in chapter 4.

Microphone Faults

The Microphone or mouth-piece is the device responsible for transmitting voice sounds to the other end during a phone call. When they become faulty, it is signified by the following behaviors;

- The user of the mobile device will hear voice message sounds from the other end of the conversation but cannot be heard.
- The user can barely be heard by the caller on the other end.
- The voice signal transmitted to the other end will be cranky, stifled by noisy interference.

Testing, Troubleshooting & Repair Action Steps

To repair Microphone or Mic or Mouth-piece faults, follow the steps below;

i.   First of all, confirm the behavior of the mobile device by initiating a call. If the user at the other end cannot hear you while you can hear the voice, then there is a problem.

ii.   Next, turn OFF and disassemble the mobile device.

iii. Locate the Microphone and detach/disconnect it from the motherboard.

iv.   Observe the PCB contact pads for the Microphone contacts (2 pins or cords for positive [+] and negative [-] electrical supply) for dirt, oxidation or corrosion.

v.   Clean the PCB contact pads thoroughly whether you observe the presence of dirt, oxidation or corrosion or not.

vi.   Use your multimeter to take readings from the Microphone (Mic or mouth-piece). Resistance values for a good one ranges between $700 \sim 1700\Omega \pm 100$. Reading is taken only with +ve probe to +ve terminal of Mic and −ve probe to −ve terminal of Mic and not the reverse.

vii. Connect back the Microphone if the values are good or replace with an alternate good one and test. If ok, end.

viii. If not ok, use cleaning fluid with brush and thoroughly clean the entire motherboard with focus on the electronic components around the microphone contact pads vicinity. Most times by design the control components are directly on the reverse side of the PCB parallel to the same spot as the Mic or peripheral component being controlled. This helps to remove any surface short-circuit agent like rust between surface mounted components.

ix.   Then turn ON the rework station and run a moderate temperature stream of hot air on the PCB with focus on control electronic elements around the Mic's vicinity. This is to correct open-circuit connections for deteriorated solder joints between the components and the motherboard.

x.   Test the Microphone again by powering ON the device. If ok, end.

xi.   If it is not ok, power ON the motherboard and test for the presence of voltage at the contact pads for the Microphone. Begin components and motherboard IC (in this case audio IC) troubleshooting and repair procedures as learned in chapter 6 "Electronics Fundamentals" and the section "IC BGA Soldering and Repair" in chapter 4.

Ringer Faults

The ringer or loudspeaker is the device responsible for sound alert, music and other notifications to a user. When they become faulty, it is signified by the following behaviors;

- The user of the mobile device will not hear the ringtone when called by another mobile device user or telephone.
- The device rings but the user can barely hear the sound from the other end or other multimedia and notification sounds are very low.
- The sound signal from the phone will be cranky, stifled by noisy interference.

Testing, Troubleshooting & Repair Action Steps

To repair ringer or buzzer faults, follow the steps below;

i.   First of all confirm the behavior of the mobile device by initiating a call to the device from another phone or check the phone 'settings>sound>Alert Type>Volume'. The volume should be high enough and the alert type should not be 'silent' or 'vibrate only' option. If the settings are ok…

ii. Next, turn OFF and disassemble the mobile device.

iii. Locate the ringer and detach/disconnect it from the motherboard.

iv. Observe the PCB contact pads for the ringer contacts (2 pins or cords for positive [+] and negative [-] electrical supply) for dirt, oxidation or corrosion.

v.   Clean the PCB contact pads thoroughly whether you observe the presence of dirt, oxidation or corrosion or not.

vi. Use your multimeter to take readings from the ringer. Resistance values for a good one ranges between 8~10Ω ±1. Older monotonic ringers read between 15-18Ω. Don't worry if you hear the continuity beep sound.

vii. Connect back the speaker if the values are good or replace with an alternate good one and test. If ok, end.

viii.   If it is not ok, use cleaning fluid and brush and thoroughly clean the entire motherboard with focus on the electronic components surrounding the speaker contact pads' vicinity. Most times by design, the control components are directly on the reverse side of the PCB parallel to the same spot with the speaker or peripheral component being controlled. This helps to remove any surface short-circuit agent like rust between surface mounted components.

ix.   Then turn ON the rework station and run a moderate temperature stream of hot air on the PCB with focus on control electronic elements around the speaker vicinity. This is to correct open-circuit connections for deteriorated solder joints between the components and the motherboard.

x.   Test the speaker again by powering ON the device. If ok, end.

xi.   If it is still not ok, power ON the motherboard and test for the presence of voltage at the contact pads for the speaker. Begin components and motherboard IC (in this case Audio IC) troubleshooting and repair procedures as learned in chapter 6 "Electronics Fundamentals" and the section "IC BGA Soldering and Repair" in chapter 4.

Vibrator Faults

Vibrators provide silent alert notifications. They rarely develop faults although just about any device can fail. Inside it is a control unit which has a small DC motor that drives a gear. Attached to the gear, there is a small weight mounted off-the-center on the gear. When the motor spins the gear/weight combination spins at 100 to 150 RPM, the off-center mounting causing a strong vibration.

Testing, Troubleshooting & Repair Action Steps

Follow the following steps to repair a vibrator failure.

i.   First of all confirm the behavior of the mobile device by initiating a call to the device from another phone or check the phone 'settings>sound>Alert Type>Vibrate & Ring or Vibrate Only'. If the settings are ok but the phone does not still vibrate. Then…

ii. Next, turn OFF and disassemble the mobile device.

iii. Locate the vibrator and detach/disconnect it from the motherboard.

iv. Observe the PCB contact pads for the vibrator contacts (2 pins or cords for positive [+] and negative [-] electrical supply) for dirt, oxidation or corrosion.

v. Clean the PCB contact pads thoroughly whether you observe the presence of dirt, oxidation or corrosion or not.

vi. Use your multimeter to take readings from the vibrator. Resistance values for a good one ranges between $8\sim16\Omega$ ±1.

vii. Connect back the vibrator if the values are good or replace with an alternate good one and test. If ok, end.

viii. If it is not ok, use cleaning fluid and brush and thoroughly clean the entire motherboard with focus on the electronic components surrounding the vibrator contact pads vicinity. Most times by design the control components are directly on the reverse side of the PCB parallel to the same spot on which the vibrator or peripheral component being controlled is mounted. This helps to remove any surface short-circuit agent like rust between surface mounted components.

ix. Then, turn ON the rework station and run a moderate temperature stream of hot air on the PCB with focus on control electronic elements around the speaker vicinity. This is to correct open-circuit connections for deteriorated solder joints between the components and the motherboard.

x. Test the vibrator again by powering ON the device. If ok, end.

xi. If it is still not ok, power ON the motherboard and test for the presence of voltage at the contact pads for the vibrator. Begin components and motherboard IC troubleshooting and repair procedures as learned in chapter 6 "Electronics Fundamentals" and the section "IC BGA Soldering and Repair" in chapter 4.

Video/Graphics/Display faults

The visual output unit of mobile phones is the LCD (Liquid Crystal Display). LCDs get damaged in a number of ways ranging from the following;

- LCD Glass (screen) breakage.
- Ink blots covering the entire screen.
- No visual elements (dark screen or blank lit screen).
- Presence of visual elements without background LED lighting.
- Part or whole of the Touchscreen not responding to input.

LCDs like almost all the peripheral components of the mobile phone motherboard are field replaceable units. This means that the unit should be replaced completely when they develop a fault instead of attempting to repair them. This does not eliminate the possibility of technical improvisation. Display faults could be caused by any of the following;

a. Mobile device impact on hard surfaces.
b. Water or other liquid damage.

Testing, Troubleshooting & Repair Action Steps

The following action steps should be taken for a faulty display unit.

i.   Determine first and foremost that the mobile device can transmit and receive calls. Although in some cases, as a result of the screen blindness the device's power-ON routine may not be completed especially if a user input is required like a "Yes" or "No" pop-up menu question.
ii.   Next step is to Turn OFF and dismantle the mobile device.
iii. Disconnect the LCD unit from the motherboard if it is not permanently soldered to the motherboard.
iv.   For LCDs with fused flex connectors; with socket-end permanently soldered to the PCB, clean the contacts and re-solder its multiple pin contacts. If the LCD has a detachable socket or clip

on the PCB, clean both the flex connector's socket-end pins and the PCB socket pins. Re-solder with soldering iron one pin after the other. Use of hot air stream from the blower should be avoided because the heat will melt the plastics housing the contact pins.

v. For LCDs with separate detachable flex connectors, both ends of the flex connector (LCD-end socket and PCB-end socket) should be cleaned to remove dirt, oxidation or corrosion. Then reflow the solder under the pins using soldering iron one after the other.

vi. Clean the entire PCB focusing on the Display unit area.

vii. Reconnect the LCD unit and test. If ok, end.

viii. If it is not ok, change the LCD flex with a new one. If ok, end.

ix. If it is not ok, change the LCD and connect with old flex connector. If ok, end.

x. If it is still not ok, change both the LCD and its flex connector. If ok, then both are faulty simultaneously. This is often the case with fused LCD and flex scenario but rare when the flex connector and LCD are separable.

xi. If change of the entire LCD assembly does not solve the problem, and either the old LCD and Flex or the new ones are confirmed to be in good condition, then the investigation shifts to the PCB. The entire display system could fail too - LCD, flex, PCB control components (electronics and display IC) and this occurs when there is liquid damage.

Caution: It is the technician's responsibility to verify that the new parts being swapped with the old part in the device is in good condition before further investigation on the motherboard. Unlike other components that can be tested with the multimeter, the LCD cannot be tested in like manner. The alternative is to test them on another similar device or try as many new replacement LCDs or flex connectors as are available. This is usually a dicey situation especially for permanently soldered flex connectors or fused LCD and flex units. Whether it was a single unit purchased at a parts store or the technician has the parts in stock, multiple testing of LCDs or flex connectors without success results in loss of money if damaged in the process. In cases where the technician purchases one at a time from a mobile phone parts store, the sellers hardly accept a return part (good/bad) once it has been soldered and you cannot blame them would you? Your soldering skills must be perfect or you may be the problem as well.

xii. Then check the socket on the PCB. Begin a track trace between the socket and the surrounding discrete electronic components. Apply the motherboard electrical level troubleshooting steps learnt in chapter 6 "Electronics Fundamentals" and the section "IC BGA Soldering and Repair" in chapter 4.

Touchscreens

Touch Screens are available in different sizes. Their flex connectors usually have four (4) contact pins: (+), (-), (Rx), (Tx). They are usually controlled by the CPU and operating system software. In some Mobile Phones an intermediate Interface IC or Screen Touch IC is present instead.

Touchscreen problems manifest in the following ways;

- Whole or partial section of the screen not responding to touch input.
- One or more keys or icon not responding to touch.

Testing, Troubleshooting & Repair Action Steps

To repair a touch screen problem;

i.   Check the surface of the touchscreen for any scratch or physical damage.
ii.   If the touchscreen is a resistive type touchscreen, go to the device settings and recalibrate the touchscreen.
iii. Turn OFF and dismantle the mobile device to its component parts.
iv.   Disconnect the touchscreen connector contact from the motherboard. Most of them have sensors which are detachable.
v.   Clean the contacts thoroughly with cleaning fluid and reconnect it back.
vi.   Test the touchscreen to confirm if the problem is solved.
vii. If the problem persists, replace with an alternative good touchscreen.

viii. Test again if the problem is solved.

ix. If problem is not solved, troubleshoot PCB tracks and motherboard control elements. Carry out reflow soldering on the touchscreen controller IC or change. See section "IC BGA Soldering and Repair" in chapter 4.

x. Consider reloading the mobile device software before or after the step ix above if problem persists.

Keypad Faults

Keypads are input user interface devices through which the mobile device receives command and control signal. They preceded the current prevalent virtual keyboard input system in touchscreen technologies. They consist of buttons arranged in a multi-grid array of rows and columns which bridge two separate physical electrical contacts when pressed down. The buttons are setup in a matrix format. This allows a microcontroller IC to 'scan' the output pins to detect which of the buttons is being pressed.

The resulting analog electrical signal is fed into an ADC converter connected to a BCD (Binary Coded Digits) decoder that is either separate or integrated into the CPU. The output is displayed on the LCD.

When keypads fail, the following symptoms are observed;

- All or few specific buttons produce no output on the display unit.
- Key press causes the mobile device to restart or reboot.
- Response to key press is very slow in producing an output or desired action.
- Key press produces unexpected outcomes than is normal on the display unit.
- Response to key press requires very hard pressure on the buttons.
- The back-light on the keyboard is not functioning or remains permanently ON.

The following are probable causes of malfunction of keypads;

a. Oxidation or corrosion of keypad contacts due to liquids.
b. Liquid on the motherboard (PCB).
c. Corrupted operating system software.
d. Virus activity.
e. Faulty control elements or ICs.
f. Damaged keypad buttons, part or whole unit.

Testing, Troubleshooting & Repair Action Steps

Follow the steps below to troubleshoot and repair keypad faults.

i. Whether it is a physical keypad or touchscreen, determine if the behavior is symptomatic of a software fault. If it is, flash the phone. But for hardware check…

ii. Turn OFF the mobile device and remove the battery, SIM and Memory card.

iii. Dismantle the mobile device using a precision screwdriver set.

iv. Test the keypads in a partially disassembled state. This is because when in its assembled form, if there is a permanently pushed down side switch (side volume control buttons, camera etc), it will affect the keypad functionality.

v. If it is not ok, locate the keypad assembly on the front fascia of the mobile device and detach it from the motherboard. There are usually 2 or 3 layers consisting of plastic button pad or carbon, a thin cellophane material laced with gum and concave cylindrical contacts array (*the concave form is such that it makes contact with the PCB's outer ring gold pad when at rest, on its outer edges. The upward curve at the center makes for non-contact with the inner ring gold pads except when pressed down, then it closes the circuit by bridging to two rings*) that is stuck to the PCB. Carefully peel off this cellophane. Do not tear or apply cleaning fluid on the gum. It will neutralize its sticky property making it unable to be fixed back in position after repair.

vi. Clean the motherboard dual concentric circular gold contact pads (outer and inner circular pads separated by a ring). The outer ring for Rows while the inner ring is for columns. See image below;

Figure 7.2a: Keypad PCB Contact

vii. Using a sharp blade, scratch out oxidation coatings or dirt on the concave circular shiny metal contacts stuck on the reverse side of the cellophane material. Be careful to retain their positions on the material. Align and stick the cellophane back to the PCB contact pads.

viii. Partially assemble the device, enough to power it ON and test the keypads one after the other.

ix. Problem solved? End. If not, conduct a test between direct presses of the keys on the flat cellophane covered contacts and using the outermost button overlay on the cellophane. If the problem is from the outermost buttons, change. Else …

Figure 7.2b: Detachable Keypad PCB covered with cellophane

x.   Also conduct a test between direct bridging of the motherboard contact pads with a screwdriver and pressing the cellophane's concave circular metal discs on the PCB contact pads. If the fault is with the discs, you may change the whole material or discs one after the other.

xi.   If the problem persists, change the keypad assembly for cases where it is a detachable unit with a flex connector. Where it is not a separate unit from the PCB, test for continuity between rows and columns. If broken, reconnect PCB track. If ok, then keypad matrix is ok.

xii.   Trace the electrical connection and condition of the keypad control electronic components. Reflow with rework soldering station's blower or use soldering iron to resolder each component's contacts one after the other. If they are ok, test the keypad again after reflow.

xiii.   If problem still persists, next step is to reflow the keypad IC (Microcontroller) and apply the knowledge gained in chapter 6 "Electronics Fundamentals" and the section "IC BGA Soldering and Repair" in chapter 4.

Switch Faults

When switches fail in mobile devices, it is evidenced by an obvious non-responsiveness to a desired function. For instance;

- When the power switch is pressed, the device should power ON/OFF, else it has failed.
- When the side volume key is pressed, it should either increase or decrease volume, else it has failed.
- When the camera button/switch is pressed, it should activate camera functionality, else it has failed.

Testing, Troubleshooting and Repair Action Steps

A failure to bring about the above listed responses may not always mean that the switch is the problem. Other such related faults have been discussed in other sections.

If however the fault at hand is determined to be with the switch, take the following actions;

i.   Turn OFF the device and remove the battery, SIM and Memory Card.

ii. Locate the relevant unresponsive switch and determine what type of switch you are dealing with based on the knowledge shared earlier about switch types.

iii. If the switch is observed to be physically damaged, change immediately.

iv. If there is no observable physical damage, test with multimeter to confirm if the switch is functional or not (See *'How to Test Various Components –Switches'* in Chapter 4).

v.   If it is functional, resolder its contacts on the PCB and test. If it is damaged and therefore non-functional, replace with a new one.

SIM and Memory Card Faults

SIM cards are the storage units in which telecommunication companies store the communication codes and subscriber information necessary for maintaining access to the mobile network. Memory cards on the other hand are secondary extended memory chips used to provide extended capability to the mobile device to store user data.

There are a few faults associated with these two devices which we shall discuss shortly. Different ways these units fail are as follows;

SIM Card Faults

a. 'No SIM card' or 'Insert SIM card' is displayed by the device's display unit just as it does when none is inserted, even though a SIM is inserted properly.

b. SIM card is properly inserted but the device is not recognizing the presence of Network.
c. 'Invalid SIM card' is displayed on the screen when SIM is inserted.

Testing, Troubleshooting and Repair Action Steps

i. Turn OFF the device and remove the battery.
ii. Based on the information output by the system's display unit when SIM is inserted, take the following actions.
iii. For (a) above, confirm with another good SIM card if the mobile device's output would display the same message. If not, the problem is with the first SIM card. CHANGE SIM. If the same message is displayed (meaning that the device does not recognize SIM), the problem is with the device.
iv. Next, dismantle the mobile device.
v. Check the SIM slot. The SIM slot has 6 contact pins that interface with the SIM card. Ensure that each pin has connectivity with the PCB contact pads.
vi. If any pin is broken, change the unit. If the pins have lost connectivity, resolder and test.
vii. If SIM slot unit is OK, first do a thorough cleaning of the PCB with focus on electronic components around SIM slot area. Reflow surrounding electronic components with hot air. Test the SIM again.
viii. If problem persists, locate the SIM microcontroller chip (IC)- usually made of a very small glass in square shape. Apply hot air reflow process to the chip with moderate hot air stream. Apply good soldering skills learnt in an earlier chapter. Test again.
ix. If problem persists, change microcontroller chip.

These steps above apply to all error messages in which the technician has determined that the SIM card itself is not the faulty device. If all else fails, do a flash programming of the mobile device.

Memory Card (MMC) Faults

When a phone is not reading the MMC, it is most often a hardware failure. However, sometimes the insertion of a memory card results in the mobile device restarting or rebooting. In that case, it might be a software problem.

Testing, Troubleshooting and Repair Action Steps

Check whether the memory card is working or not in another device. If not, replace it. If yes, then proceed as follows;

i.   Turn OFF the mobile device, remove the SIM, MMC and disassemble.

ii.   Turn straight any bent pins (if there are bent pins) of the Memory card slot/connector.

iii. Also clean the MMC socket with cleaning fluid and resolder its contact terminals. Test. Is it ok? End.

iv.   If not ok, reflow the (BGA heating procedure) MMC IC or change it.

v.   If problem persists, carry out a reflow of the microprocessor. (Reason: All the connections of the MMC terminate at the microprocessor).

Network Faults

In earlier chapters, we learnt that a mobile phone is basically a radio, although digital mobile phones use the same radio technology in a different way. For instance, digital phones change analog voice signal into binary information (1 and 0) and then compress it, allowing multiple (up to ten) digital phones to occupy the same frequency spectrum equivalent to that occupied by one analog cell phone. Communication takes place over a network. The basic functionality of a mobile device therefore, is to communicate over wireless network media.

Any mobile device that fails to gain access to the network or communicate effectively over the network media has essentially become a brick.

Inside the mobile phone, there are lots of components and ICs which their failure will result in network connectivity problems. However, just like other fault correction processes, troubleshooting and fixing network related faults in mobile phones follow a systematic process.

Some common causes of network faults are;

- Antenna pads corroded, dirty or antenna unit not making proper contact with the antenna contact pads.
- The track between the antenna and the antenna switch (Tx/Rx switch) is broken.
- Antenna switch not performing its functions hence damaged.
- Damaged power amplifier.
- RF filters (Rx/Tx Saw Filters) may be damaged.
- RF signal generator (VCO) not functioning.
- RF processor (Analog baseband) not functional.
- Corrupt or invalid IMEI or software damage.

Mobile devices with Network access faults exhibit the following observable traits;

- "No Network" / "No Access" On Screen (*Antenna/Antenna switch wire tracks broken, dirty contact pads, or dry broken soldered joints*).
- Carrier Network ID displayed on screen without a single network signal icon bar. (*Software fault, require flash programming*).
- No outgoing calls but receives calls only (*Power Amplifier faulty*).
- User not reachable (No Call Reception) but can make calls (*Check Antenna Switch/ RF processor*).
- Signal bars show full on power on and disappear especially when trying to make or receive call (*check Power Amplifier [PA]*

especially (+ve) power supply line to it. Also track between Tx signal from PA to Antenna switch or change PA).

Testing, Troubleshooting and Repair Action Steps

To repair network issues take the following steps;

i. Go to the mobile device's settings>Network settings>...and ensure the multi-band select is ON. For smartphones, there are options for GSM only or 2G, 3G (WCDMA or HSPA) or both etc. This is to ensure that temporary network communication parameters available in the user's environment relative to the selected band or mode did not cause the network failure.

ii. If all network settings are correct, next is to power cycle the mobile device by switching it OFF for 15 minutes before switching it ON again. Observe the booting and network initialization routine. If the network service is restored, problem solved; If not then next step.

iii. Check the phone's IMEI by dialing the code - *#06#. The 15 digit IMEI number should appear on the screen and it should correspond to that written on the back label of the phone. For double SIM phones, two number sets will appear for each SIM card slot. If the IMEI is bad, it will show a wrong number, write "invalid" or show question marks "????". Te solution is to use an appropriate software tool to re-write or repair IMEI. If IMEI is ok, next...

iv. Power OFF the device, remove the battery and disassemble the unit for PCB access.

v. Using soft brush and chemical solvent clean the entire PCB assembly, focus on antenna pads and dry. Test to confirm if problem is solved before next step.

vi. If the problem persists, check if the antenna is properly connected with its pins to antenna contact pads (improvisation is allowed by making jumpers where necessary between antenna and antenna pads) and re-solder the antenna contacts and surrounding discrete electronic components. Test after re-soldering process.

vii.   If the problem persists, Trace the track between the antenna and the antenna switch (Tx/Rx Switch) and ensure connectivity if broken. This is because network search, network identification and authentication are carried out by the baseband processor in sync with the antenna switch/antenna pair. Test before next step.

viii.   If the problem persists, although RF filters rarely get damaged, reflow-solder these components.

ix.   If the problem persists, re-solder the antenna switch contacts. If it is still not ok, remove the antenna switch and make jumper between its Tx, Rx lines and antenna pads. Test before next step.

x.   If the problem persists, the main component in the RF section is the RF processor. In some phones it is a BGA chip while some others in the older models, they are SMT Chips with visible side pins. Carry out reflow soldering with care. Damaged RF processor leads to dead phone in many mobile phones.

xi.   The mobile phone connects to the network using its software with network control protocols to control RF hardware components and perform some frequency tuning together with the CPU. This means that some network faults are as a result of corrupted software. If all else fails, a software flash programming is necessary as a last resort.

Camera Failure Faults

Cameras are integrated into mobile devices to provide users with the added capability to take snapshots and process still and motion pictures. They also fail just like other functional units in the mobile device. Some symptomatic behaviors when they fail are;

- The device outputs a message "Camera module not ready"

- The display becomes dark with no images in view when camera is activated
- No response when camera is activated

Testing, Troubleshooting and Repair Action Steps

After checking the mobile device settings to confirm that all settings are in order, take the following steps;

i.   Turn OFF the device, remove SIM, MMC and disassemble the device.
ii. Use brush to clean the camera connectors with IPA or any other solvent and test. If ok, End.
iii. If the problem is not solved replace Camera.
iv. If the problem persists, replace the Camera module (slot).

Restarting/Rebooting Mobile Device Faults

Mobile devices like mobile phones, tablets, PDAs etc may experience automatic intermittent power cycling issues when an abnormal condition exists in their circuitry. A mobile device has a power cycling fault if;

- It reboots continuously.
- It reboots during a phone call (Transmit or Receive).
- It reboots when the keypads are being used or a particular action is taken by the user after functioning normally over a period of time.
- It gets excessively hot intermittently (overheating) and then reboots.

Take the following actions to repair:

i. Remove the battery and disassemble the device if power OFF fails to activate.
ii. Remove all peripheral units attached to the PCB.

iii. Service the PCB using brush and cleaning fluid. Using hot air, carry out reflow procedure on the whole PCB components. Test.

iv. If the problem persists, with the device dismantled, connect the PCB to power supply (battery or D.C power supply). Attach peripheral units one after the other because any one of them could be the cause.

v. Switch ON the device and allow it to be ON for at least 2 minutes.

vi. Lay your thumb on the various ICs and other components on the PCB. Feel to determine which component is getting excessively hot.

vii. If there is any such component, remove and replace that component or IC. For ICs, carry out reflow soldering procedure. If problem is not solved, remove the IC and re-ball (BGA soldering procedure).

viii. If there was no overheating component or IC, reassemble the device and carry out Flash programming or boot sector formatting with the appropriate software tool.

ix. If step (viii) fails, the Microprocessor is the faulty component. Dismantle the device again and carry out reflow/BGA soldering repair procedure on the Microprocessor. After any such repair on processors, flashing the phone is a must.

x. But if the rebooting occurs during phone calls, both the PA (Power Amplifier) and CPU (Microprocessor) are possible suspects, especially the PA.

PCB/Motherboard Faults

The Printed Circuit Board PCB, Mainboard or Motherboard of a mobile device provides surface mount space and wiring circuitry for every electronic component or device that make up the mobile phone. PCBs develop faults and as well damage beyond repair. In chapter 6 of this book, details about the motherboard were fully discussed. Like I said earlier, knowledge and understanding about the device one is fixing and the functionality of its component parts makes for a better technician. It enhances your technical judgments and speeds up your capacity to deliver in good time ditto to earn good money.

PCB faults occur in one or more of the following ways;

a. Short-circuit in the internal wiring
b. Open-circuit in the internal wiring
c. Damaged contact pads for surface mount components

The above 3 common ways a PCB can fail could all be traceable to water or any other salty or mineral liquid.

Water Damage Faults

Water is not good for electronics especially in an enclosure like mobile phones. Once water is trapped underneath the ICs or the surface of the PCB, it causes corrosion. Corrosion occurs as a result of oxidation of the metal contacts which creates rust, deteriorating the contacts of the surface mounted components. As corrosion spreads, the resistance between circuit components drops. On the surface, the rust creates bridges between adjacent components that by design should not be connected together. These 'bridges' are short-circuits. Pits and cracks also occur in places where current freely flowed before the liquid damage. This results in what is called electrical 'open-circuits'. The affected components may fail permanently or temporarily pending the removal of the 'short-circuit' or reconnection of the 'open-circuit'. Also, corrosion may eat up the fibrous coating of the PCB in an irreparable manner.

Testing, Troubleshooting and Repair Action Steps

Cleaning the Motherboard

Electronic boards are cleaned using various chemical solvents. The recommended chemical for mobile phone PCBs is Isopropyl Alcohol (IPA) also called Isopropanol. It is an effective cleaning agent that dries as quickly as it is applied leaving no harmful residue on the motherboard like acidic oils. It dissolves oils, alkaloids, gums, natural resins etc. and removes thermal pastes from IC packages. Because of their relative high cost, most technicians resort to using readily available fluids like Methylated spirits.

Methylated spirits are actually ethanol mixed with Methanol and some poisonous additives. In some cases they are dyed to change their color. They also contain a little quantity of Isopropyl alcohol and other chemical additives. The disadvantage of using methylated spirit is that it leaves residue of toxic oils on the PCB after use. When used, a technician must carefully dry out (burn out) the oily molecules with continual streams of hot air especially underneath the ICs. There are cases where use of IPA to clean a water damaged phone would instantly restore the phone to normal working conditions whereas on alternatively using Methylated spirit, the PCB refuses to power ON until after painstaking drying routines are applied.

If one is using an ultrasonic cleaner, you have to immerse the PCB in a soap solution and wash thoroughly with brush before putting it into the machine. Before that, you must detach delicate peripheral units like camera, LCD, microphone, speaker, ringer etc from the PCB and kept aside safely.

Whatever you do, recognize the importance of keeping a PCB as dirt-free, water-free, oil-free, and alkaloids-free as its pre-fault condition. Like I wrote earlier about the mindset of a technician, your foremost objective should be to return a faulty device to that state or condition in which the manufacturer made and introduced it into the market. If it was initially functioning, your mental state should be such as to eliminate with every process possible, any foreign causative agent introduced into the device that may be preventing it from normal operation. That way, solving problems will be a lot easier.

PCB Short- Circuit

When short-circuit conditions exist in a mobile phone PCB, the mobile phone will shut down completely. This is what is commonly regarded as a 'dead phone' condition because it came to the technician dead – non-responsive, whether temporarily or permanently.

Short circuits are conditions whereby a PCB wiring which consists of two distinct parallel electrical polarity wires or conductors, positive (+) and negative (-) have their paths crossed at any point in the circuit. In PCBs however, wires are replaced with printed copper tracks.

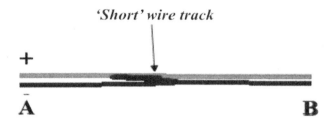

'Short' wire track

+

A   **B**

Short circuits on PCBs can create any of the following faulty behavior in a mobile device;

   a. Power-On failure
   b. Overheating of the mobile device
   c. Fast battery drain
   d. Mobile device frequently freeze or hang
   e. Restarting/Rebooting of mobile device.

Testing, Troubleshooting and Repair Action Steps

To test if a motherboard or PCB is short-circuited;

   i. Turn OFF the mobile phone or device and disassemble it.
   ii. Using your multimeter for continuity testing, locate the battery terminals of the device. There are usually different types of battery contacts: 2-terminals type, 3-terminals type and the 4-terminals type. Whichever type the device came with, the first and the last pin counting from left to right are the positive (+) and negative (-) contacts respectively. The battery-side contacts have the mark (+) and (-) on the battery so you may use that as a guide too.
   iii. With the positive (+) probe of the multimeter, touch the negative (-) battery contact terminal on the PCB while the negative (-) probe is on the positive (+) of the battery terminals.

iv. If there is continuity (if using the buzzer point and it beeps or using normal resistance measurement, it reads 0Ω), the PCB is 'shorted' (short-circuited).

v. If using a D.C supply machine, select a supply voltage equivalent to the mobile device's battery output voltage. Connect the probes: (+) probe to (+) battery connector terminal; (-) probe to (-) battery connector terminal. If there is a short circuit in the PCB, the Ammeter will output a current value in Amperes (A). If not, it will give a zero output.

vi. Clean the whole circuit-board with IPA making sure underneath all the ICs is thoroughly washed. Repeat the flow of fluid underneath the chips several times. You may need to soak the PCB for about 120 to 180 minutes in a recommended solvent before drying and then reflow soldering is applied.

vii. Test to see if short circuit still exists.

viii. Investigate the source of short circuit and eliminate it. This is how;

ix. Remove all peripheral components from the PCB and test again for a 'short'.

x. If the short circuit is no more, begin adding the components one after the other to determine the causative agent. However, if the short circuit remains, continue the investigation on the PCB.

xi. For peripheral components, determine if it is the component that needs replacement or a lack of supply at its terminals. Apply also component testing skills learnt in this book to electronic components. A track may be good but the electronics (like burnt capacitors, resistors etc) surrounding a peripheral component have failed, making it not to function. If that happens, remove the component, check if 'short' is gone and replace similar part on that spot.

xii. Test again for short circuit.

xiii. Connect the PCB to its battery, press the power switch to ON and keep it in this position for 10-20 seconds, whether the board power ON or not. Remove the battery and immediately check if any component or IC is heating. Any component which is heating up is most likely shorted. Remove it and check again. If the problem is eliminated, replace the overheating IC or component.

xiv.   If short circuit still exists, download PCB wiring diagram from the internet.

xv.   Begin a wiring track trace using the circuit diagram as a guide and a digital multimeter for continuity testing. Any two contacts which are by design not meant to intersect but are showing interconnection would be the fault line.

xvi.   If all else fails, PCB has gone beyond repair.

PCB Open-Circuit

Broken PCB wiring tracks are referred to as open-circuits. Open circuits may occur due to a broken positive (+) or negative (-) polarity electrical track, preventing the circuit from completing by stopping the flow of current. Due to the design of motherboards with multiple layers of board fused together, breaks may occur either internally or on the surface of the PCB.

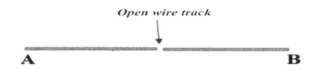

Testing, Troubleshooting and Repair Action Steps

In order to fix broken tracks in the PCB circuitry, a circuit tracing process is carried out. 'Track-tracing' is used to check for broken tracks on the Printed Circuit Boards.

These tracks are voltage and current supply lines to every component terminated on the circuit board. Any component starved of this supply cannot function. A PCB can only be 'dead' if the open circuit occurs on its power supply line between battery and the power supply system.

Therefore take the following steps to solve broken track problems;

i. Track tracing is a continuity measurement process. Get your multimeter ready on the continuity test buzzer mode selector.

ii. Determine what type of failure is being investigated ranging from power failure to component failures.

iii. Download the device's PCB wiring diagram. This is most times available if you search on the internet.

iv. Get your jumper wire roll, magnifier and soldering equipment handy.

v. Begin the trace, testing the various component interconnections, terminal to terminal according to the wiring diagram

vi. For peripheral components, determine if it is the component that needs replacement or a lack of supply at its terminals. Apply also component testing skills learnt in this book to electronic components. A track may be good but the electronics (like burnt capacitors, resistors etc) surrounding a peripheral component have failed, making it not to function. If that happens, remove the component, check if short-circuit is gone and replace similar part on that spot.

vii. If a PCB wiring diagram is not available online, Google images provide an alternative whereby other professionals in the mobile phone repair community worldwide share jumper track trace solutions that have worked. Use your sound judgment to verify and apply same.

viii. Where a track is broken, use an insulated jumper wire to make relevant cable link.

Improvisation

When there is adequate knowledge of the theoretical and practical design of a system as this book is trying to equip the reader, intelligent and creative improvisation may become handy. Technical improvisation refers to the ability of the technician to devise workable equivalent solutions relative to standard practice which were not planned before - hand but applied on the job for a particular instance.

What this means is that a situation may warrant your devising a solution based on a mix of technical experience working on several devices. For instance, there are components that are meant for a particular device model but which can be made to apply in another model for a successful solution. There are components which may not be available for a repair job for which your application of creative solutions will be needed. Whatever you do, ensure that such solutions are durable.

Some Frequently Asked Questions: Phone Hardware and Software

Q1. What is Flashing and format of a phone?
Answer: Flashing a phone is a process whereby the firmware/operating system of the phone is erased and reloaded. However, when you format a phone the arrangement of data in the phone which must have been altered or rearranged in the memory areas either by usage or virus infection is reordered and realigned with the file system to comply with the phone's default/normal programming within the Operating System. After formatting a phone, it returns to its default state; all user data are deleted and bugs or viruses are removed.

Q2. What are the different types of flash memory in a phone?

a. NOR flash and b. NAND flash

Q3. What are the various types of CPU brands in China phones?

There are different CPUs and flash types;

    A. MTK (MediaTek)
    B. SPD (Spreadtrum)
    C. TI (Texas Instrument)
    D. MSTAR CPU
    E. RDA/ Coolsand CPU
    F. Infineon
    G. Broadcom

Q4. What is the difference between NAND and NOR Flash?

(i) NOR Flash: Intel introduced the first commercial NOR type flash chip in 1988. NOR-based flash has long erase and write times, but provides full address and data buses, allowing random access to any memory location.

(ii) NAND Flash: NAND is the 2nd type of flash chip. It has faster erase and write times, and requires a smaller chip area per cell. NAND-flash

247

has about ten times the endurance of NOR flash chip. However, the I/O interface of NAND-flash does not provide a random-access external address bus. Rather, data must be read on a page block basis, with typical block sizes of hundreds to thousands of bits.

Q5. What are the labels of the different data test-points of phones?
Answer: Pin-outs data test points for software flash access and are:

RX
TX
GND
D+
D-
VPP

Q6. What is a jumper?
Answer: A short length of wire used temporarily to complete a circuit or to bypass a break in a circuit.

Q7. When a previously working phone with a software fault but good display before it was flashed, display white screen after Flash, what could be the cause?
Answer: Use of wrong flash file version may cause it. Download the correct file especially the highest available version and flash again.

Q8. When one inserts charger and the phone says "Bad contact charger".
Answer: This could be due to the result of excess of current drawn from the charger. Every phone needs a required voltage/current in order to charge a specific mobile phone. Try replacing the charger as a first step before trying out the solution in the book.

Q9. When a phone 'hangs or freezes" after power on, is it a software or hardware fault?
ANSWER: It may be either a HW fault or software fault but try the following.

i.   Remove the side volume key buttons.
ii. Check the keypad for any likely stuck-in keys. Release if any.
iii. Disassemble the phone and clean it with a solvent.
iv. Reflow solder the microprocessor,
v.   Finally try software flash.

Q10. When a phone restarts during initialization and network search what could be done?

i.   If the device is a China mobile phone, Format or full flash with any China phone software flasher. If it does not solve the problem remove or replace the Bluetooth controller IC (tested in majority of phone).
ii. If the phone is not a China phone, reflow the microprocessor or flash the phone.

Q11. When a phone boots to a white display what should be done?

Answer: First of all check if you could receive or make call.

i.   If yes then it would be HW fault, Change L.C.D
ii. If not, then it would be software problem

Q12. What does a flash file contain?
Answer: Flash files contain Firmware in some and Firmware + Operating System in Smartphones.

Q13. When a phone shows "Contact Service" what does it mean and what should be done?
Answer: The message displayed shows that one or more parts of the software are not able to execute properly, triggering the watchdog processor which is able to detect that an error has occurred. Also, when a phone is powered ON, it executes a self test routine, if one or more components fail, the message "contact service" is displayed on the screen. Therefore to fix this problem;

i.   The first action is to flash the phone. If it continues to show the message;

ii.   Disassemble the phone.

iii. Using soft brush and your cleaning solvent like IPA, service the phone by washing and drying with hot air station.

iv.   Ensure the solvent gets underneath the ICs and air- reflow

v.   Couple the phone back and power ON.

vi.   If not solved, carry out complete hardware troubleshooting and BGA reflow on the Power IC.

Finally, as a general advice again, Google-search of a phone model's name for instance with 'dead phone solution' appended will direct you to numerous solution tips other professionals applied for a specific fault which was successful. If you click 'images' after the search result, you may find soldering track PCB trace cable-section images discovered by other professionals as a shortcut to digging into circuit diagrams by yourself.

PART 3

MOBILE PHONE SOFTWARE
And
SOFTWARE REPAIR TECHNIQUES

Chapter 8

Understanding Mobile Phone Software Repair

Mobile phones and tablets are *computerized* electronic devices that comprise of both hardware and associated software component in order to function. A digital mobile phone or Smartphone is a computer device.

In part one and two modules of this book, the focus was on the hardware components, hardware tools, and hardware repair procedures required for fixing faults related to the hardware components of a mobile phone. In this part three module, the teaching will focus on software related faults associated with mobile phones/devices, the solutions and the solution tools needed.

Software faults in mobile phones require software solutions. *Mobile phone repair software tools* are programming tools designed with the capability to read and write software programs from and into the flash memory of a mobile phone for the purpose of upgrade, repair or change of corrupted software in the mobile device. Mobile phone software repair tools are therefore different from the mobile phone software itself. The mobile phone software comprises only of the written program specific only to a manufacturer's model of a phone.

Generally "Software" is a code of routines, instructions, commands or protocols that define and guide the operation of hardware, including granting access to user input commands to control a system unit to perform specific operations. Once a programmer defines a structured set of instructions for the sole purpose of influencing computer hardware to perform specific functions, it is called software.

Mobile phone or Computer software consists of programs, libraries and related non-executable data such as data stored in the phone like music, personal notes and documents, contacts, files etc. Software is non-tangible (unlike hardware it cannot be seen or touched).

Computer or Mobile phone hardware and software require each other and neither can be realistically used without the other.

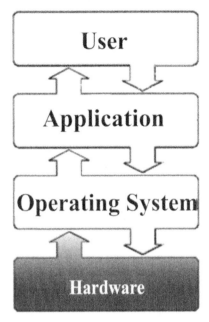

Information flow chart in a computer between Application software,
Operating system software and the User input
Source: https://en.wikipedia.org/software

Figure 8.1

Software in a mobile phone or computer can be divided into the
following categories:

Application software

These are software that uses the computer system or mobile device to
perform special functions or entertainment beyond the basic operation of
that computer device. They extend the device's utilization capacity.
There are many different types of application software for mobile phones
today. An example of this is any application downloaded from Google
play store or iTunes store etc.

System software

System software is any software that runs, operates or influences the
computer hardware directly in order to provide basic functionality needed
by users and other applications. One example of System software is the
Operating system software.

Operating System software

They are essential collections of software that manage resources and provides common services for other software (e.g Application software) that runs "on top" of them. Supervisory programs, boot loaders, shells and window systems are core parts of operating systems. In practice, an operating system comes bundled with additional software (including some application software) so that a user can potentially do some work with a computer that only has an operating system fresh out of production.

Device drivers

These set of software control specific types of device, attached to a computer. Each device needs at least one corresponding device driver. They can be likened to interpreters that interpret the communication protocols needed for both interface and operation within the computer system.

Utilities

Utility software is a computer program designed to assist users in maintenance and care of their computing devices.

Malicious software or malware

These are software developed to harm and disrupt computing devices. Examples of such are viruses, malwares, Trojan horses and any such software code which its intention is to harm the user or the device.

Mobile Phone Operating Systems (MobileOS)

A mobile operating system is the software platform on top of which other application programs can run on mobile devices. They are specifically designed to run on mobile devices such as mobile phones, smartphones, PDAs, tablet computers and other handheld devices. This is similar to the same manner Windows Operating Systems or Linux Operating Systems controls your laptop or desktop computers.

The operating system determines the functions and features available on a mobile device, including the types of third-party applications a mobile device can run as well as the hardware functionalities.

Below are some predominantly popular mobile OS in the market today. They include;

1. Android OS by Google Inc.
2. iphone OS / iOS by Apple
3. Blackberry OS by Research In Motion (RIM)
4. Windows Mobile (Windows Phone 7) by Microsoft
5. Symbian OS by Nokia
6. MeeGo OS by Nokia & Intel
7. Palm OS
8. WebOS by Palm & HP
9. Bada by Samsung Electronics

Firmware

Firmware is used to refer to microcode software that runs in electronic and computing systems held specifically in non-volatile memory devices like ROM, EEPROM or flash memory. They are low level software codes that provide control, monitoring and data manipulation of engineered products at basic level and provide services to higher level software like the operating system. In embedded systems like mobile phones, firmware may be the only program that will run on the system and provide all the functions in some phones (basic and feature phones) while combined with an operating system in others like smartphones or tablets. The flash files used for software repairs are actually firmware files. Flash memory allows firmware to be updated without physically removing an integrated circuit from the system. For basic and feature phones that mostly had smaller storage capacity and far less application software processing, EEPROMs were mostly used; NAND-flash storage with its larger memory capacity has enabled the use of larger operating system software that are feature rich, implementing a large bouquet of functions we enjoy today.

Real Time Operating Systems (RTOS)

Every mobile device or Smartphone in reality runs two operating systems instead of one. Apart from the mobile operating system that is very obvious to users and professionals like the Blackberry OS, Android OS, iOS or PalmOS etc, it also runs a proprietary (manufacturer owned/specific) smaller operating system that manages everything related to radio. A real-time operating system is required for this purpose because radio functionality is highly timing-dependent.

This operating system is stored in EEPROM in some phones or NVRAM (remember Flash is a type of NVRAM) in others and runs on the baseband processor. Real time operating system running in a mobile device is very powerful. Compared to RTOS is the Computer BIOS.

Mobile Phone Software Repair Tools' Guide

A mobile phone service technician requires the following equipment for software repair services.

- A Desktop/ Laptop computer system running on windows operating system.
- Varieties of mobile phone flasher boxes and Service cables.
- Flash files for various brands and models of mobile phones.

The list above is a basic one. It presupposes that the software repair technician is also engaged in hardware repairs and therefore possesses basic hardware repair tools. This is because in carrying out software repairs there are strong possibilities of swinging between both types of repairs. Also, to encourage a start-up technician with lean resources for purchasing a variety of flasher boxes, one flasher device should be okay to start with, provided the flasher chosen supports a wide range of mobile devices predominant within that chosen business environment.

For repair software programming (Flashing/unlock) of the following mobile device product brands, here are some recommended flasher software or boxes;

- **Nokia:** UFS Micro box /JAF box (Odeon)/ ATF box, UFS3 tornado, MT-Box for Nokia, Universal box etc.
- **Samsung:** UFS micro box /Z3 box/ NS PRO box/ Odin (Android), MT-Box for Samsung

- **IPhone:** iTunes Software
- **Blackberry:** Blackberry Desktop Software, Z3 box
- **LG:** Z3X box (LG activation), Octopus box(Smartphones) and many others
- **China phones:** Infinity box, Miracle box, Chinese Miracle2, Avator box, Volcano box and SPflash tool (Smartphone Android).

Figure 8.2: Flasher boxes

There are varieties of flasher boxes covering a wide range of mobile phones. Choosing the right flasher for a range of mobile phone devices, phone models or mobile phone manufacturers can be a daunting task for a technician based in any given job location. The technician should be guided by his market-what kinds of phones are his clients bringing for repairs or mostly used around his business environment?

Warning: The following list below is not an endorsement for any product. Cross check their market relevance, currency of information and support on these products online before making a buy decision.

Some others include the following;

Table 8.1: Flasher boxes and Their Supported Products List

SN	Software Toolbox	Products Supported
1.	Advance Turbo Flasher	Nokia models
2.	Axe Box	HTC phone service
3.	CPF-box Products	Chinese Phones (Support all serial MTK,Spreadtrum,AD,TI,Sky,Agere,Philps.SI4 904(new) and Infineon CPU), Some Samsung, LG, Motorola And support use of free 3rd party software
4.	Cyclone box	Nokia models
5.	Easy-Unlocker	Unlock a wide range of brands and models like Samsung, Alcatel, LG, Huawei etc.
6.	ET-BoX	Multiple models support. Confirm before buying
7.	Furious Team Products	Multiple product support. Very vast support of a wide range of phone brands and models. Useful tool.
8.	Genie Universal	Unlocker for Nokia
9.	GM-Box	For CDMA phones unlock/repair like Vitel, Haier, Kyocera, LG, Motorola etc all CDMA versions
10.	GSM-Server Products[Medus	So much so read up at: http://medusabox.com/eng/features/models

	a, DreamBox, Scout, Sigma Key, Smart-clip, Smart-clip 2, Smart-unlocker, Rextor cables, Pegasus]	Scout: http://forum.gsmhosting.com/vbb/f417/ For info on ALL: http://forum.gsmhosting.com/vbb/f372/
11.	GTS box	Nokia, Motorola, Samsung, Sharp, LG, Sony Ericsson and Siemens
12	Infinity-Box	Strong support for All China feature phones, some Nokia models, some Samsung models
13.	J.A.F - Just Another Flasher	Nokia mobile phones
14.	Kulankendi Box/Dongle	Nokia BB5 SL3, Samsung models, LG (2G & 3G) etc Check list here: http://forum.gsmhosting.com/vbb/f593/kulanke ndi-box-dongle-line-server-phone-supported-list-1154078/
15.	Martech products (clip, box, key)	Nokia, Panasonic, Siemens, LG
16.	Mastertools	China Android phones flash/unlock support (MTK, SPD etc)
17.	McnPro Box	China mobile phone software solutions

18.	Micro-Box.com Team Products	Blackberry, Samsung Galaxy, SAGEM, Sony Ericsson, LG, Alcatel, HTC, ZTE models support and supports use of third party software with the box.
19.	Multi-Box TEAM Products (Chinese cocktail, multi-box lite, multi-box, padfinder box)	All China feature phone models support, Multiple product support including all feature phones from Samsung, Phillips, Sendo, Sagem, Alcatel, Vitel, Maxon, Bird, Motorola, LG, Mitsubishi, Nokia, Panasonic, VK, Bleu etc
20.	MXKEY (by Alim Hape)	Nokia flasher and unlocker, Blackberry flasher and unlocker, Add-ons for HTC, Huawei, etc
21.	NEROkey	Son Ericsson unlocker
22.	NSPRO	Great support for Samsung phones - feature and smartphones. Also Blackberry 5xx, 6xx, 7xx series
23	POLAR Team Products	Alcatel, Huawei, few Samsung and ZTE phones support.
24.	Rocker Team products (RIFF box and Rocker dongle)	Alcatel, Haier, Full Samsung models (A-Z series and Galaxy models), LG, HTC, Huawei, few Nokia, few Motorola, few Sony Ericsson, Micromax models, Pantech, Sierra, Toshiba,ZTE and a mix of other various models and brands.
25.	T-BOX Products	China phones flasher box

26.	Saras Boxes (UFST, HWK, Twisterflasher, n-box. UFS 2 and UFS 3 Turnado flasher)	Nokia, Samsung, Sony Ericsson, LG phone models and more.
27.	SMTi	Sagem, Vodafone, ZTE, LG, Alcatel, Coral, J-Max, Huawei, Samsung 3G models,
28.	SpiderMan	China feature phone models
29.	SPT BOX	Samsung tool for all feature and smartphones Software works with USTPro2 and infinity box.
30.	Super Doctor Box (MTK-BOX)	Chinese Android mobile phones support
31.	Test-box 2	China MTK Tool, Samsung 3G (A-M series), LG 2/3G models, Nokia Tool, ZTE, Asus HDD/Bios master password tool, HTC unlock, Alcatel unlock, Hovatel, Sierra, Qualcom Vodafone, some CDMA, Motorola, VK mobile, Maxon, Benq, Nec 2G/3G, Sony Ericsson, Vitel, Panasonic, Sanyo, Siemens, Phillips, Toshiba, Blackberry Unlock, etc
32.	TGT Products	China mobile phones support
33.	Ultimate-Sam Box / dongle	Samsung Mobile phones Unlock/Flash
34	Universal box	Nokia, Blackberry and Sony Ericsson unlocker
35.	UST Pro II	Samsung feature phones Unlock/flash/Repair

36.	Volcano box	Full China phones support (All CPUs) and Samsung Smartphones, ZTE, Huawei (All models), HTC(Qualcomm CPU) support, iPhone IMEI check service.
37.	VygisToolbox	LG, Sharp, Benq, Maxon, Sanyo, Newgen plus added Alcatel support.
38.	Miracle Box	China Mobile phone support
39.	Z3X-Team Products	Samsung, LG, Blackberry, Benq-Siemens and China phones Editor
40.	Infinity Box	All China phone models, some Samsung, Some Nokia , ZTE, Motorola models. Multi-brand unlock/flash/repair tool

The above listed flasher software tool boxes are products designed by their respective manufacturers to provide interface between the mobile devices being reprogrammed or flashed, unlocked or repaired and the computer. The mobile phone software program files (OS or firmware) are usually downloaded and stored in the computer system. In order to transfer these files properly into the mobile phone/device, there has to be a communication link between the computer and the mobile phone/device.

Computers have in-built communication ports which include;

- Serial ports
- Parallel ports
- USB (Universal Serial Bus) ports
- Ethernet ports
- VGA (Video Graphics Adapter) ports
- PS/2 ports

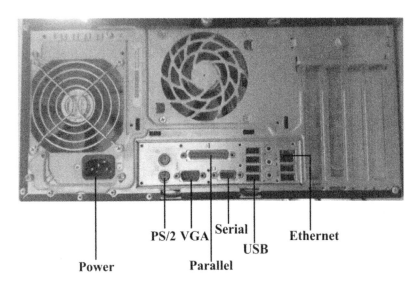

PS/2 VGA **Serial** Ethernet
USB
Power Parallel

Figure 8.3: Computer ports

The USB technology has overtaken the older serial and parallel port systems although they still exist on the main boards of computers. Every product designed for interface in any way with a computer these days are fitted with USB ports. This includes mobile phones.

However, it is not all mobile phones whose software files (firmware or OS) may be transferred into its ROM or flash memory directly through a USB/serial/parallel cable connection to the computer. If it were mainly so, programmers who write software programs for phone repair will go hungry due to piracy and free internet downloads. Also, the repair software application for most mobile phones is not provided freely by their manufacturers. Third-party application developers with access to the mobile product's APIs (Application Programming Interface) leveraged the opportunity to create repair software applications referred to as flasher boxes.

Mobile phone flasher boxes or simply "flashers" are mainly used for the following;

- To recover user data from dead or faulty mobile phones that otherwise will not provide access to data stored on their internal memory.
- To update or replace software that is stored in the mobile phone's Read Only Memory (ROM) or Non-Volatile Flash Memory

(NVRAM). This software as we have learnt here is also commonly referred to as "firmware" and is usually pre-installed on phones by the manufacturer of the phone such as Nokia, Samsung, Sony-Ericsson, RIM etc.

- To add language support and set regional settings for mobile phones. For instance, changing language settings can enable a user that bought a mobile phone device with a firmware that has no Italian language support by default to re-flash it with Italian supported firmware.

- Flashers can also be used to repair corrupted IMEI or illegally used to change the IMEI number of some mobile phone devices. This in effect enables criminals to illegally re-enable stolen or lost mobile phones which may have been barred from the network by telecommunication carriers in some countries.

- They are used for unlocking SIM restrictions, User security locks, carrier based locks or call restrictions. SIM unlock is legal in some countries and illegal in others

Features and Components of Flasher Boxes

Mobile phone flashers comprises of a combination of;

- The Software suite and Installation drivers.
- The hardware (USB flasher device).
- Service cables.
- Flash files for various supported mobile phone brands and models.

There are two main categories of Software flasher tools:

- Original (Branded) software tool boxes

- Cloned or Cracked (Non-branded) tool boxes or software

Table 8.2: Features of Original and Cloned Flasher Tool boxes/ Software

Original (Branded) Tools	*Cloned (Non-branded) Tools*
They have well known names and model numbers.	They are much cheaper than branded boxes
They have unique serial numbers.	They combine the phone support of more than one branded flasher box.
Some boxes need activation. Software, updates and support is provided for these boxes. The level of support varies depending on the box manufacturer.	They support the addition of a smartcard from branded flasher boxes.
It is easier to get support for them in forums and on other support websites. Most major manufacturers have dedicated active threads on GSM Forum by ZFrank.	Do not usually come with any software and/or drivers and places the responsibility on the buyer to find the software from other sources. No after sales support
They are widely used by professional repair service technicians.	Usage is rare among good repair professionals.
The boxes are usually sold with quality service cables.	Some come with a few service cables; others do not come with any.
They are sold by recognized retailers and an "Authorized reseller list" is often found on the manufacturer's website.	They are sold in the open market.
Their USB interface serve as a power source so they do not usually require an external power supply to function.	Some require the use of external power source not included in the purchase.

Flasher dongles

These are also used for mobile phone flashing but differ from the flasher boxes in their minimal functionality. Most dongles are used as extension cards to flasher boxes; can serve also for remote unlocking and de-branding of phones.

MX Key dongle

CS Tool Dongle

Source: Ipmart.com
Figure 8.4a: Sample Flasher Dongles

Flasher Cables and Interfaces

The flasher box typically connects to the mobile device through a special cable made for that phone model referred to as a "Service cable". One end of the cable is the standard RJ-45 Ethernet networking cable interface which connects to the RJ-45 port on the flasher box. The other end is a matching phone's USB/Data port connector or a set of data test point contact pins that make contact with the mobile phone's Joint Test Action Group (JTAG) or the Mbus/Fbus connections.

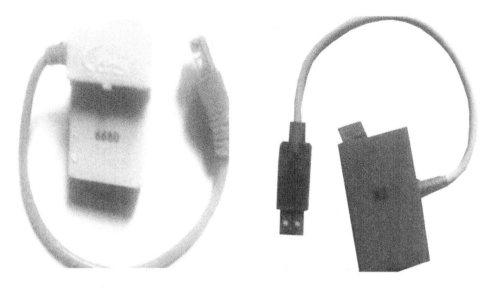

Figure 8.4b

Mobile Phone Software Faults Diagnosis

The following symptoms lead to the diagnosis of a phone's behavior as a software fault;

- When a phone is frequently restarting automatically.
- When a phone is frequently switching off automatically without the power switch pressed or switch-OFF initiated by the user.
- When the phone switches OFF or reboots as soon as a particular folder like gallery, message inbox or other is opened.
- When some of the phone's applications which came with the OS refuse to function properly.
- Incomplete booting stuck at logo.
- When a phone does not switch-ON, especially without physical damage related reason. This could be as a result of a corrupted OS.
- When a phone frequently freezes or hangs.
- When a phone processes its applications, user requests and commands very slowly.
- A phone starts up but is blank, inoperable and possibly with some indication light.
- A phone displays "Contact Service" or "Contact Retailer".

Mobile Phones Viruses

Viruses are malicious codes written with intent to cause harm to mobile or computer devices. A mobile phone virus is basically the same thing as a computer virus which comprises of unwanted executable files that "infect" a device and then replicates to other devices. In the history of mobile phones, the first known mobile phone virus appeared sometimes in 2004 known as Cabir.A. At that time, it infected only a small number of Bluetooth-enabled phones. In 2005, another virus known as "Commwarrior" virus arrived on the scene. Technicians who were knowledgeable in those days made a kill financially from these two viruses including this author. Commwarrior replicated by way of both Bluetooth and MMS transfers. Once you receive and install the virus, it immediately starts searching for other Bluetooth phones in the vicinity to infect. At the same time, the virus sent infected MMS messages to every phone number in your address list. Commwarrior was probably one of the most effective viruses to date because it used two methods to replicate itself.

A mobile phone virus or worm spreads via;

- Internet downloads
- MMS (multimedia messaging service) attachments
- Bluetooth transfers from other phones
- From a PC connection

In the past, phone-to-phone viruses almost exclusively infected phones that were running the Nokia Symbian operating system.

Virus Infected files usually show up disguised as applications like games, security patches, add-on functionalities, pornography and most freeware.

Obstacles to Viruses' Mass Replication

- Lack of auto-installation capability in most viruses.
- The methods of spread.

- Basic Phones which can only make and receive calls are an obstacle as they are not at risk.
- Lack of uniformity in mobile operating systems worldwide unlike the predominance of Windows OS for computers. The large number of proprietary operating systems in the mobile phone industry is one of the obstacles to mass infection.
- The Android OS which is the dominant OS in the Smartphone market segment currently is based on the Linux OS kernel which is not affected by viruses written for windows based computers. Some malwares and viruses are now existing which affect Android OS systems like the monkey test virus.
- Mobile phone-virus-writers have no flat Windows-level market share to target, so any virus will only affect a small percentage of phones.

Effects of Virus Infections on Mobile Phones

- A virus accesses and/or deletes all of the contact information and calendar entries in your phone.
- Viruses cause financial loss to users since they sometimes send infected MMS messages to every number in the phone book which costs money to send.
- Some viruses delete or lock up certain phone applications or crash the phone completely so that it is bricked.
- Viruses may be malwares that spy user data (such as monitor calls and listen to conversations, SMS, Chats etc) and steal financial information, which is a serious security issue.

Mitigating the Effects of Virus Infection on Mobile Phones

i. Turn off Bluetooth discoverable mode. Set the phone to "hidden" mode so that other phones cannot automatically detect it and send to it a virus. This is done on the Bluetooth options menu.

ii.   Install security antivirus software on client phone and eliminate virus. Many developers have developed security software for mobile phones. Some are for free downloading, some for user purchase and some intended for mobile phone service providers.

iii.   Check security updates to firmware files and flash phones with updated versions of software. This is necessary where the virus has infected the phone in a way that locked out user interface access to carry out (ii) above.

Mobile Phone Software Tools Installation Guide

The appropriate software for each type of flasher box is usually made available through the official support site for the flasher box manufacturer. Each flasher box has a unique serial number which is usually displayed in the software suite's user interface dialog box after it has been properly installed. Also, when you purchase the flasher box from an accredited reseller or directly from the manufacturer, you are allotted a username and password for access to secure resources on their web servers.

It is required that the right driver for both the flasher box and various types of mobile devices are chosen. This information can be gotten from the flasher box manufacturer's support sites where they update the drivers frequently. Sometimes an older version of a USB driver and software bundle may run perfectly with some mobile phone models while a newer USB driver and software bundle will not work with that same device.

Before using a flasher box;

- USB drivers for the flasher box hardware in addition to the phone repair software should be installed in the computer **before** connecting the USB cable to the flasher box.
- If a specific version of the repair software does not work properly with a particular mobile phone model or range of phone models, it is recommended that both the flasher box's repair software and its associated USB drivers be completely uninstalled from the

computer system. Reboot the computer after uninstall completes and try another USB driver and software version until the appropriate driver and software match is found.

- Obtain information about the best version of driver for each type of device from mobile phone repair forums or in the flasher box's support site. GSM forum remains a rich resource site for technicians.

- A Flasher box's specific guidelines are usually available on the flasher box manufacturer's website. Read these guidelines for directions.

- Flash-files (firmware files) for each brand, model or type of mobile device supported by a particular flasher box are also available for download from the flasher box manufacturer's website. This is the reason it is best to buy a branded flasher box. Some flash-files are flasher box-specific for given models of phones. Get the information from there as well. Flash-files are also available on many sites shared by other repair professionals. Be cautious about using any off-the-internet file.

- Finally be computer literate.

Computer System Requirements for Software Flash Repair

The following are the required provisioning on any desktop or laptop computer a technician wishes to use for mobile phone repair software flash programming. This section is meant to serve as a guide to the reader to organize the system for the task of repairs.

Hardware Requirements

- 250 GB Hard Disk Drive- HDD (Minimum requirements) extensible with external storage up to 2 Terabytes or more of hard disk storage
- 2GB RAM (Random Access Memory) minimum requirement
- 2.30 GHz Processor (minimum requirement)

Software Requirements

Computer desktop or Laptop running Windows Operating System (32-bit or 64-bit Operating System is fine although you may encounter some useful applications that would require a 64-bit system. So why not have a 64-bit system). Windows XP (support has been retired by Microsoft)/ Windows Vista / Windows 7/ are all sufficient for most applications.

WinRAR

WinRAR is Windows version of the RAR archiver - a powerful tool which allows one to create, manage and control archive files. There are several versions of RAR, for a number of operating environments: Windows, Linux, FreeBSD, Mac OS X.

There are two versions of RAR for Windows:

+ Version with graphical user interface - WinRAR.exe;
+ Command line console (text mode) version - Rar.exe.

WinRAR and WinRAR self-extracting modules require Windows XP or later. The application is important to the technician because most flash files and other useful files downloaded from the internet are in the archived format. Compressed archives combine multiple files into a single file to make them easier to transport or save on disk space. Zip is the most-widely used format, used by the Windows operating system. RAR is also a very popular and flexible format. Without the application installed in your computer, the archived useful content cannot be extracted.

One great benefit of having your files in .zip or.rar format is that viruses will not corrupt the files. It is a recommended practice to extract any needed file for flashing, use it, delete the file to conserve disk space (leaving the main file as a .rar or .zip file) and repeat the same process each time the file is needed to protect against virus.

Here is a screenshot that shows how these files look;

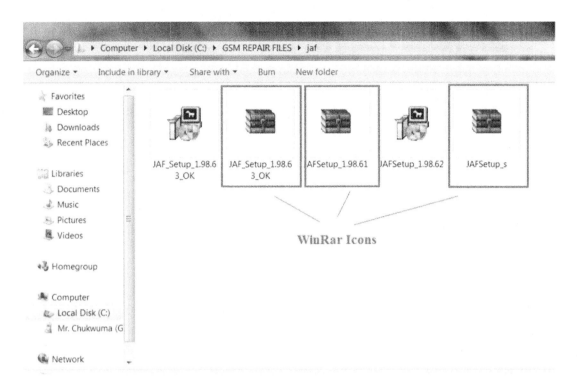

To extract the needed file, right click on it as below and select "Extract Here" or "Extract…" which will open the file path menu to direct the extraction to any desired location in the computer.

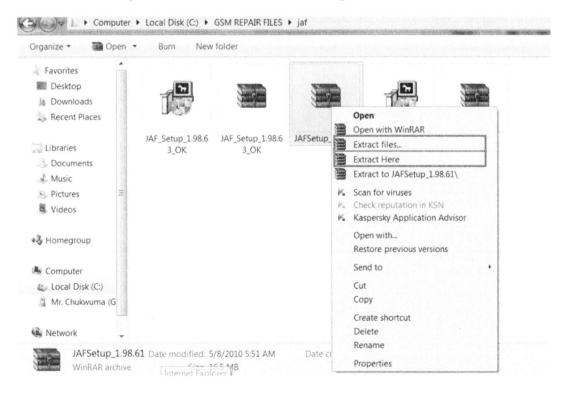

Nokia PC suite

Nokia PC Suite is Nokia's suite of applications used to edit, store, and synchronize your Nokia mobile phone data with a Microsoft Windows based PC system. With this software installed in the computer, you can;

- Back up personal data from a phone to a PC and also restore personal data from your PC to any supported phone.
- View Nokia phone files and folders on the PC.
- Manage a Nokia mobile phone in Windows Explorer as a Windows Portable Device or with Nokia Phone Browser, depending on the operating system and Microsoft software installed on your PC.
- Transfer video, image and other files between a Nokia phone and PC.
- Update/Install Nokia phone software and so on.

In as much as these are some simple services a technician may offer to clients, it is necessary too to do a system backup when a phone is about to be flashed, to minimize data loss. An up-to-date version of the suite also contains Nokia connectivity drivers for all Nokia phones that may be connected to the system for repairs using other third-party applications. The Drivers are installed automatically when you install Nokia PC Suite. In order to establish a connection between your phone and the PC you need to have drivers installed on your PC.

The connection to a PC is via any of the following;

- USB connection cable and a compatible port on your PC.
- Serial connection cable and a compatible port on your PC.
- Infrared (IrDA) port on your PC.
- Bluetooth wireless technology equipment and software.

iTunes

The iTunes software or application is Apple's (the manufacturer of iPhones, iPads, iPods) support platform for offering a range of services to end users of their products, for the product. The Apple iPhone runs on their proprietary mobile Operating System called iOS. Using the iTunes desktop application, a support technician or user can;

- Update the iOS system software for the iPhones, iPods and iPads.
- iTunes is used for restoring failed iPhones, iPod or iPad to factory settings during which the latest versions of the software with additional functionalities are installed.
- iTunes is also used for backup and restore operations for user files, music, videos and other data.
- When an iPhone, iPod or iPad is disabled due to forgotten password, iTunes is used for restoring the phone.

The iTunes store which is part of the application suite has a sophisticated interface and a large library of media and applications.

iTunes is also a jukebox software player for playing and downloading music. It lets users of Apple products add to, organize and play their digital media collections on the computer as well as sync it to a portable device.

If you are going to be fixing iPhones, iPads and iPods as a mobile phone support technician, then you should have latest versions of this application installed on the computer.

Blackberry desktop software

The BlackBerry Desktop Software links the content and applications on your BlackBerry smartphone or BlackBerry PlayBook tablet with your computer. With this software you can synchronize your organizer data and media files, backup and restore your data, manage your smartphone applications, and even use your smartphone as a modem to connect to the Internet from your computer. You can also use the BlackBerry Desktop Software to switch smartphones or tablets as well as write firmware files into the phone.

Microsoft.NET framework

This is a software framework developed by Microsoft for use by application and software developers to serve as a universal, reusable software environment that provides particular functionality as part of a larger software platform to facilitate development of software applications, products and solutions.

However, it is needed by certain mobile phone repair applications to function in the computer system. Its absence in the system will make those applications not to function, so it is required that one installs it in the computer system.

Antivirus

Antivirus programs help to protect the computer system from malicious software and viruses. Seeing the huge amount of files and applications required for mobile phone repairs, it will amount to a huge loss of data if the system has to be formatted because of virus attack. It is therefore one of the most sensible things to do to protect your investment.

Recommendation

Ensure that you search online and download the above listed software. Install them all whether you will use them or not as they provide the system with needed drivers. Include also;

i. **Lumia Device Updater**
ii. **Nokia Device Updater**
iii. **Samsung Kies**
iv. **Sony PC companion**
v. **New PC studio**

Chapter 9

Understanding Software Repair Terminology and Procedures

Flash Programming Terminologies

"Bricked" Phone

When a mobile device would not switch ON in any way, and therefore is in a non-functional state due to either a serious configuration error, corrupted firmware, or a hardware failure, it is regarded as 'Bricked". A phone in that state for all intents and purposes, is as useful as a brick. When a mobile phone is stuck in a boot loop, it is not "fully" bricked; also a phone that boots straight into recovery mode is considered as a partially bricked phone.

Bricking a device also usually results from a failed attempt to update a device. Most electronic devices especially smartphones and tablets have an update procedure that must not be interrupted before completion. Should there be an unwanted condition like interruption by power failure, user intervention, or any other reason, the existing firmware may be partially overwritten and unusable. The risk of software corruption can be minimized by taking all possible precautions against interruption during such processes.

"Bricking" can also be caused by installing the wrong firmware, firmware version, firmware with errors or for a different revision of the hardware and by viruses or other malicious software. Bricking is classified into two types: soft brick and hard brick.

Soft bricked devices will boot unsuccessfully and get stuck on boot logo, or reboots continuously. Sometimes it shows a white screen when in use. Some of the major reasons for soft brick are;

- Software bugs.
- Viruses/malwares.
- Corrupt firmware installation.
- Attempted rooting failure.

- Flashing a custom recovery image to a device with a locked boot loader.
- Invalid memory caches.
- Wrong read/write permissions.

Flashing or system reset (hard or soft reset) that clears all the internal memory can recover a device from a soft brick state. For instance Blackberry phones usually show a single red light while iOS devices show a completely black or white screen with only an Apple logo when bricked.

Hard bricked devices on the other hand are what mobile phone technicians generally regard as "dead phone". No sign of activity or life; Non-responsive no matter what the user does, despite having adequate operating battery power. Hard bricking could also be as a result of software related faults which can be traced to any of the following;

- Wrong selection of firmware for installation or flashing.
- Interruptions during the flash process.
- Wrong keypad code command syntax.
- Software bugs.
- Using a wrong flash procedure than recommended by the repair software manufacturer.

IMEI

IMEI means International Mobile Equipment Identity, a unique 15-digit international serial number used to identify a mobile phone or device to a mobile phone network. This number can be used to identify illegal or stolen mobile phone devices. Whenever a mobile device is switched-ON or a call is made on it, the network provider's switch checks the IMEI number of the handset and then cross reference it with a blacklist database. If that IMEI is on the blacklist then the network will either block signals to the phone or allow signals but block outgoing or incoming calls. IMEI's importance is such that if it is missing, wrong, or corrupted, there will be no network service in the mobile device.

Flashing

Flashing is a process whereby existing firmware or data in a mobile phone's EEPROM or flash memory is overwritten with a fresh firmware code or new data. This can be done to upgrade a device, repair or fix bugs, swap a mobile service provider for network locked devices or just to install a new operating system. Some manufacturers like Apple for instance require over the air upgrades whereby the device is connected through the internet to the manufacturers' web server for the process.

Custom ROM/Stock ROM

Although ROM in computer terminology means Read Only Memory (A memory storage which once written, can neither be edited nor deleted), in Android OS community parlance it means firmware for Android phones and tablets. Changing or installing a ROM in a phone is similar to installing a new operating system on a desktop or laptop computer.

Android is an open source software which is supported by a vast community of developers that continually modify the code by adding features, customizations, and improvements to its stability and the product is what is referred to as Custom ROM.

Custom ROMs are replacement firmware for Android devices created by third-party software developers which provides features or options not found in the Stock (the device manufacturer's) OS. Custom ROMs are often built from the official files of Android or kernel source code. Examples of popular Custom ROMs are CyanogenMod, Paranoid Android, MIUI, and AOKP (Android Open Kang Project) etc.

Stock ROMs on the other hand are the Android firmware installed by the original equipment manufacturers (OEMs) in smartphones running the Android mobile operating system. The companies customize and brand the phones to give it a unique look and feature that is proprietary. For instance, a Samsung phone and an LG phone just purchased off the shelf may be running the same version of Android OS. But when you switch both phones ON, each one would display their company brand name and the desktop environment may look different, with different widgets, wallpapers etc and even accompanying third-party apps.

Rooting

Rooting is the process that provides users with full administrator control and access to an Android smartphone or tablet. This is often done in order to bypass carrier or handset-maker limitations or restrictions. The moment a phone is rooted you can replace or modify applications and system settings, run specialized apps and so on. Root access compromises device's user data security.

One major reason to root a phone is to replace the operating system with a ROM (in this sense it means another software developer's version of the OS) that also gives a user more control over details. This is commonly referred to as *flashing a custom ROM*. The process of rooting an Android phone is different for each device and that is why this book can only point you to online resource links as long as you have understood the concept.

Other advantages of rooting include;

- Rooting provides the ability to uninstall (rather than disable) any unwanted apps and games that are preinstalled in phones which take up enormous storage space even though they are rarely used.
- Rooting enables faster platform updates. Custom ROMs can be flashed to access new released features once a device is rooted.
- Rooting makes available additional optional settings and control.
- Rooting a phone makes it possible to install new apps, gain more device management options and additional security functionality more than what is possible with the usual Android stock OS.

Note that when a phone is rooted, warranty becomes void; however, flashing a stock ROM can reverse the warranty status to original state. Few examples of apps that add new levels of functionality to a rooted Android phone include ROM Toolbox Pro, SetCPU, Titanium Backup, Touch Control, and Cerberus anti-theft and so on. So if you want to root a phone, not to worry. Here is a link to where you can find easy step-by-step guides for different models;

http://www.androidcentral.com/root

Updating a Phone

Updating a phone simply means downloading firmware or OS files of higher versions with either bug fixes or add-ons/features into the device. Updating a phone's software reduces its internal storage as the new software instructs the phone to create more storage space designated for system use. While it is impossible to manipulate the "read only" memory part of the phone using end user tools, it is possible using developer tools.

Read/Write/Update/Download

Various flasher box software interfaces use different language choices on their radio buttons. Apart from "read" which is usually for reading files and information from the phone, the rest (write, update, upload) are meant to transfer the firmware files into the device being flashed.

Android ADB driver

This (Android Debug Bridge) is a small application which auto installs in the computer to support all android devices that may be connected to the system for firmware flashing or any other operation including models like Samsung, Google Nexus, Motorola, HTC, LG, Infinix or other MTK phones, Huawei etc.

Download the "15 seconds ADB Installer" from;

http://androidmtk.com/download-bst-android-adb-driver. This installer was created by XDA developer "Snoop05".

USB DFU.exe

DFU stands for Download Firmware Utility or Device Firmware Update and as the name implies it can be used to flash both stock and custom ROMs of android phones/tablets especially for Broadcom android devices.

In iPhones, DFU mode which is Device Firmware Update mode is usually the mode of last resort when all other effort to recover the phone into a normal state fails. DFU mode in this case, different from "recovery mode" puts the device into communication with iTunes on windows, although the boot loader or iOS has not been loaded yet allowing the device to be recovered from any state.

Booting, Bootloader and the Booting Process

No human being falls asleep instantly and neither does anyone wake up from sleep in an instant, fully conscious and active 100%. Sleeping and waking is a process. Machines tend to be built as imitations of nature and God's creation.

In computing systems therefore such as mobile phones, booting is an initialization process of a computer system. When a computer system assumes normal operational run time environment, ready to accept inputs and produce outputs, booting has been completed. If the booting process began from an OFF state to normal operational state, this can be regarded as "Hard booting". Soft booting is when the system boots up from a partially OFF state like hibernation, standby mode or sleeping mode.

A **boot loader** is a tiny separate program or code resident in ROM or Flash memory which is designed to automatically load an operating system into the main (working) memory of the computer and run it after completion of the power-on self-tests (POST). In a computer system, the operating system is resident in secondary memory like Hard disk storage. Embedded systems like mobile phones however do not have such large storage space and are designed to boot fast, almost immediately after power ON. Therefore, such devices usually have operating system software or firmware in ROM or flash memory, so that the device can begin to function with little or no loading as the loading can be pre-computed and stored on the ROM when the device is made. This is where basically the boot sequence of a computer desktop/laptop differs from that of a mobile device. The boot sequence for mobile devices' CPUs/DSPs or microcontrollers (SoC- Socket on Chips) usually include a boot ROM with boot code integrated directly into their IC. This allows their processor to perform self-boot and load boot programs from other sources like NAND flash, SD or eMMC etc.

This feature is often used for system recovery purposes when the usual boot software in non-volatile memory gets erased or corrupted. It is therefore possible to take control of a system by using hardware debug interface such as JTAG, connected to flasher boxes to write the boot loader program into bootable non-volatile flash memory by instructing the processor core to perform the necessary actions needed to program non-volatile memory.

From the earlier teaching about mobile phones' (especially smartphone) processors whereby there exists dual core processors in a master-slave relationship, the DSP could be booted by the CPU or Application processor which is the Master that boots first from its own memories and then controls overall system behavior - booting of the DSP as well as its role in the system. The DSP in most cases do not have its own boot memories and relies on the master processor to supply the required boot code.

Mobile Phone Flash Programming Process

Having read about all the ways mobile phone software faults manifests or a phone becomes bricked as well as the causes or sources of bricking in a mobile device, we shall now examine the procedures and processes involved in proffering solutions to bricked phones through flash programming.

Flashing as has been defined in this book is simply a process whereby a technician uses mobile phone flasher devices and software to reload a new, updated, valid firmware or operating system into a bricked mobile device thereby replacing the corrupted one.

It is also important that every detail of the structure of the mobile phones, their memories and the relationship with the microprocessors is both understood and internalized in memory. Note that Flash programming operations cannot take place if any of the *Flash memory, microprocessors, data communication ports* or the *power management IC* of the phone is faulty. These hardware components must first be functional and **properly soldered** to the PCB. For this reason, during a flash operation, the technician must intuitively monitor the communications from the flasher box program output on the computer screen and respond accordingly.

Mobile phone flasher devices as has been listed in this book are of various brands, types, and support levels. Here we shall be teaching a general all encompassing procedure although each device is different. In a subsequent section, we shall discuss specific platforms for some popular mobile phone brands in the market.

The Flash Procedure

The following steps must be completed by a technician who wants to flash a mobile device;

- ✓ Download and install all the required **drivers** for both the phones and the flasher boxes to be used on the computer system. Mobile phone drivers are mostly needed for repair software that is not interfaced to a flasher box. If you are flashing with a flasher box, phone drivers are not needed to be installed on the computer system individually.
- ✓ Download and install **setup files** for the flasher boxes on the computer system. Most setup files include the device drivers.
- ✓ Install the flasher device. Each device follows a laid out routine. In most cases they follow a similar device installation pattern. Observe the installation routine in the next section of this book.
- ✓ Download and install the repair software suite for specific flasher boxes you want to use on the computer system.
- ✓ Download, extract and label appropriately (in individual folders for each mobile device model) the mobile device's firmware files or flash files on the computer system. Flash files used for some specific flasher boxes are unique to those flasher boxes and available only in their support websites and GSM forums. If you do not purchase a valid legitimate branded flasher box from the manufacturer's authorized resellers, you will not gain access to support areas to download flash-files and other useful resources. Some files may be used across platforms.

Having completed all software and hardware device installations needed for the repair flash programming process, the technician will need to understand each **repair software's** user interface parameters;

- Functions of the Radio buttons

- Communication port settings
- Flash process action timing
- Flash file 'Type' selection

Once the above listed parameters are known and understood, the flash process is easy and straight forward. Just click on the button marked "Flash/Write/Update Firmware/Download" etc depending on whatever language was used on the software interface that represents "flash" or unlock.

Other parameters that constitute actionable command operations are;

- Write Operations (IMEI, Phonebook, Full Flash, PM)
- Factory Settings
- Format
- Read Operations (Flash, IMEI, Lock Code or Security Code, Phonebook, Gallery)
- Erase (Full Flash, Security Areas, etc) and so on.

The repair interface programs are usually designed with multi-view window tabs that grant access to the user to execute a whole lot of programming options possible with the flasher box used.

Fastboot Android Protocol

Fastboot is a protocol as well as a tool used for diagnostics purposes in Android phones. Developers integrated the Fastboot protocol into Android devices software development kit (SDK), although some may not have it. As a protocol it defines a communication process that puts the phone into bootloader or Secondary Loader mode, giving access into the device such that custom images can be written into the various disk partitions of the Android device by connecting the phone through USB to the computer. It could be recovery.img files, system.img file, logo.img etc. As a tool, the Fastboot tool when used provides a command-line interface through which a user can modify, wipe or load those images into the phone.

In order to use the Fastboot tool to perform diagnostic operations on a phone, the phone must be put in Fastboot mode through a combination of keys on the phone. For example, the POWER + VolumeUP or VolumeDOWN and Home button keys in some. After enabling the protocol on the device itself, it will accept a specific set of commands sent to it via USB using a command line. Some of the most commonly used fastboot commands include:

- **Flash** – rewrites a partition with a binary image stored on the host computer. Syntax is; "fastboot flash <type of file-name> {space}<name of file>"
- **Erase** – erases a specific partition. Syntax is; "fastboot erase <type of file-name or partition name>
- **Format** – formats a specific partition; the file system of the partition must be recognized by the device. Syntax is; "fastboot format <partition-name>".
- **Unlock/Lock** – For unlock/relock of bootloader. Syntax is; "Fastboot oem unlock" and "fastboot oem lock".

Most Android-based smartphones have a procedure through which the device can be placed into this mode in order to execute commands through user interface flash tools created for that purpose.

Most direct USB flash tool software programs require that the user puts the device into a specific mode before the flash software can execute flash/unlock/format or other service operations on the mobile device.

Some Platform-Specific Flash Programming Procedures and Interface

Below is a view of some popular brands' repair procedure to drive home the skills required to provide software repair solutions to clients. A grasp of these procedures will surely give you an insight into the flashing process and the needed confidence that you can do it. While it may not cover all there is to the process as each repair process may differ due to a combination of factors related to the nature of the fault, it will provide the reader with a great start.

Blackberry Firmware Update, Upgrade and Repair

To carry out software repairs, update or upgrade of Blackberry phones, the technician should follow the following steps using the blackberry desktop software. However this is not to mean that there are no third-party flasher boxes for working on Blackberry mobile devices.

There are, as seen in the earlier table of flasher boxes. However follow the procedure below;

i. Download and install Blackberry desktop software, the latest version available.

ii. Download and install the blackberry firmware software for each device you wish to repair, upgrade, etc.

iii. Go to the computer system directory: My Computer>Local disk(C:) > Program Files > Common Files > Research In Motion > Apploader >

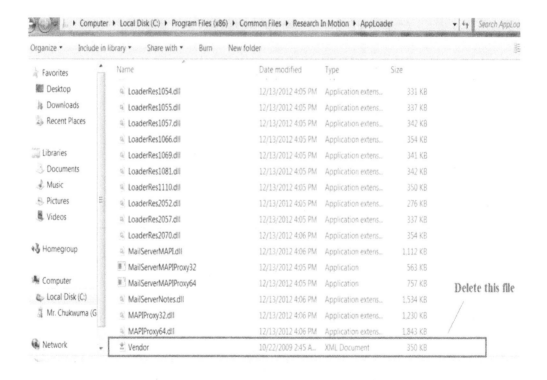

iv. Delete the "vendor.xml" file. (If left, it will lock the phone to a specific service provider customizations)

v. Run the apploader by double clicking on the icon. It is an application loader wizard which will guide you through the process of loading a Blackberry OS or firmware software into the blackberry phone.

vi. Connect the device using the USB cord. Ensure there is sufficient battery power in the device. After plugging in the device, click "Next".

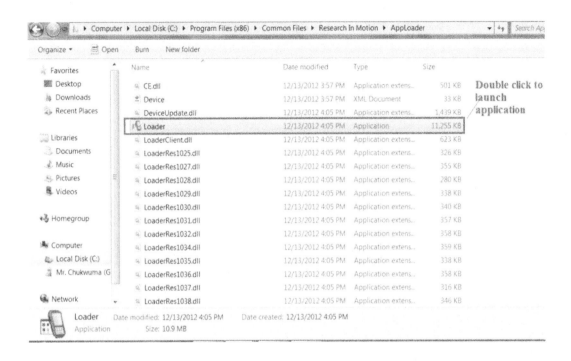

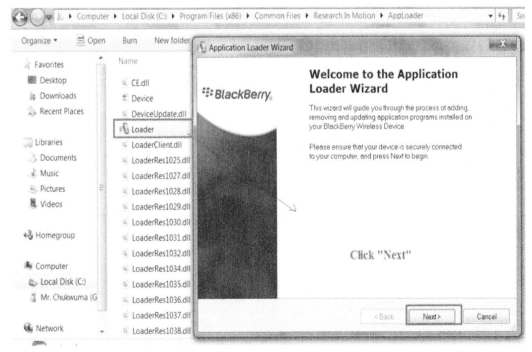

vii.   The wizard guides you through the installation of the OS. If the device is detected properly, the next screen will show the PIN of the device. When you click "Next", you will be prompted to make selections of features and application settings as desired. Do that and monitor the process till it is finished.

iPhone Update, Restore, Upgrade and Repair

Using iTunes software requires first and foremost that the iTunes software be an up-to-date one. Download and use the most current update from the iTunes web server to avoid "error code" conditions and wastage of gigabytes of subscription data. To carry out software repairs, update or upgrade of iPhones, iPads, and iPods, the technician should follow the following steps:

i.   Ensure that the iPhone, iPad or iPod device has enough battery power.
ii.   Run the iTunes software on the computer system.
iii.   Connect the device to the computer's USB port.
iv.   Place the device in recovery or DFU mode and follow the prompts from your computer screen.

Note that all iOS device software support for update, restore etc are done online through a direct internet connection to the iTunes support server.

All the steps and guidelines including what to do in case you encounter errors with an error code displayed are listed on the apple support site. I will leave the links to all such relevant documentations here without need to repeat such procedures here.

Visit http://www.apple.com/uk/support/itunes/
     https://support.apple.com/en-ng/HT201442

How to Enter Recovery and DFU Modes

Recovery Mode

To put an iPhone into recovery mode;

•   Locate the power button and the home button of the iPhone.

- Run the iTunes software application on the desktop.
- Connect the phone to the computer using its USB cable.
- The phone should be powered OFF if it is ON already.
- Press and hold the Power button and the Home button simultaneously. Do not release the buttons as an apple logo appears. Only release the power button but continue holding the home key until a black screen with USB-to-charger symbol appears.
- The iTunes software will pop out a notification that it has detected a phone in recovery mode with the option to update and restore phone.
- Select restore or update as desired.

DFU Mode

To put the iPhone into this mode;

- Locate the power button and the home button of the iPhone.
- Run the iTunes software application on the desktop.
- Connect the phone to the computer using its USB cable.
- Turn off the device.
- Press and hold the power button for 3 seconds.
- Then press the Home button, making it a simultaneous Power + Home button press for 10 seconds.
- Release the power button after the 10th second but continue to hold the Home button.
- After the 15th second, release the Home button with a black screen and iTunes software will notify that it has detected a device in recovery mode. Note that in DFU mode, the screen is usually black with nothing on the screen.

Nokia Basic, Feature and Smartphone repairs

To carry out software repairs, update or upgrade of Nokia phones, we shall be teaching this lesson using as our example the JAF flasher box among many other flashers that can be used for Nokia basic and feature mobile phones. Microsoft has taken over Nokia but the lessons still apply when using flasher boxes for flashing all classes of mobile phones. There are other software tools that serve for flashing Nokia phones. For instance, you may download and install "Infinity BEST (BB5 Easy Service Tool) by Infinity Box-team" for direct phone to computer USB flash process and begin immediately to make money flashing Nokia BB5 phones. A simple Google search for flash-file by typing for instance "RM-721 flash file" will give you the necessary MCU, PPM and CNT files! The software interface is simple. Select the "flashing" tab; checkmark "Dead Mode", the "Flash" button becomes active. Click "Flash" and follow instructions on the screen by pressing power button when it demands for that. Pronto! That is a simple illustration of how easy it is to start earning if you are focused.

Note that the tutorial below, just like the others used for other platforms covers everything any technician need to know about software flashing. The difference across various flasher box software interfaces or routines is very little. It is similar to a man or woman who registered to learn how to drive a car. The vehicle used for teaching may be an old rickety model of Volkswagen Beetle or Peugeot 504 or whatever old model car. But after learning how to drive, the learner goes ahead to drive various newer models of cars including the ones yet to be manufactured in future. The technician should follow the following steps below to use the JAF flasher box.

JAF - Just Another Flasher is a software box manufactured by Odeon Team. JAF just like other great Nokia software tools like Saras' Twister and UFS series boxes provide support for Nokia basic and feature phones. Nokia generations of phones are named according to a series of mobile baseband technologies implemented in their phones. There are Digital Core Technology generations, DCTx starting from DCT-L (L for Linda), DCT-3, DCT-4 and then BB5 (Base Band 5) models which are all supported by JAF. Each of these series has different software page views integrated into the software interface, accessible with a click of a button.

Note that JAF product support has waned! This is just for teaching purposes.

DCT-L View

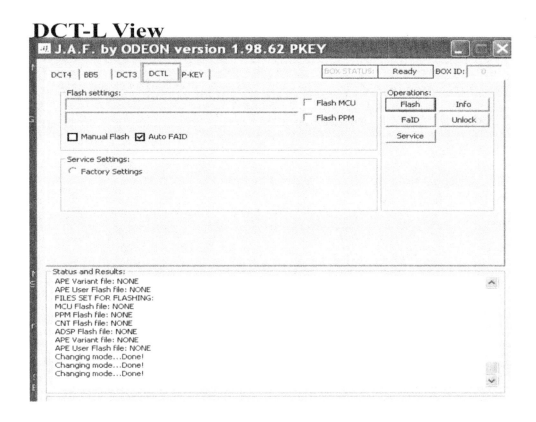

DCT-3 View

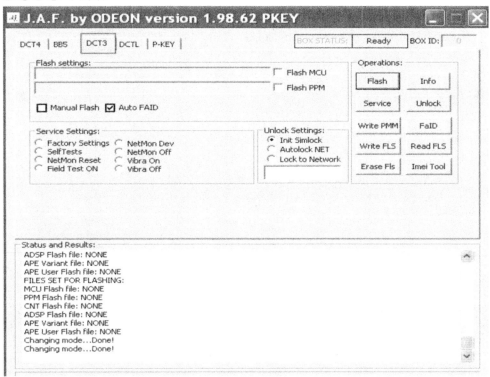

DCT 4-View

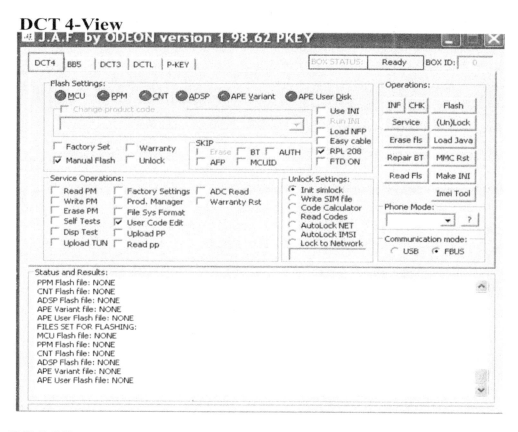

BB5-View

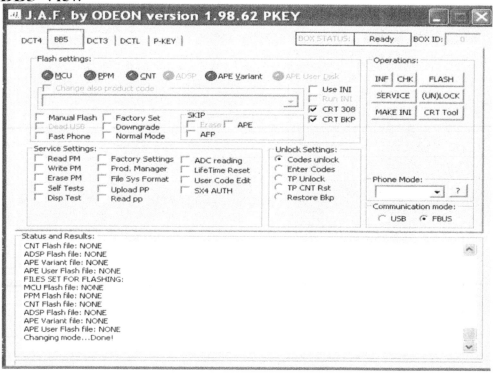

It has one main interface but different views.

You may not bother about the list of models under each category. But in case you do, here is a link to such a list;

http://forum.gsmhosting.com/vbb/f299/guide-nokia-model-dct1-dct2-dct3-dct4-4-bb5-etc-list-hear-638998/

Almost all software interfaces would not allow a flash/unlock process if the wrong phone model is connected for a given classification, so all that a technician is required to do is change mode with a click. Having an idea is also good so you may go through the list to save time switching modes and also to be sure of what you are doing thereby ruling out that any communication error is due to a wrong mode selection.

Now let us take it step by step;

i. Assuming you own a JAF box flasher or any other flasher, download the setup files. The latest version is usually in the support website for that flasher box. *Always download setup files compatible with the Windows operating system you are running on your computer*.

ii. JAF initially debuted with a hardware P-Key dongle that grants access to the software suite when installed and plugged into the computer system along with the flasher box. Later, it was cracked into a software emulation program by OGM development called "JAF Full P-Key Emulator by OGM development". Download it too. Without this program, you cannot gain access to the JAF software suite.

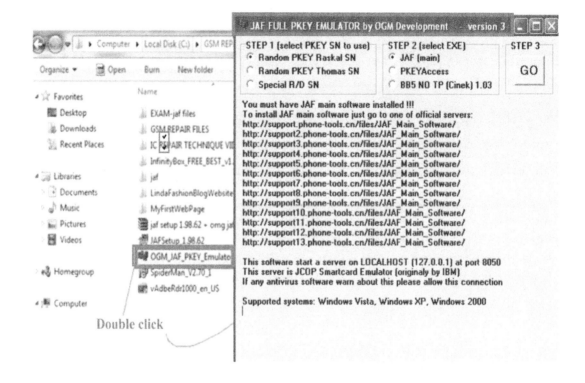

STEP 1 (select PKEY SN to use)

● Random PKEY Raskal SN
○ Random PKEY Thomas SN
○ Special R/D SN

STEP 2 (select EXE)

● JAF (main)
○ PKEYAccess
○ BB5 NO TP (Cinek) 1.03

STEP 3

GO

You must have JAF main software installed !!!
To install JAF main software just go to one of official servers:
http://support.phone-tools.cn/files/JAF_Main_Software/
http://support2.phone-tools.cn/files/JAF_Main_Software/
http://support3.phone-tools.cn/files/JAF_Main_Software/
http://support4.phone-tools.cn/files/JAF_Main_Software/
http://support5.phone-tools.cn/files/JAF_Main_Software/
http://support6.phone-tools.cn/files/JAF_Main_Software/
http://support7.phone-tools.cn/files/JAF_Main_Software/
http://support8.phone-tools.cn/files/JAF_Main_Software/
http://support9.phone-tools.cn/files/JAF_Main_Software/
http://support10.phone-tools.cn/files/JAF_Main_Software/
http://support11.phone-tools.cn/files/JAF_Main_Software/
http://support12.phone-tools.cn/files/JAF_Main_Software/
http://support13.phone-tools.cn/files/JAF_Main_Software/

This software start a server on LOCALHOST (127.0.0.1) at port 8050
This server is JCOP Smartcard Emulator (originaly by IBM)
If any antivirus software warn about this please allow this connection

Supported systems: Windows Vista, Windows XP, Windows 2000

iii.   Run the JAF Setup.exe file. It will run and automatically create a folder named "Odeon" in the location: My Computer>Local disk>Program files, where all drivers and files for JAF operation on the system are dumped.

iv.   After the setup is finished, plug in the JAF box into any of the computer's USB ports. Windows' "Add New Hardware Wizard" menu will appear to aid the installation of the JAF box. Do not select the option to go to Windows Update as it will try to connect to the internet.

v. Select the option to install the hardware automatically and click "Next" when it is **not** a fresh installation on the system. However as a fresh installation, select the advanced option as below.

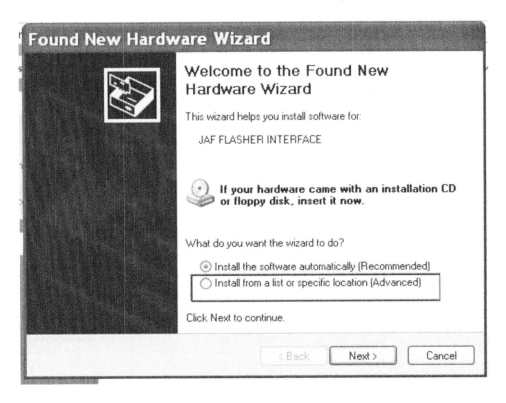

vi.   A file path menu will come up. click "Browse" button and direct the wizard to Local disk>Program files>Odeon>JAF USB Driver as shown below;

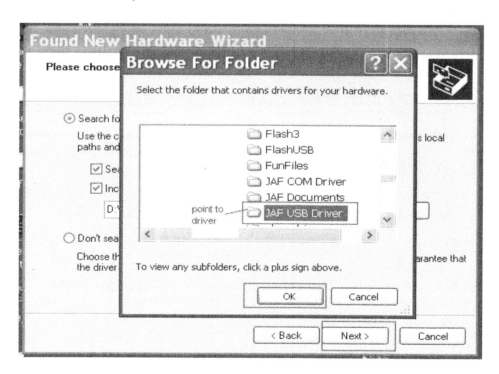

vii. Click "Ok" to complete the selection. Click "Next",

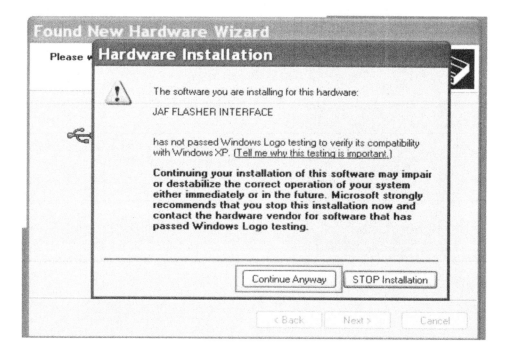

and the wizard will pick the files from the location to install on the system;

viii. Select to "Continue Anyway" and watch the installation complete. Click "Finish" and wait to allow the wizard initiate a second process to install JAF serial ports.

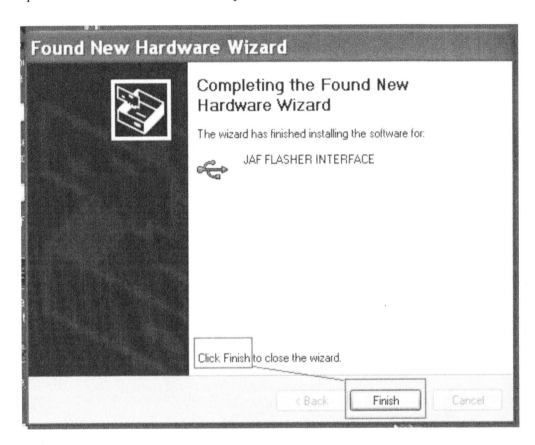

ix. Follow the same routine of clicking "Next" and "agree" to install unknown hardware when prompted.

x. The wizard will inform you with a window bottom notification that "New hardware was installed successfully" or not. Take note of this.

xi. Next, extract the OGM JAF P-Key emulator on your desktop and run by double clicking on the extracted file as shown above.

xii. Click on "Go" button and it will open the flasher software interface.

That ends the flasher box installation phase.

Installation of JAF Flash Files

The next action is to install the flash-files appropriately;

Flash-files are usually compressed into .zip or .rar files and other formats. There is also the auto installer package with an InstallShield wizard. In whichever compression format the files come, unpack the files just like you will tear open an envelope containing a letter. For JAF, flash-files are located by the JAF software by looking in the file directory;

Local Disk[C:] > **Program Files** > **Nokia** > **Phoenix** > **Products**

Therefore, all flash-files to be used by the JAF software for flashing the mobile device should be extracted to the "Products" folder. However, all the folders in this file path are either created automatically when you run a flash file that came as an auto installer package or manually. Each file should be labeled appropriately with the model number of the phone it is meant for or the software type name.
Example; Nokia 1100 or RH-18 refers to the same phone model.

The Software Interface and JAF Flash-File Selection

It is important to know what the various buttons in the software interface are meant for. It is not often that a technician may have occasion to make use of some of the buttons on the software interface.

Experience has shown that during the lifecycle of most mobile or other

electronic devices, there seem to be certain specific faults that are associated with a model such that it is distinct to that model relative to others which explains that.

Let's take a look at some of these buttons;

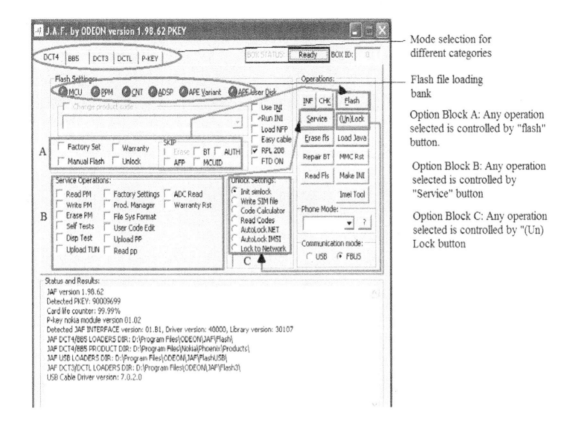

The image above clearly explains or identifies the buttons used to change mode for the appropriate DCT-X category of phone that needs to be flashed. Also, the flash-files selection buttons are indicated for loading the right type of file into the software which will transfer it to the phone during the flash process.

Three blocks are also identified for selecting optional commands that the software is expected to execute on the phone. Block "A" permits multiple selection of command operations during the flash process. It falls under "Flash settings" alongside flash-file selection banks.

Therefore the technician may checkmark multiple operations as seen in the image below;

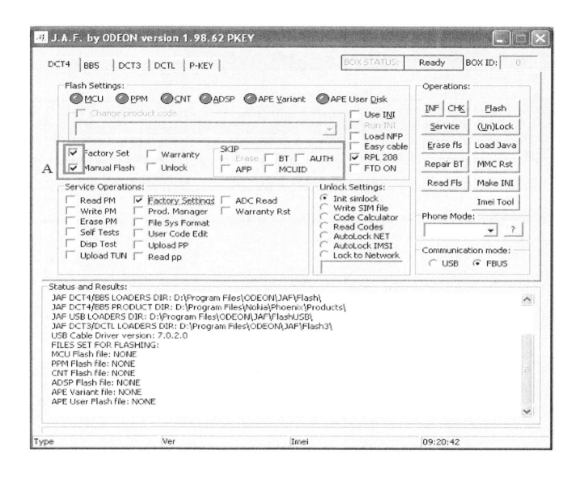

Factory Setting: When you checkmark this option it means that the software will perform factory settings immediately after flash operation.

Manual Flash: It means the software would not carry out automatic flash-file selection but the user will manually select the appropriate files for flashing.

Warranty: Check-marking warranty option is used to reset the mobile device warranty setting.

Unlock: It means that the software is expected to perform unlock operation on the security areas of memory immediately after flash process.

SKIP: Skip is a sub-block for selecting optional operations that should be excluded during the flash process. Most times when experiencing errors and incomplete flash process, it may be due to faulty memory sectors for Bluetooth, authentication, reading MCU-ID, AFP (After Flash Processing), which are indicators of faulty hardware (Processor, Bluetooth chip etc) but which if skipped may allow the process to complete and the mobile device to still function albeit sub-optimally. In such situations, select skip "x" where x is any of the options available.

Block "B" is for service operation settings controlled by the "Service" button. It is a single-select command block as only one service operation can be performed at a time. Block "B" is also not active during the flash operation. It consists of stand-alone commands that can be performed once a phone is connected to the flasher box.

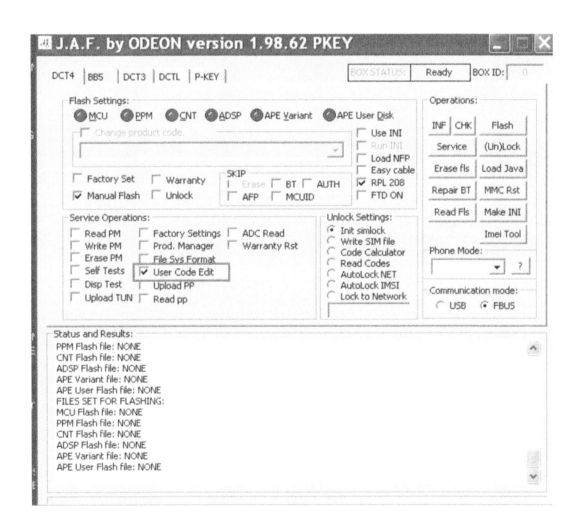

In the image above "User Code Edit" is selected. This is used to read codes used to lock phones. It can also be used to lock a phone by typing 'in' user codes and activating it by clicking the service button.

Other important service operations include;

1	Read PM (Permanent Memory)	Used to extract copy of PM file from a healthy phone to load into a faulty one with network fault.
2	Write PM	For writing the PM files to the phone
3	Erase PM	For erasing old PM files before writing the new one
4	Self Tests	When you click on "self tests" a menu pops up listing almost all device hardware tests possible. It gives a pass/fail result which can guide the technician on possible hardware failure points.
5	Display Test	For testing the health of the screen
6	Factory Setting	To restore a phone to factory settings.
7	File System Format	Sometimes a faulty file system might prevent the installation of flash files. Format and then flash
8	Upload PP (Product profile)	To upload a device profile though rarely available from the manufacturer.

Other important buttons are;

CHK: The "chk" button is used to check connectivity and communication between the phone, software interface and the flasher box without which no operation is possible. It is a very vital button. You run check before operating any other button since without communication nothing else works.

INF: The "inf" button is used for reading information from the phone such as the software type present, the software version in the phone, the IMEI number of the phone, the service cable type required for connecting the phone as well as automatic loading of the flash-files for flashing the phone using the device's product profile. Avoid using the files loaded if and when you use this button. Use the information it presents such as file version, IMEI, service cable information etc. Select "Manual flash" instead.

FLASH: This button begins the flash process after loading the flash-files and performing CHK. Select "YES" to any pop-up menu question after you click on "FLASH".

(UN)Lock: This button is a dual function button for Unlock/Lock operation. The button controls Block "C" in the image above depending on what is selected among the listed unlock/lock operations. Some unlock operations will pop-up a menu requiring you to select the MCU file for that phone model before carrying out the unlock process. Select appropriate file and version.

IMEI Tool: This is used to repair or change IMEI of mobile devices. All other buttons in the "operations" block will perform functions according to their names. It is usually not necessary to erase flash before flashing. If you flash directly, erase operation follows writing operation. If the problem persists, then "Erase fls" first before flashing. This empties the flash chip and may require writing PM after flashing. The communication mode to the flasher box is FBUS by default using the RJ-45 service cable. There is also optional USB connection.

Flash-File Selection

To select flash files, click on the "flash-files bank" buttons. Since this tutorial is an example, it is pertinent to note that the naming of files is different for most flasher boxes and phone types too. Nokia flash- files comprise of these components;

305

i.	MCU.SW file	- Microprocessor (or Master) Control Unit binary files
ii.	PPM file	- Post Programming Memory which contains Languages present in the phone's flash-files.
iii.	Image (CNT) file	- Content Pack which contains Gallery, Multimedia, games etc. files.
iv.	ADSP	- Advanced Digital Signal Processor files for Phones that have DSPs.
v.	APE	- Application Processor Engine for Nokia's early specimens of smartphones.

To recognize the right files to flash with is usually a difficult task for new technicians. The first three files are the full flash-files for most feature and basic Nokia phones. Sometimes, even with the omission of image (CNT) files, the faulty device may be restored to normalcy. If not, flash with the complete three files selected.

Let us identify these files!

Depending on the nature of the flash-file package downloaded, two versions for the older models take the following formats;

Example: Nokia 5130 model

Software type is RM-495

Flash files are: MCU   - rm495_07.97.mcusw   18.634 MB

PPM   - rm495_07.97.ppm_a   13.328 MB

Image or CNT   - rm495_07.97.image_a   8.208 MB

This type of flash file package is easy to select since the file type's name is included in the file naming scheme. Note that the number "07.97" represents the flash-file software version. Always select and use higher file-versions. Also a file selection set for flashing must have the same version for MCU, PPM and CNT.

Finally, for PPM and CNT files, the alphabet that distinguishes one language from another MUST be same for both in a file selection set.

If ".ppm_**a**" is selected, then ".image_**a**" must also be selected, not for instance ".image_**s**".

The second type of file follows the format below;
Example: Nokia 5130 model;
Software type is RM-495;

Flash files are: MCU   - rm495_07.97**0**   18.634 MB

           PPM   - rm495_07.97**a**   13.328 MB

       Image/CNT - rm495**0_nai**7.97**a**   8.208 MB

If this set of files were encountered by an untrained 'newbie' to flashing, it will be difficult to locate the appropriate flash-files. That will be a problem.

There are also RPL files which restore service provider data on Nokia phones. You notice a field "RPL 208" pre-selected by the software to backup the resident RPL files in a phone before flashing. In BB5 phones, if you try to unlock a phone and it shows "CONFIG KEY: FFFFFFFFFFFFFFFF" or "counter 10/10" or 3/3; you need RPL file to complete the process.

Hardly do flash-file package extracts contain only three files. They usually contain volumes of files out of which you have to choose only three (3) distinct files. Therefore observe the highlighted identifiers above in bold. To select MCU file, click MCU tab;

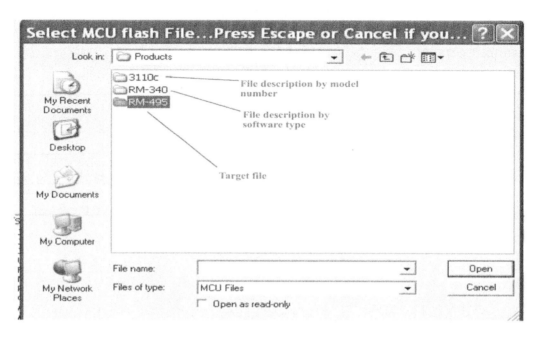

In the image above, a menu for file selection path pops up. Double-click to open the file folder or highlight it with a click and select open. The next window below shows the list of files out of which the appropriate flash-file type is selected. If MCU tab was clicked to reach this point, then ".mcusw" file must be selected. Do not load a ".ppm" file into the location for ".mcusw" or vice versa. The same goes for image file.

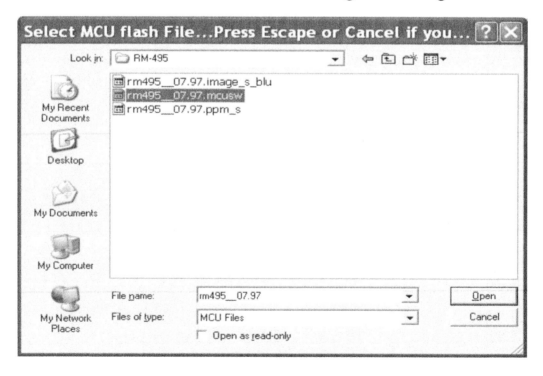

After the file is selected the deep green color on the main software interface changes to light green! Do the same for ppm and image files as shown in the two following screenshots below;

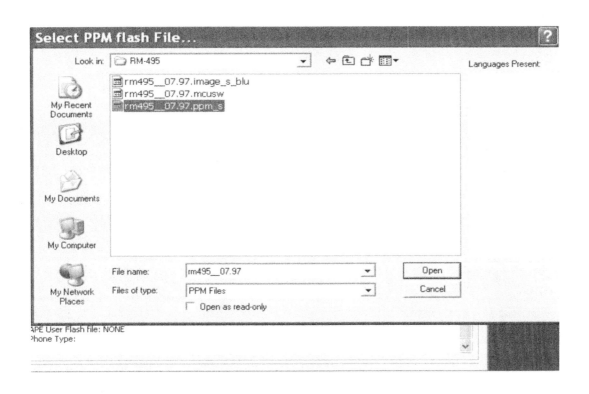

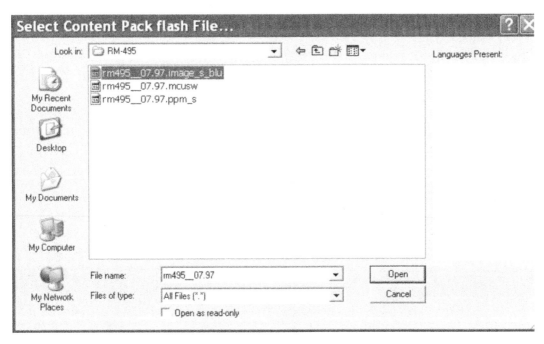

When all files are loaded, the interface looks as shown below;

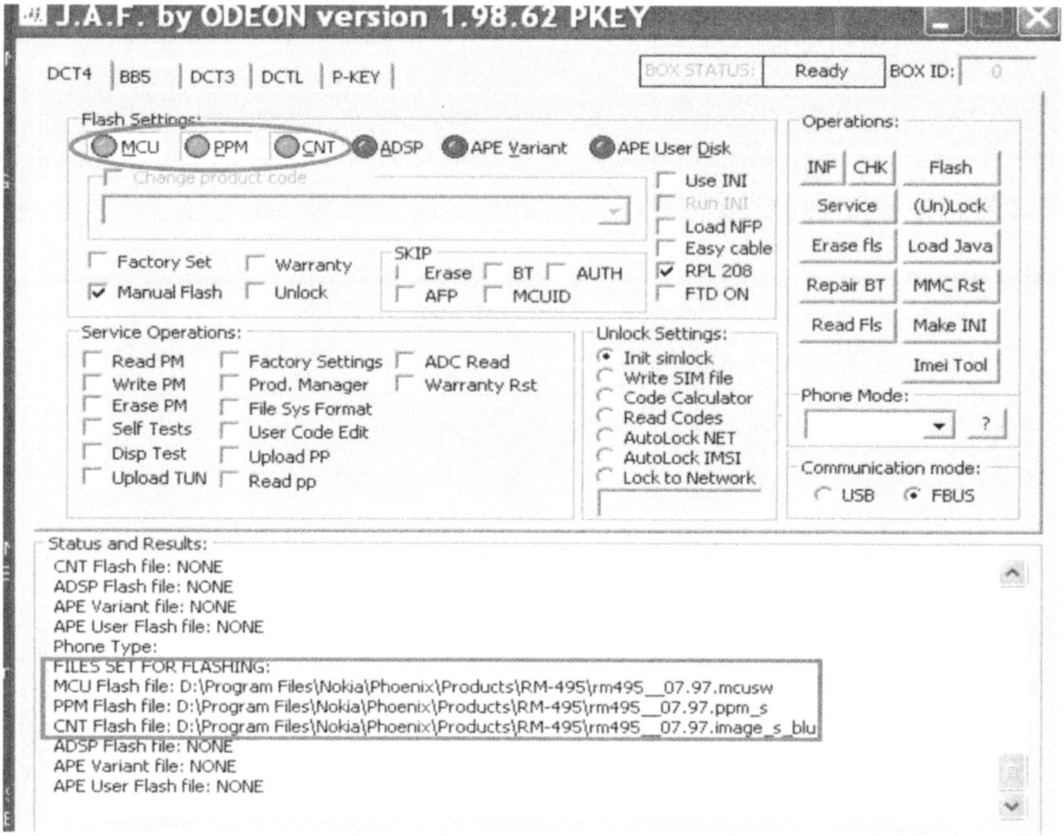

Next is to click "flash" provided a "CHK" output is ok without communication errors.

Newer models of Nokia flash-files are of the format below and also difficult to decipher if you are new, whether you are using JAF or other software flasher;

As an example, let us identify the files for Nokia E51:

Software type is RM244;

rm244_40034011.01U	7/4/2009 1:35AM	01U File	3,796 KB
rm244_40034011_prd.c00	7/4/2009 1:34AM	C00 File	54,816 KB
rm244_40034011_prd.v05	7/4/2009 1:41AM	V05 File	23,189 KB

MCU files are usually the highest size file, followed by PPM and Image files in that order.

MCU   rm244_40034011_prd.c00

PPM   rm244_40034011_prd.v05

Image   rm244_40034011.01U

Another one is Nokia N97, software type RM-505, version 20.0.019

RM-505_20.0.019_prd.core.C00	10/28/2009 12:03...	C00 File	103,799 KB
RM-505_20.0.019_prd.rofs2.V11	10/28/2009 12:19...	V11 File	22,368 KB
RM-505_507_20.0.019_uda_3_001.uda.fpsx	10/28/2009 12:20...	FPSX File	8,212 KB

I have arranged the files in the order MCU, PPM, Image files from top to bottom above. The file extension ".prd.core.c00" is the binary MCU file, the file with extension ".prd.rofs2" is the PPM file and sometimes the language country name is included while the ".uda.fpsx" extension is for the image file.

Once the right files are selected, flashing is straight forward. Any error that may result should follow a cable to phone hardware communication troubleshooting steps.

China Phones Software Repairs

China phones refer to a group of mobile phones under certain identified platforms based on the base microprocessor technologies used for manufacturing these mobile phones. MediaTeK (MTK) processors are the most popular featured brand common with China phones.

MediaTeK is a popular chip manufacturing company based in Taiwan that mostly outsources their products and their largest demands come from the Chinese mobile technology market. There are other notable base chips in China phones as was listed in the F.A.Q earlier. For instance for iTEL Spreadtrum (SPD) MCUs, you need to use Research Download software, a free tool too.

In this section, the tutorial will only focus on SP Flash tool usage. Flasher boxes trend over a period and new ones debut with greater improvements just as new mobile phones and tablets are being manufactured. So for a book that will be around for decades, name dropping or recommendation of specifics is impractical. This book will be helping people many years ahead on how to master the basics. For instance, where will Miracle box or infinity box be in say 10 years time? That, I cannot predict. But there will always be new flasher box products for all generations.

To carry out software repairs, update or upgrade of China phones, the technician should use any of the current software flasher boxes besides direct USB, using MTK/SP flash tool software. There is **MTK flash tool** for china feature phones while **SP flash tool** is for china Smartphones.

To flash using SP flash tool;

- You need the USB cable to connect the phone to the computer.
- You need the USB drivers for each phone you are connecting to the computer to be detected correctly.
- You also need the Custom ROM or firmware file for each phone downloaded into a folder.
- Then you should download (it is <u>freely</u> available online in different versions) the SP flash tool as well as a USB DFU.exe file. Use the USB dfu.exe file to remove or uninstall previous drivers from the system.
- Open the computer system's device manager;
- Connect the USB cable to the phone you want to flash with a custom ROM without battery (some may require battery);
- Once you connect, you should see MTK preloader; Right click on it and select "update Driver". A pop-up menu appears as below;

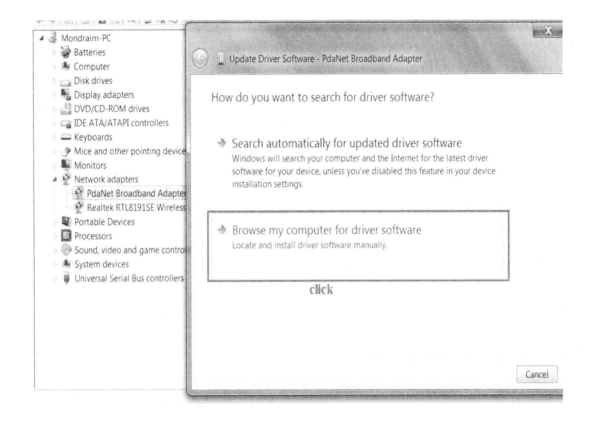

- Select "Browse my computer for driver software" and point to the folder where you saved the phone's driver. Be sure you select the right folder that matches your Windows version.
- When you select the driver you may get a message that the driver is not digitally signed,; then you may have to disable driver signature enforcement by;

i.   Rebooting the computer
ii.   Press "F8" continually until a screen appears as below
iii. Select "Disable Driver Signature Enforcement"

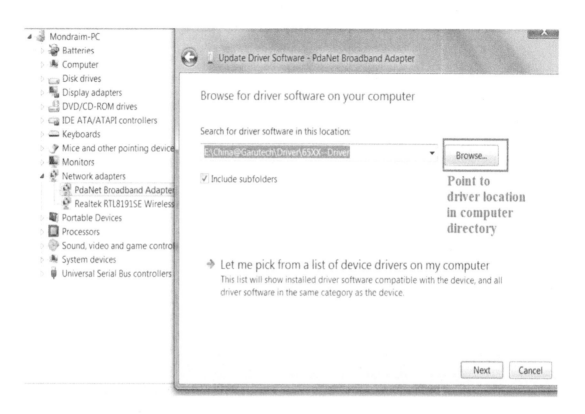

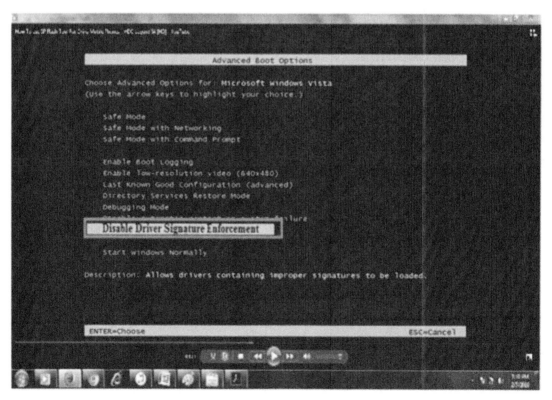

- Now back to the flashing process; ensure the custom ROM you want to flash is extracted into a folder. For instance here is a Tecno H6 file.

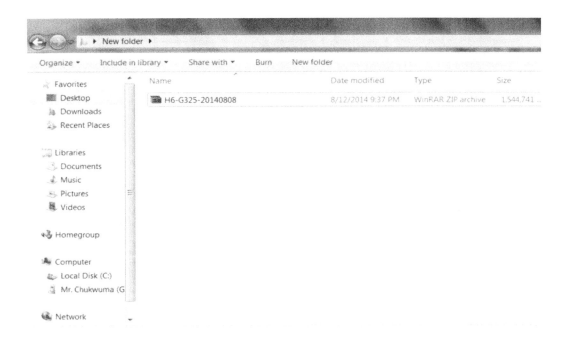

- Right click and select "extract here" option

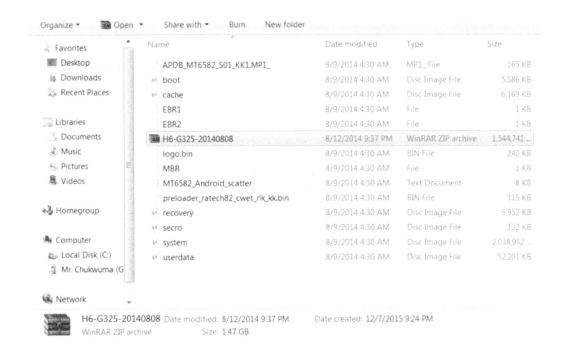

- You can see all the files extracted. The one of importance which you will point to later as you click "Scatter loading" below is the "scatter.txt" file. Select the file "**MT6582_Android_scatter**" as seen in the screen shot below circled in red;

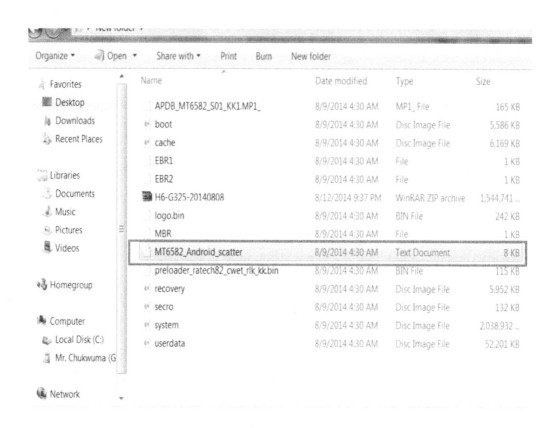

- Next, run the SP flash tool program and click on "scatter loading". You may notice that the "Scatter.txt" file is only 8kb in size. It is normal. The scatter file only helps to aggregate together all the partition component files needed for flashing. The main files run into gigabytes in size.

So don't let it bother you.

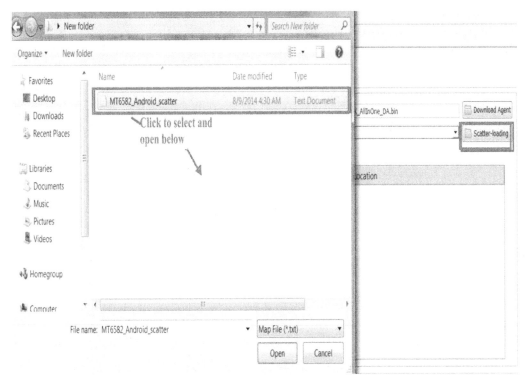

The Android scatter file contains information on the device structure with the memory map of the image file and loads all the flash file components into the flash tool in preparation for the flash process. The Android smartphone is basically like a hard drive consisting of several partitions. While one of those partitions holds the Android system files, another holds all the app data accumulated by users and others for backend processing by the phone. Note that all the files that are required are check-marked and has a file path to indicate their location in the computer system. If you do not want to flash a file, for instance "Recovery", just uncheck the selection of that particular file. The list includes;

i. **PRELOADER** – *Specific to each device and must be present in every custom ROM extract or the phone cannot enter download mode. The preloader communicates with the computer during flashing by making the phone to be detected as a port which should be flash-able. Downloading a wrong pre-loader can brick a phone. If not needed, never flash the preloader (Do not check-mark it)*

ii. **MBR** – *Master Boot Record(first sector of any partitioned drive which invokes Volume Boot Record that holds the boot code)*

iii. **EBR1** – *Internal memory storage partition for apps installation (2GB)*

iv. **BOOTIMG** – *Boot code file partition for device booting. boot.img contains the kernel and RAMdisk, critical files necessary to load the device before the file system can be mounted*

v. **UBOOT** – *Universal Bootloader*

vi. **Recovery** - *It contains the recovery system as an alternative boot partition that lets the device boot into a recovery console for performing advanced recovery and maintenance operations on it.*

vii. **SEC_RO** – *Important file for IMEI write/repair and Baseband processor*

viii. **LOGO** – *Boot logo*

ix. **EBR2** – *Phone storage which acts as Memory card if no memory card is installed (6GB). Once a memory card is* *installed, it becomes a dormant, wasted memory space. It can be reconfigured to benefit a client user, freeing up more memory storage space.*

x. **Android** – *Android OS partition for system image*
xi. **Cache** - *This partition stores frequently accessed data and app components. It is an internal memory temporary storage.*
xii. **USER_DATA** - *This partition contains user's data like contacts, SMS, settings etc. Factory reset on a device usually clears this partition.*

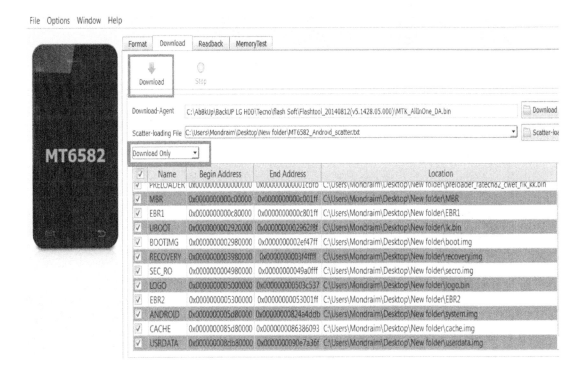

- Once everything is checked, next is to click "Download" button. There are other options in the drop-down menu beneath "scatter-loading file" such as "Format All + Download", "Firmware Upgrade". They are controlled by the "Download" button.
- After clicking on the download button, connect the phone-turned OFF, without battery (in some cases with battery) to the computer.

As soon as that is done, the flash process begins. It will take a while. Wait until a green circle appears, with "Download Ok" written.

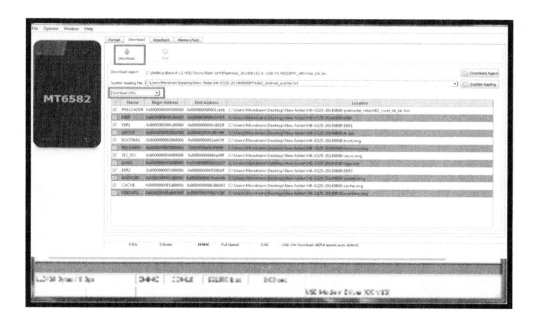

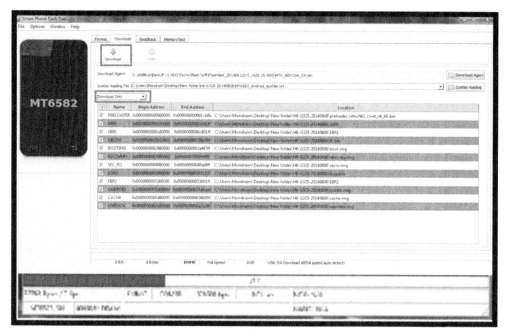

First you will see red horizontal stripe, then purple, yellow and then the green circle in that order.

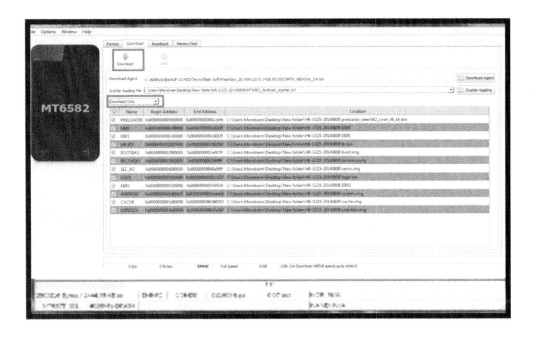

- After you see the green circle, next disconnect the phone from the system, attach the battery and press the Power ON button. It may take a little while to boot. Do not worry until it powers ON.

The process above is for flashing the whole custom ROM. If you want to flash just a part of the ROM, just deselect all other check-marked items in the scatter loaded list above. There are times you may need to format first, before flashing the ROM.

Flashing Samsung Phones

From the table of flasher boxes in Table 8.1, a technician may select any or all of the support tool boxes that support Samsung flashing/unlock. But for the purposes of helping a start-up technician, who may not have ready cash to invest in tool boxes, let me walk through a simple tutorial on how to use the Odin software just like I did with the Blackberry and SP Flash tool tutorial. The Odin software is a support tool from Samsung originally meant to be used exclusively in Samsung support offices. If you go to any Samsung service outlet, ask the support staff if they use Odin. One answer I got was "How do you know about that. Yes we do".

Ok, let us do a quick rundown.

i. You have a Laptop or desktop computer.
ii. You have USB cable for phone to computer communication.
iii. You have a Samsung phone that is bricked.
iv. You want to flash or reload the Operating system/firmware.

The next items you need are;

i. Samsung firmware files for that particular model of Samsung you want to flash. Go online and download the firmware flash-files. **Find links in the "Resource Links" section at the end of the book**

ii. Odin software. There are many versions of Odin software. Find an up-to-date version.

The components of the Samsung firmware files on the software interface, depending on the version of Odin being used are;

a. AP file (Modem file); type .MD5
b. BL file; type .MD5

c. CP file; type .MD5
d. CSC file; type .MD5
e. A file name (varies); type .pit file
f. PDA button is for the main software in older versions of Odin
g. Phone button for Modem files in older version of Odin
h. Bootloader for new bootloader files

The Pit files will only be needed if firmware updates needs to change the phone's partition layout which is rarely required. But if the partition table is corrupted, .pit file will be required. Do not bother about using the pit file except as needed. ***Select files according to the radio buttons seen on the software interface.***

Before the Flash Process

a. Ensure that your computer system has Samsung Kies installed which enables Samsung device drivers in the system.
b. After installation of Samsung Kies, close the application, download and install the Odin.exe software.

The Flash Process

To begin the flash process;

a. The firmware files extracted into a folder need to be selected one after the other by clicking on the respective buttons on the software interface.
b. After selecting the files, next is to put the phone into download mode by pressing some key combinations. Turn the phone off and then press simultaneously the VolumeDown + Home button + Power button. A pop up warning sign will appear with options; "Press VolumeUp to continue OR VolumeDown to cancel". Therefore press volume up and it will put the phone in download mode.
c. Run the Odin software to begin.
d. On the software interface, ensure these two options are check-marked; "Auto Reboot" and "F.Reset Time".

e. Plug the mobile phone into the computer. Allow time for the drivers to install and then wait for the section "ID: COM" on the software interface to change to the color blue.

f. Press start to begin the flash process. As soon as the process begins, do not remove the USB cable or turn OFF the computer or any other form of disruption.

g. After the flash process has ended, the phone will reboot. If the software experiences hang/freeze during this operation, you may detach and re-attach the USB cable and Odin should continue the process.

Software Repairs' Questions and Answers

You have learnt the procedures and processes involved in flashing a mobile device either by using a software flasher box or by using freely available service software with direct USB connection to the computer. If you have studied the previous sections keenly, I am confident that you can begin earning a few bucks right away with your computer system.

One more sound advice is that you must learn how to query the Google database or internet library. I think it is safe to say "Google is your best friend". Let me use some random case scenarios to further teach you some software tips.

Q1. What flasher tool boxes are recommended that would make the best tools for all phones and tablets' support out of the long list in table 8.1?
Answer: As advised earlier, this book serves to lay both the foundation and standardize professional practices for both beginners and practitioners. In the field, there are lots of experience and knowledge to build upon to grow, using a mix of software tool boxes depending on your market size. This book will be around in years to come and for a first timer to the book, it would be wrong to name any software tool relevant as at the time of writing this book, but which may have become less of a choice among technicians with the introduction of much more powerful tool boxes in future.

However for those who are reading the book within the first 2 years of publication, it is safe to do a free advert for some powerful flasher boxes in the market at the moment;

i. Miracle box complete with CM2 (Chinese Miracle2) add-on software. CM2 is very powerful to support multiple Chinese mobile phones in the market with different CPUs (MTK, SPD, Coolsand, etc). Its current drawback is the lack of support for 6680/8800 SPD CPUs. One great feature Miracle box has is the ability to read files and "save as scatter file". The same file can then be used by other flasher tools or even the freely available SP flashtool. With CM2 and even Miracle box, a feature, "SmartAV" can easily remove viruses and correct multiple software issues even without flashing the phone.

ii. Volcano is a multiplatform flasher box and I recommend it as a must-have tool box.(Refer to Table 8.1 for supported products or its website)

iii. Infinity box is a superb product. Include infinity box dongle, infinity Best dongle and CM2 activation. Infinity box has been around for years with continuous support from the infinity box team. They have a history of consistency with support and all files are in their download area.

iv. Z3x box with normal and pro activation is good as it supports Samsung, LG and even has activations for other products.

v. Octopus box is a great software tool to have in your kitty

vi. UFS software tool box products are great too.

Note that in the field, there are solutions for phones which will require that one apply the use of multiple software flasher boxes before success. One flasher box may fail to repair a phone while another will repair the same phone. The possession of multiple software tool boxes is what gives one technician an edge over another. Invest along the way!

Q2. After flashing a phone and any hardware malfunction like a non responsive touchscreen, keypad etc results, what should one do?
Answer: Reload the operating system; find another good version of the firmware/flash-file and re-flash the phone.

Q3. I have an iPhone/iPad that is locked to iCloud account with forgotten login details.

Answer: Upgrade/restore the phone using iTunes software.

Q4. I want to remove Google account or Samsung account from a Smartphone or Tablet that is stuck at the "sign in" screen.

Answer: To remove the Google account or Samsung account in a phone use OTG cable, with a flash drive connected to the OTG cable; download Samsung activation bypass ".apk" file into the flash drive. Next plug the OTG cable (with connected flash drive) into the phone stuck on Google account;

i. The memory card content will open through the phone's file manager, click on the ".apk" file and run it to install.

ii. Next, the phone "settings" menu will be opened automatically by the installed ".apk" file.

iii. Go to "reset" in the phone and do a factory reset. Reboot the phone and follow through with the usual phone setup routine by following the prompts.

iv. If a phone is stuck on "Samsung account" and not "Google account" as explained above, follow the same procedure.

v. But for Samsung account, instead of reset, create a new Samsung account with the "Add Account" tab or use a personal active account and use Wi-Fi connection to sign in.

vi. Exit "Settings" menu. Return to activation screen. Sign in with the newly created account or if an active account was used earlier, it will appear at the "Username" input field. If so, input password and sign in.

vii. Once you sign in, go to account settings and remove account.

OTG Cable

Q5. I am trying to restore an iPhone/iPad but the iTunes software is showing error 3194 (or any other code)

Answer: This error code appears when a user is using an older version of iTunes software and will lead to the technician or user exhausting Gigabytes of data. It also means that the iTunes software could not reach the Apple server even with a good internet connection. Confirm that the iTunes software you are using is the latest version. For any other error code, copy the error code and search the Apple website. There are a list of error codes with suggested solutions in their web support server or just copy the output on your system and paste it in the Google search form. It will return multiple results with suggested solutions including from those from Apple.

Q6. I have an LG Smartphone that boots and get stuck on the appearance of logo. What do I do?

Answer: Download the firmware file for the phone and flash it. You may also download and use KDZ updater. It is a free tool. Search on Google or check the "Resource Links" section at the end of the book.

Q7. Flashing a rogue, un-trusted firmware flash-file to a phone may damage a phone permanently. What precaution can one take to avoid such situations?

Answer: The best standard procedure in this period that there are several file sources online, with greater difficulty differentiating original models from Chinese clones is;

    i.   Back up flash before any flash operation if your source for the file gives you reason to worry and even if you trust the file.

    ii.   Remove the software interface's checkmark (if it has) for "Erase flash" during the flash operation.

That way, should the flash process experience a hitch or the phone behaves abnormally after flash or dead, you may revert to an earlier status by re-flashing with the backup.

Q8. I have flashed Custom ROMs for Gionee Smartphone but the phone refuses to switch ON after flash. What could be the problem?

Answer: This situation is specifically related to phones that have dual copies of firmware for different storage capacity flash memory. Gionee firmware files for instance are of two editions. There is the 4GB edition and the 8GB edition. Infinix Hotnote has similar issues. The best solution is to locate a similar phone as the faulty one and read files from there, using Chinese Miracle2 (CM2).

Q9. I Used Smartphone tool (SP Flashtool) to flash a phone that hangs and freeze on the appearance of logo, an error "BROM ERROR: S_NOT_ENOUGH_STORAGE_SPACE (1011)" appears on the screen. What is the solution?

Answer: Try to flash the phone using a flasher tool box. If you experience a similar error code, the problem is from the embedded memory card (eMMC) – Flash memory. It may have become damaged. Try eMMC repair with BGA reflow soldering. If no success, change eMMC chip with a new one and flash the phone. Otherwise the phone may be permanently bricked.

Q10. How do I carry out eMMC Repair?

Answer: Requires Hardware BGA soldering and a good flasher box to repair.

Q11. When I unlocked a phone using unlock code, I inserted SIM cards of various networks but although the phone is unlocked, there is no network service in the phone. What is the solution?

Answer: First, confirm that the phone shows its baseband in the settings menu.

   i.   Go to Settings>About>Baseband. Is "Baseband" version entry missing?

   ii.   If the baseband entry is missing in the settings, then use a good flasher box like Miracle box (CM2) or Volcano to repair or write NV.

   iii. In some cases the problem may be as a result of a single band phone with IMEI number starting with the digits, "01". Most networks in African regions like Nigeria for instance do not recognize phones with IMEI starting with digits '01" after unlock operation. Repair NV using CM2 (Chinese Miracle 2) software or other flasher box.

Q12. When I insert SIM card into a phone, it reboots. Is it a software problem or hardware problem?

Answer: First of all, confirm if the phone will reboot (without SIM inserted) if you dial and call an emergency number like 112 or any other local emergency number. If the call connects without rebooting of the phone, the problem is software related. Flash the phone using an up-to-date flash file with a good flasher box. But if there was a reboot when emergency call was made, then the problem is hardware related. The phone's power amplifier is faulty. Carry out a BGA reflow soldering repair on the power amplifier chip. If it still fails, change the power amplifier (PA). Check online too for PA jumper diagrams for that phone model.

Q13. I have an iPhone 2G phone. I restored the phone using iTunes software but it is showing the message "activate with iTunes". What is the solution?
Answer: To solve;

    i.   Put the iPhone in DFU mode (explained previously).
    ii.   Download a custom firmware (different from original stock firmware).Using the iTunes software, flash the custom firmware into the iPhone.
    iii. Allow phone to activate network and restart.

OR

If you flashed the phone with original stock firmware, Download and use pawnage tool or use Redsnow tool to jailbreak and unlock the phone.

Q14. After flashing a Chinese Smartphone, it recognizes no network. What is the solution?
Answer: Check the phone's IMEI using *#06# as a first step.

    i.   Root the phone
    ii.   Carry out IMEI repair using a good Chinese phone supported flasher box.

Q15. After flashing SPD CPU Smartphone (example iTel inote) using Research Download software, the phone is dead. What is the solution?
Answer: It is recommended that when flashing iTel SPD phones, especially if the initial problem is a lock related issue, select and flash only "User data". In this case, re-flash the phone. Only this time, remove checkmark for "NV" before flash. It will solve the problem.

Q16. What version of SP Flashtool is best?

Answer: SP Flashtool has several versions which support different MTK CPUs. Get the up-to-date version that supports a particular CPU you want to flash.

Q17. How do I de-brand a network locked phone?

Answer: Download and install (flash) upgrade firmware on the phone. If it still asks for code, unlock with software and input 00000000 or any default code.

Q18. When a phone is displaying "Unknown Baseband" and null or invalid IMEI number, what is the solution?

Answer: If the phone is a Chinese model Smartphone, use a good Chinese software flasher to repair unknown baseband and write IMEI back to the phone. For instance, Chinese Miracle 2 (CM2) has a feature in its software interface for repair of unknown baseband. Check the baseband version by dialing *#1234#. If it does not display the baseband version, then the baseband chip may be damaged or require reflow soldering. If it shows, then root the phone and repair IMEI.

Q19. When a Smartphone is flashed and it refuses to power ON, refuses to connect or be detected by the computer system even when the Fastboot or download mode key combinations are pressed. What should a technician do to connect and repair the phone?

Answer: Create and Use a "Force-boot" cable. It is a modified USB-boot cable using a CA-101 cable type. To make the cable to force-boot a phone into download mode;

   i.   Take the USB cable and open the connector head. See image below.

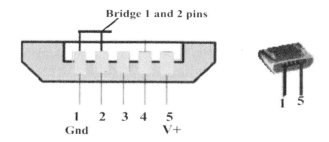

ii.   The ground, GND pin counting left to right of the USB cable's plug is the negative pin. Shunt it to its neighbor, pin 2.

iii.   If bridging the cable is difficult to do, disassemble the phone and bridge the corresponding pins in the phone's USB charging connector with a tiny drop of lead. **After flashing, ensure you separate the pins.**

Having succeeded with the process, as soon as the phone is connected, it enters download mode and enables the flash process.

Web Links to Useful Resources

1. http://www.needrom.com for smartphone Custom ROMs
2. http://www.imeidata.net for confirming originality of a phone through its IMEI and then get the appropriate ROM for the phone.
3. http://www.phoneinfo.com to check a phone's status using IMEI
4. http://firmwarefile.com/walton-primo-f4b.d for ALL phone firmware files.
5. http://lg-firmware-rom.com for LG smartphones. Just type the phone's IMEI and its file appears.
6. https://www.androidmtk.com/download-lg-usb-drivers for LG Android drivers.
7. http://www.icloud.com/activationlock to check the icloud status of an iPhone.
8. http://forum.xda-developers.com/showthread.php?t=961956 for latest Samsung Android ADB drivers.
9. http://www.driverscape.com/download/cdc-serial for cdc-serial driver.
10. http://www.romkingz.com for custom ROMs of Android phones
11. http://www.hovatek.com for MTK ROM files support.
12. http://droidblaze.com.ng/2015/07/list-og-tecno-stock-roms-download-links.html to access links to Tecno files
13. http://forum.gsmhosting.com
14. http://www.google.com

Chapter 10

Mobile Phone User Interface Settings and Codes

Incorporated into the Mobile phones' menu system is the "settings" option whereby every device provides the user with the capability to set some user preferences on the device. Among these options is the ability to clear internal memory caches, reset the device to factory settings etc. In some cases, there are hidden code routines that reset the EEPROM or contents of the NVRAM or Flash memory. The latter is possible especially in some devices where the manufacturer loaded two copies of firmware. One is active while the other one is stored in ROM or flash memory where normal operating processes cannot corrupt the files. They then include a keyboard-input hidden code routine which only trained personnel can use. When activated, it clears corrupted active version of firmware by copying a stored copy of firmware over the active version as a replacement. In some others a minimal bootloader firmware is designed to be enabled by an internal "reset switch or jumper" which when pressed can reload the main firmware. You must have seen some phones or other devices that have a tiny pin-hole somewhere on the body which serves as a reset switch when pressed with a needle tip.

It is important that a technician understand the workings of these systems even in such simple ways as is attempted to be achieved in this practical book. When the level of understanding is of good depth, a great technician is in the making and that is the major purpose of this book. If it motivates the reader to dig deeper for knowledge on these topics or even pursue further formal education in electronics, what a joy!

Hard Reset is a manual method of formatting a device with keypad input combinations which deletes the device's user data in the internal memory. This is the same as factory reset or master reset. Hard reset does not affect data stored in the memory card. Hard-reset deletes all downloaded data saved in the phone which includes phone contacts, music files, pictures, videos, apps/app settings, SMS messages etc. Hard reset returns the phone back to its original settings and is also referred to as factory reset.

Soft Reset on the other hand is simply power-cycling the mobile device which forces the clearing of the DRAM or Main memory (recall that it is a volatile memory that loses its contents when it loses power). This is necessary when the device hangs or freezes and become unresponsive.

To do this, just press the power-button continuously until the phone shuts down. Then reboot the device. This should be done before a hard reset is necessitated. Some phones have optional feature that allows ONLY reset of the phone settings without deleting user data. This option is also a soft reset routine and solves some settings related faults.

Warning: Never do a hard reset on any phone without adequate battery charge and be sure the client has no concern for data loss (who doesn't?). Where possible, create a backup first.

#*SECRET CODES*#

Don't get carried away with secret codes. It is important that while they are handy tools sometimes, wrong application of an unverified code could lead to fatal consequences. Don't get scared. Just be cautious.

*#06#: To view ALL mobile phone's IMEI (International Mobile Equipment Identifier).

NOKIA:

  i.   *#0000#- To view ALL Nokia phones' model number, software type, software version, and release date.
  ii. *#7780#- Hard reset for Nokia phones. Clears user locks and some settings related bugs.
  iii. *#7370#- Formats Nokia feature/multimedia phones
  iv. + 3 + Calling button + On/Off switch (Press the three buttons simultaneously) to manually format Symbian series 60 Nokia phones that freeze/hang.
  v.   Control + Shift + F + On/Off switch pressed simultaneously will format Nokia communicator mobile phones and clear non-OS damaged faults.

vi.   12345 – Default Security Code when prompted in the security settings.

Samsung Phones

i.   *2767*3855# - EEPROM reset code that clears user locks, user data and minor memory errors that affect the normal operation of the phone.

ii.   *2767*3855# - Master EEPROM reset code that clears non-OS damaged faults.
Note: Be sure it is absolutely necessary before issuing this factory data reset command.

Other ways of resetting Samsung phones is through the settings menu. If it is possible to access the system menu, then;

➢ Select the settings option >'Backup and Restore'> 'Factory Data Reset'>'Reset Phone' and select "Yes" to confirm ERASE.

OR

➢ Switch off the mobile device.
➢ Press and hold the side Volume Up and Volume Down keys simultaneously or in some – Volume Up (or Volume Down) + Home button).
➢ Press and hold the Power button (now all 3 keys simultaneously) until the phone vibrates. Wait until the Android logo appears on screen. When it appears, release all the buttons.
➢ An options menu screen comes up –Navigate to "Wipe data/Factory reset" option using the volume down button. To select this option use the power button.
➢ Next, scroll down to "Delete all user data" using the volume down key and select it with the power button.
➢ The device will be formatted. Finally scroll to and select the option – "Reboot system now" using the power button. The

process will start and complete in less than a minute and the phone will restart automatically.

This works for Samsung Smartphones running on Android. These key combinations are important when access to the system menu is blocked by the prevailing fault. It is good to try these methods for any software related or lock issue before using a flasher or repair software solution. Note that some Samsung phones differ in the initial key combinations.

Try any of the following;

> Power key + Volume Up + Volume Down **or**
> Power key + Volume Up + Home button **or**
> Power key + Volume Down + Home button

iii. *#0*# - check the screen clarity with this code in all Samsung phones including latest models.

iv. 0000, 000000 or 00000000 - Default Security Codes when prompted in security settings

China Phone Models

China Basic/Feature phones

- To change phone language to English language, try *#0044# or *#001# and send.
- To set default language: type *#0000# Send.
- To enter the engineering mode, without SIM inserted, type*#3646633# send.
- To Reset defaults (phone/user code reset to default): *#9998*7328# (hold #).
- To Reset defaults (phone/user code reset to default): *01763*737381#.
- To Reset Factory settings ***000*.
- To unlock phone code, only press***847# without SIM card.

China Smartphones on Android

Apply any one combination key press as below to open menu options;

> ➢ Power key + Volume Up + Home button OR
> ➢ Power key + Volume Down + Home button
> ➢ Power key + Volume UP + Volume Down

Once the Android logo appears, release the power button until the menu screen appears. Scroll to "wipe/Factory settings" and select using the power button. All the procedures described under Samsung apply too.

Blackberry Mobile phones

To reset the custom/user settings of Blackberry phones;

i.   From the Home screen, press the Menu key.
ii.   Select "Reset Settings".

As shown below;

iii.   Tick the settings option to set to default as shown below;

iv.   Click Apply, then Yes to confirm.

To perform Hard Reset on Blackberry phones

Remove the battery instantly without normal shutdown procedure for about 10 seconds. Then reinsert it into the phone. This will clear up internal memories and minor application hang/freeze issues.

To perform Soft Reset on Blackberry phones

Press ALT + Right Shift key + Delete.

To perform Soft Reset twice

Press ALT + Right Shift key + Delete.

The screen will go blank for a few seconds. When the screen comes back ON, repeat the combination;

ALT + Right Shift key + Delete one more time.

To Wipe All Data stored on Blackberry phones

i.   Select the Options app under the All tab.
ii.   Select Security.
iii.   Select Security Wipe.
iv.   Check the items you wish to remove

v. Type blackberry in the box, then tap Wipe.

It will take a few minutes for the device to wipe all of the data. The phone will then reboot and restore to factory default settings.

To Reboot/Reset BlackBerry

Press the Left Shift key + Alt + Delete buttons simultaneously. It will reboot the device.

HTC Mobile Phones

Default security code – Try 0000, 1234, or 9999.

To access HTC phone information, Type *#*#4636#*#*

To carry out diagnostic HTC function Test for its hardware, Type *#*#3424#*#*

For direct factory reset, type *#*#7780#*#*

For direct factory format, type *2767*3855#

For LCD test, type *#*#0*#*#*

For Melody test, type *#*#0673#*#* OR *#*#0289#*#*

Hard Reset

Go to settings or apply any one combination key press as below to open a menu with options;

- ➢ Power key + Volume Up + Home button OR
- ➢ Power key + Volume Down + Home button
- ➢ Power key + Volume UP + Volume Down

Once the Android logo appears, release the power button until the menu screen appears. Scroll to "wipe/Factory settings" and select using the power button. All the procedures described under Samsung apply too.

LG

Before trying unlock codes on LG phones, note that some codes will require the presence of a SIM card while others may not. Some will open a menu through which access is granted to the lock settings input form. Try any of the following codes;

3845#*275#

2945#*660#

2945#*71001#

3845#*660#

1809#*660#

##4636#*#* to access phone information menu

2945*#331#

Chapter 11

Trade Secrets and Service Center Operational Guide For Success

Every business segment in life has its set of rules, members' attitudes, and guidelines for success. These informal and sometimes formal rules may be termed "secrets" whereas they are just part of the same universal ethos that governs practical living on earth.

To work is to live!

Don't get me wrong. There are hidden practices in most fields that an uninitiated in that line of business will fail if there is lacking, an adequate grasp of these pros and cons. Experience as often said, is the best teacher. Therefore in concluding this book, based on practical experiences gathered over the years in offering technical support to various kinds of individuals; it is important to use those experiences to formulate a set of guidelines that would help a start-up technician avoid the mistakes and pitfalls of others before them thereby leading to success.

It is therefore rather to be considered more as a business advisory than as a cast iron rule.

The Purposeful Technician

Like every other vocation man is engaged in, there must be a vision backed by purpose. Dr Myles Munroe states it most succinctly that "if the purpose of a thing is not known, abuse is inevitable". The technician who wants to succeed must have a vision. It would be helpful for such a person to ask and answer some pertinent questions like;

Why do I want to do this job?

There must be a burning desire and interest behind offering technical service. One must see himself as that "go-to" person when there is a problem. One must possess the hunger to be the solution others are seeking to technical issues. That someone, must not be irritated by any kind of persons but like a medical doctor, be ready to deal patiently with all persons.

And that someone must have a sense of adequate compensation (not greed) for offering the best service necessary.

Why this particular line of business?

There must be a sort of desire to belong to a certain professional group. Every profession in the world has an imitation. Every good product as well has the fake or substandard equivalent. What kind of professional one chooses to be is dependent on that person's world view. It does not matter what anyone does to make money and be counted as successful; what matters is the responsible pursuit of excellence. Be a master in deed not on paper. Observe that every vocation on earth whether rated low or high has produced successful men. Success is a personal choice. *Therefore to be a technical support personnel who attracts men and women of all cadres, class and financial status especially with a private information storage device such as a mobile phone, places one in the corridor of power!* What is done with such power is up to the technician.

Where do I want to be, in say, the next five years?

There must also be a plan towards an end. Every business is an investment vehicle. In order to travel from city A to city B that are oceans apart for instance, a man would arrive city B only after utilizing several types of transport. This is similar to businesses and the journey of life. Therefore to succeed, your final vision must be the driving-force for your performance in the present preoccupation-in this case if you have chosen mobile phone and tablet repairs.

The Character for Entrepreneurial Success

A good technician should possess the following character traits for success. They include but not limited to the following;

- Discipline
- Integrity
- Persistence
- Capacity
- Honesty

- Patience
- Courtesy
- Resourcefulness

Discipline: You need discipline to excel. It is discipline that drives you to the workshop early in the morning and keeps you in your position until closing hours without being distracted by any concern than to attend to and meet your customer's needs. Operate like an established corporate organization. Even though you are the only staff, imbibe the corporate culture for success. This discipline begins from day one - whether the patronage has begun or not.

Integrity: Integrity is more precious than gold. It is your integrity which is at play in the way and manner you handle client's devices that will announce you to others. It is your integrity that will drive some clients to offer you greater business benefits aside your primary technical support services compensation. Don't think no one is taking notice – indeed its smell is everywhere around you. For instance, never exchange one component of Mr. A's device with that of MR. B's with the justification that at a later time, you will purchase a replacement. It is not the same thing. Respect your client's device components because the quality and lifecycle of one part differs from another. Respect also the privacy of their data. When you do so though in secret, there is that invisible helping force that is all-seeing who will withdraw his help to your business. **Never sacrifice your integrity on the altar of expediency.**

Persistence: A technician should not be one who gives up easily. In fact success knows no man who easily gives up in life. In proffering solutions to mobile devices, you must persist and get it done or you lose a great market share to your competitors.

Capacity: Without both mental and technical capacity, the technician will function as a robot. This means that only knowledge gained at the time of training is that technician's currency of capacity. This is wrong. Keep abreast of knowledge-online and offline. Learn everyday and be creative.

Honesty: The technician must be honest, no matter the circumstance. Earn what is due to you but be honest. There is no universal pricing policy. To do this, you must be clever enough to differentiate between information to be shared, not to be shared and how to share it to your clients.

Patience: Without patience, one is prone to giving up easily. Be patient by applying diligence. Impatience leads to the loss of other virtues including those listed above.

Courtesy: It is often said that the customer is king. Above all things treat them with utmost respect. However do not be bullied into losing your personal self esteem. If your conduct is guided by what you have read so far, you should at most times be in the right. But yet be courteous and create a respectful work environment that will pave way for mutual trust - and trust brings quality patronage.

Resourcefulness: A technical solution provider must have an uncanny ability to cope with unusual or difficult situations. Every day in a workshop is different, presenting the technician with different devices' fault challenges. If you hate monotonous jobs, this is a great place to test your love for variety and excellence.

Useful Work Routine Guides and Customer Service

Below are some tips to serve as operating principles specifically for mobile phone technical support technicians. It is important to learn the proper steps to take when faced with the following;

- The task of troubleshooting and repair of a mobile phone
- Billing a customer
- Time management
- Dealing with troublesome clients
- General Service centre operational routines

The task of troubleshooting and repair of a mobile phone

Whenever a faulty device is brought to the "Mobile Phone Service Centre" (to be referred to in this teaching as MPSC), as a solution provider, believe that every problem can be solved and receive the device.

Do not be intimidated by any of the following;

- ✓ The personality of the client.
- ✓ The sophistication of the mobile device.
- ✓ The complexity of the reported fault.

If you were not competent, neither of these listed factors would have permitted the challenge to be directed your way. *Be confident.* Why?

i. It will inspire your client to retain your services.
ii. You will negotiate better financial compensation for almost the same repair routines because all devices are first and foremost ELECTRONIC devices!

Fault manifestations are usually different in nature, so never expect to have seen it all. *Never inspect or attempt repairs on a device in the presence of clients.* Why?

i. It is unprofessional especially where a device is of a very high sophistication/complexity to you - this is relative. Another technician who may have handled a similar phone and issue will see it as a common fault. It is unprofessional because due to the pressure of prying eyes, you may be forced to take a wrong action that required a relaxed, studious observation before action.
ii. It reduces your capacity to negotiate adequate compensation. (There are cases where this works in the reverse – (where some braggadocio in front of the client intimidates for benefit and that device is known to the technician like the back of his palm).

Be clear about the client's complaints, the current general status of the device, the clients' expectations, and what you agreed to render as a service. Why?

i.   To avoid unnecessary bickering and quarrels within your business environment. One incident will rub your business wrongly no matter your level of excellence.
ii. Document the transaction contract.
iii. Carry out a thorough visual inspection on the device.

Ask relevant questions about the device history before and after the fault occurred. Why?

i.   It is a very quick way for fault prognosis (A forecast of the outcome due to an earlier cause based on your technical knowledge). Ask questions like "what happened before the fault? Is it a reoccurring phenomenon? Is it a victim of liquid spillage? Did it experience heavy impact on a hard surface? Did it just occur spontaneously without a user action?" Questions that establish possible causes of failure and areas of focus for repair.

ii. To protect your integrity in case of buck passing when the device may have passed through wrong technical procedures.

Based on knowledge, determine mentally on the distinction between a software and hardware fault before billing the client. Why?

As you have learned in this book, there are software repairs and hardware repairs. Each type of repair procedure factors into the eventual cost of repairs. To buttress this point, let us see some few determinant observation checks;

✓ A broken, blank, white or cracked LCD screen needs to be determined as a hardware or software issue. Observe if the device can power "ON" by any noticeable activity like lighting, keypad or ring tones on it, call reception and transmission etc. These are signs of LCD problem which is hardware. If not consider software repairs.

✓ When there are partially responsive or totally unresponsive keys, then a hardware/software related Keypad Malfunction issue is at hand. Usually it is hardware fault though.

✓ When the phone consistently restarts (auto-reboot) or automatically turns off; on a scale of 10, 8 is software related while 2 is hardware fault.

✓ Or the phone is stuck on logo only, without responding while in use or running any application. That is a software problem.

The above listed are not all there are but enough to drive home the point am making. Also note that over time in the field, experience would take over in making these critical judgment calls at the wave of a hand.

Billing the Customer

Before accepting to do a job or begin to do a job, ensure there is a job order. Part of your initial discussions with the client helps you to mentally estimate all the possible costs based on;

- The probability of parts change and replacement parts' cost.
- Your established standard service fee for any hardware repair.
- Your established standard service fee for any software repair.
- A combination of any one, two or three of the above.

By all means avoid overpricing or ripping off your customers. Learn to give more value than is being paid for in cash by each customer. Strike a balance between overpricing and under-pricing your services. It is never good to demand additional pay after an initial agreement. Be consistent with your standards and focus on the quality of your service, in this way you will gain the customers' trust and make your business successful.

Time Management

One of the killers of successful MPSCs is the inability to space out their service delivery time for each job order and meeting deadlines for collection even while successful with the repair jobs. You must estimate accurately what time it will take to satisfy each customer.

While it is a first-come-first-serve system at the job order collection time, it is not the same with job order completion time as it is based on;

- Which job requires the least effort, time and money for replacement parts;
- Which job brings in the fastest income and probably the fattest too;
- Which job takes up valuable time that requires study and probably research at a later non-rush hour!

One of the worst case scenario that can also undermine an MPSC's competence value and drive traffic away quickly on a work day is when customers converge for collection almost at the same time or period of time, one after the other with first time customers present and the technician or his reception staff mostly returning unrepaired customers' devices. Wrong timing!

It is like visiting a clinic or hospital where a lot of dead patients are being recorded at an alarming rate. You will surely check out, citing any kind of excuse. Timing is very important here, with wisdom. Even if it so happens that those who converged at such a time you are about engaging new clients are those whose devices failed repairs for good reasons having done your utmost best, do any of the following;

- Have them wait out the time you are engaging new clients to clear your reception area. Bad news is bad market!
- If all persons present are for collection of their devices, should you have to announce one bad news, be sure there are two other successful ones to accentuate your competence; by the way, start with the successful jobs!
- When there are more failed jobs than successful ones, rather than make such announcements, choose to delay their collection than allow three or four disappointed, disgruntled and dissatisfied people show there exasperation around your premises in unison. It is negative publicity to your brand. However, the sweetest moment is when discharging multiple successful jobs simultaneously – they all will be singing the praise of that centre and that is positive PR.

Whereas producing excellence is the ultimate goal of this book, these scenarios do play out in reality at some time or another. Some received jobs are already dead on arrival, sometimes due to the actions of the owner or some other MPSCs. That cannot be your fault and should not be allowed to rub your business wrongly when competence is actually in place. Be wise!

Most importantly, do not allow the impatience of some clients to force you to undermine your reputation by returning failed jobs. Calmly explain and educate them especially for additional time.

Your competence matched with technical acuity and intuition should be applied on stubborn situations that would require your keen application of delay. Delay the discharge of that device until your perseverance pays off. Your primary duty is to deliver on the job and that helps you build a powerful reputation quickly. If you lose that job to another MPSC that delivers success, imagine what damage to your competence and hence patronage. Word of mouth de-marketing is powerfully destructive.

Dealing with Difficult Clients

In every business, there are usually bound to be troublesome situations. How you handle such situations will make or mar your business whether you are in the right or wrong side. What to do?

- ✓ Recognize troublesome personalities on time and follow duly established processes and standard business procedures. Usually they are the ones seeking a relaxation of such standards at collection point. It is stated earlier but to state it again, do not relax it for anyone.
- ✓ If an issue of dispute yet arises, focus on the damage the effect is having or going to have, should it be allowed to linger. Hence find a quick compromise and discharge such a person even if at a financial loss otherwise use the full weight of the law.
- ✓ By all means avoid them. Yes you can – and do not be the problem yourself by doing the right, sensible, fair, honest, just, effective and efficient job always.

General Service Centre Operational Routines

An MPSC should basically be run on the following service routines that would help make her services delivery easy and profitable. A start-up may not have all that is required for standard operations but can grow from stage to stage, level to level with time. It is possible to pick out those that are within reach for any service capacity level or stage.

They include;

- Register and document jobs and maintain records which include a database of your client list with contact information. This is helpful for targeted marketing and numerous opportunities in future. Note their device status after repairs to identify those among your positive PR leads.
- Stock replacement parts. This eases your operations and operational cost. If finance is yet a challenge, establish a relationship with one or two sources that deliver efficiently your needs.
- As you grow, employ and train your front office support staff effectively as that is where the money is made – at collection; and that is where money and patronage is lost too!
- Keep your computer system hooked to the internet and support forums like GSM forum by ZFrank.

Think Numbers!

Finally in concluding this book, I want to encourage you as an entrepreneur to think in terms of numbers. How much of your product or service that can reach the highest number of the population is the key to success.

Here is wishing you success ahead.

Shalom!

To God Be the Glory.

Notes

[1]. Hill, Napoleon "Specialized Knowledge Personal Experiences or Observations" (chapter 5), Think and Grow Rich (1960 revised edition), Fawcett books, New York.

[2]. Ibid.

[3]. "Communication". Wikipedia (https://en.wikipedia.org/wiki/Communication), Accessed 28 October 2015

[4]. http://www.dictionary.com/browse/mobile

[5]. "GSM" (2015). Wikipedia, (https://en.wikipedia.org/wiki/GSM), Accessed 27th October 2015.

[6]. "1G". Wikipedia (https://en.wikipedia.org/wiki/1G), Accessed 27th October 2015.

[7]. 3rd Generation Partnership Project (June 2015). "3GGP TS45.001: Technical Specification Group GSM/EDGE Radio Access Network; Mobile Station (MS) - Base Station System (BSS) interface; Radio Link Control / Medium Access Control (RLC/MAC) protocol; section 10.0a.1 - GPRS RLC/MAC block for data transfer". 12.5.0. Retrieved 2015-12-05

[8]. Welt. H. Anatomy of contemporary GSM cellphone hardware, April 2010, http://laforge.gnumonks.org/papers/gsm_phone-anatomy-latest.pdf Accessed on 11 January 2015.

[9]. Baseband processor (2015), http://en.wikipedia.org/wiki/Baseband_processor Accessed on 14th July 2015.

[10]. "RAM". Wikipedia, (https://en.wikipedia.org/wiki/Random-access_memory)

[11]. Ibid.

[12]. "Flash Memory". Wikipedia
(https://en.wikipedia.org/wiki/Random-access_memory)

[13]. ibid.

[14]. "Integrated circuits". Wikipedia,
(https://en.wikipedia.org/wiki/Integrated_circuit)

[15]. ibid.

[16]. ibid.

About The Author

Chukky Oparandu has setup and managed six regional mobile phone service centers within the last twelve years; taught and mentored over two thousand mobile phone service professionals and thousands of computer technicians in partnership with governments, NGOs and individually over the past six years. He holds a Master of Science degree (MSc.) in Information Technology, Bachelor of Engineering in Electrical/Computer Engineering and a National Diploma in Electrical/Electronic Engineering. He also holds multiple industry standard certifications from major OEMs like Cisco Systems and Oracle. He consults in Information and Communication Technology, a training consultant who has mentored a good number of individuals who run successful businesses.

Chukky personally teaches seminars nationwide in Nigeria and some African countries covering Mobile Phone Repairs, PC/ Laptop Hardware and Software (including troubleshooting, maintenance, repairs, and upgrade) and Internetworking. His classes are never boring as he has a knack for making complex topics both understandable and entertaining. If you have 10 or more people to train, Chukky can design and present a custom seminar for you or your organization's needs.

He is the MD/CEO of Mondraim Contractors Ltd and Executive Director, Programs and Operation at MCOMS Training Consult Ltd, Abuja, Nigeria. He is married and blessed with three lovely kids.

Contact Chukky through email:

ceo@mondraim.com
http://www.mondraim.com or
http://www.mondraimnigltd.com

Printed in Great Britain
by Amazon

81829699R00208